Exploring Autodesk Revit 2021 for Structure

Includes Application of Robot Structural Analysis Professional 2021

(11th Edition)

CADCIM Technologies

525 St. Andrews Drive
Schererville, IN 46375, USA
(www.cadcim.com)

Contributing Author

Sham Tickoo

Professor
Purdue University Northwest
Hammond, Indiana, USA

D1088346

CADCIM Technologies

Exploring Autodesk Revit 2021 for Structure, 11th Edition
Sham Tickoo

CADCIM Technologies
525 St Andrews Drive
Schererville, Indiana 46375, USA
www.cadcim.com

ISBN 978-1-64057-093-1

www.cadcim.com

DEDICATION

*To teachers, who make it possible to disseminate knowledge
to enlighten the young and curious minds
of our future generations*

*To students, who are dedicated to learning new technologies
and making the world a better place to live in*

SPECIAL RECOGNITION

*A special thanks to Mr. Denis Cadu and the ADN team of Autodesk Inc.
for their valuable support and professional guidance to
procure the software for writing this textbook*

THANKS

*To employees of CADCIM Technologies and
Tickoo Institute of Emerging Technologies (TIET)
for their valuable help*

Online Training Program Offered by CADCIM Technologies

CADCIM Technologies provides effective and affordable virtual online training on various software packages including Computer Aided Design, Manufacturing and Engineering (CAD/CAM/CAE), computer programming languages, animation, architecture, and GIS. The training is delivered 'live' via Internet at any time, any place, and at any pace to individuals as well as the students of colleges, universities, and CAD/CAM/CAE training centers. The main features of this program are:

Training for Students and Companies in a Classroom Setting

Highly experienced instructors and qualified Engineers at CADCIM Technologies conduct the classes under the guidance of Prof. Sham Tickoo of Purdue University Northwest, USA. This team has authored several textbooks that are rated "one of the best" in their categories and are used in various colleges, universities, and training centers in North America, Europe, and in other parts of the world.

Training for Individuals

CADCIM Technologies with its cost effective and time saving initiative strives to deliver the training in the comfort of your home or work place, thereby relieving you from the hassles of traveling to training centers.

Training Offered on Software Packages

CADCIM Technologies provides basic and advanced training on the following software packages:

CAD/CAM/CAE: *CATIA, Creo Parameteric, SOLIDWORS, Autodesk Inventor, Solid Edge, NX, AutoCAD, AutoCAD LT, Customizing AutoCAD, AutoCAD Electrical, and ANSYS*

Architecture and GIS: *Autodesk Revit (Architecture/Structure/MEP), AutoCAD Civil 3D, AutoCAD Map 3D, Autodesk Navisworks, Bentley Staad.Pro, Oracle Primavera P6, MS Project, ArcGIS, and Raster Design.*

Animation and Styling: *Autodesk 3ds Max, 3ds Max Design, Autodesk Maya, Autodesk Alias, Pixologic ZBrush, and CINEMA 4D*

Computer Programming: *C++, VB.NET, Oracle, AJAX, and Java*

For more information, please visit the following link:
https://www.cadcim.com

Note
If you are a faculty member, you can register by clicking on the following link to access the teaching resources: ***https://www.cadcim.com/Registration.aspx***. The student resources are available at ***https://www.cadcim.com***. We also provide **Live Virtual Online Training** on various software packages. For more information, write us at ***sales@cadcim.com***.

Table of Contents

Chapter 2: Getting Started with a Structural Project

Chapter 3: Setting up a Structural Project

Chapter 4: Structural Columns and Walls

Chapter 5: Foundations, Beams, Floors, and Open Web Joists

Chapter 6: Editing Tools

Chapter 7: Documenting Models and Creating Families

Chapter 8: Standard Views, Details, and Schedules

Chapter 9: 3D Views, Sheets, Analysis, and Reinforcements

Chapter 10: Linking Revit Model with Robot Structural Analysis

Preface

Autodesk Revit 2021 for Structure

Autodesk Revit is a Building Information Modeling software developed by Autodesk. The structural tools in Revit are primarily used in structural engineering and they help the users to design structural models using both parametric 3D modeling and 2D drafting elements. The Revit building information model comprises of a physical representation of a building which is fully associated with analytical representation. The building information model in Revit can be used for structural designing, production of drawings, coordination of the project, and also for third party structural analysis application.

The **Exploring Autodesk Revit 2021 for Structure** textbook explains the concepts and principles of Revit Structure through practical examples, tutorials, and exercises. This enables the users to harness the power of BIM with Autodesk Revit for their specific use. In this textbook, the author emphasizes on physical modeling, analytical modeling, rebar modeling, and quantity scheduling. Also, this textbook covers the various stages involved in analyzing the model in Robot Structural Analysis software. This textbook is specially meant for professionals and students in structural engineering, civil engineering, and allied fields in the building industry.

In this textbook, special emphasis has been laid on the concepts of structural modeling, which have been explained using relevant graphical examples and illustrations. The accompanying tutorials and exercises, which relate to the real world projects, help you understand the usage and abilities of the tools available in Autodesk Revit for Structure. Along with the main text, the chapters have been punctuated with tips and notes to make various concepts clear, thereby enabling you to create your own innovative projects.

As you go through this textbook, you will work on tutorials and exercises that can be used to build a complete project. Each of these tutorials and exercises, though complete in themselves, will be a step toward accomplishing the larger projects.

The main features of this textbook are as follows:

- **Project-based Approach**
  The author has adopted a project-based approach and the learn-by-doing theme throughout the textbook. This approach guides the users through the process of creating the designs given in the tutorials.

- **Real-World Designs as Projects**

  The author has used real-world building designs and architectural examples as projects in this textbook so that the users can correlate them to the real-time designs.

- **Tips and Notes**

  Additional information related to various topics is provided to the users in the form of tips and notes.

- **Learning Objectives**

  The first page of every chapter summarizes the topics that are covered in that chapter.

- **Self-Evaluation Test, Review Questions, and Exercises**

  The chapter ends with Self-Evaluation Test so that the users can assess their knowledge of the chapter. The answers to Self-Evaluation Test are given at the end of the chapter. Also, the Review Questions and Exercises are given at the end of the chapters and they can be used by the instructors as test questions and exercises.

- **Heavily Illustrated Text**

  The text in this book is heavily illustrated with about 200 line diagrams and screen capture images.

Symbols Used in the Book

Note

The author has provided additional information to the users about the topic being discussed in the form of notes.

Tip

Special information and techniques are provided in the form of tips that help in increasing the efficiency of the users.

New

This symbol indicates that the command or tool being discussed is new in the current release of Autodesk Revit

Enhanced

This symbol indicates that the command or tool being discussed has been enhanced in this release.

Formatting Conventions Used in the Textbook

Please refer to the following list for the formatting conventions used in this textbook.

- Names of tools, buttons, options, browser, palette, panels, and tabs are written in boldface.

  Example: The **Beam** tool, the **Modify** button, the **Structure** panel, the **Home** tab, the **Properties** palette, **Project Browser**, and so on.

- Names of dialog boxes, drop-downs, drop-down lists, list boxes, areas, edit boxes, check boxes, and radio buttons are written in boldface.

  Example: The **Options** dialog box, the **Column** drop-down in the **Structure** panel of the **Structure** tab, the **Name** edit box in the **Name** dialog box, the **Chain** check box in the **Options Bar**, and so on.

- Values entered in edit boxes are written in boldface.

  Example: Enter **4'** in the **Offset** edit box.

- Names of the files saved are italicized.

  Example: *c03_Industrial-Complex_tut2.rvt*

- The methods of invoking a tool/option from the ribbon, **File** menu, or the shortcut keys are given in a shaded box.

  Ribbon: Architecture > Build > Column drop-down > Structural Column
  File menu: New
  Shortcut Keys: CTRL+N

- When you select an element or a component, a contextual tab is displayed depending upon the entity selected. In this textbook, this contextual tab is referred to as **Modify | (Elements / Components)**

  Ribbon: Modify | (Elements / Components) > Modify > Move
  Shortcut Keys: MV

Naming Conventions Used in the Textbook

Tool
If you click on an item in a panel of the ribbon and a command is invoked to create/edit an object or perform some action, then that item is termed as **tool**.

For example:
Beam tool, **Structural Column** tool, **Isolated** tool
Filled Region tool, **Trim/Extend to Corner** tool, **Rotate** tool

If you click on an item in a panel of the ribbon and a dialog box is invoked wherein you can set the properties to create/edit an object, then that item is also termed as **tool**, refer to Figure 1.

For example:
Load Family tool, **Beam** tool, **Wall** tool
Structural Wall tool, **Visibility/Graphics** tool

Figure 1 *Tools in the ribbon*

Button

The item in a dialog box that has a 3d shape like a button is termed as **button**. For example, **OK** button, **Cancel** button, **Apply** button, and so on. If the item in a ribbon is used to exit a tool or a mode, it is also termed as button. For example, **Modify** button, **Finish Edit Mode** button, **Cancel Edit Mode** button, and so on; refer to Figure 2.

Figure 2 *Choosing the Finish Edit Mode button*

Dialog Box

In this textbook, different terms are used for referring to the components of a dialog box. Refer to Figure 3 for the terminology used.

Figure 3 *The components of a dialog box*

Drop-down

A drop-down is one in which a set of common tools are grouped together for creating an object or performing some action. You can identify a drop-down with a down arrow on it. These drop-downs are given a name based on the tools grouped in them. For example, **Wall** drop-down, **Component** drop-down, **Region** drop-down, and so on; refer to Figure 4.

Figure 4 Choosing a tool from the drop-down

Drop-down List

A drop-down list is the one in which a set of options are grouped together. You can set various parameters using these options. You can identify a drop-down list with a down arrow on it. For example, **Type Selector** drop-down list, **Units** drop-down list, and so on; refer to Figure 5.

Options

Options are the items that are available in shortcut menus, drop-down lists, dialog boxes, drop-down lists, and so on. For example, choose the **Zoom In Region** option from the shortcut menu displayed on right-clicking in the drawing area; refer to Figure 6.

*Figure 5 Selecting an option from the **Type Selector** drop-down list*

Figure 6 Choosing an option from the shortcut menu

Free Companion Website

It has been our constant endeavor to provide you the best textbooks and services at affordable price. In this endeavor, we have come out with a Free Companion website that will facilitate the process of teaching and learning of Autodesk Revit 2021 for Structure. If you purchase this textbook, you will get access to the files on the Companion website.

The resources available for the faculty and students in this website are as follows:

Faculty Resources

• **Technical Support**
  You can get online technical support by contacting *techsupport@cadcim.com*.

• **Instructor Guide**
  Solutions to all review questions and exercises in the textbook are provided in this guide to help the faculty members test the skills of the students.

• **Revit Files**
  The Revit files used in tutorials and exercises are available for free download.

Student Resources

• **Technical Support**
  You can get online technical support by contacting *techsupport@cadcim.com*.

• **Revit Files**
  The Revit files (*.rvt*) used in tutorials and examples are available for free download.

• **Learning Resources**
  Additional learning resources at *https://revitxperts.blogspot.com*

If you face any problem in accessing these files, please contact the publisher at *sales@cadcim.com* or the author at *stickoo@pnw.edu* or *tickoo525@gmail.com*.

Video Courses

CADCIM offers video courses in CAD, CAE Simulation, BIM, Civil/GIS, and Animation domains on various e-Learning/Video platforms. To enroll for the video courses, please visit the CADCIM website using the following link: *https://www.cadcim.com/video-courses*.

Stay Connected

You can now stay connected with us through Facebook and Twitter to get the latest information about our textbooks, videos, and teaching/learning resources. To stay informed of such updates, follow us on Facebook (www.facebook.com/cadcim) and Twitter (@cadcimtech). You can also subscribe to our You Tube channel (www.youtube.com/cadcimtech) to get the information about our latest video tutorials.

Chapter *1*

Introduction to Autodesk Revit 2021 for Structure

Learning Objectives

After completing this chapter, you will be able to:
- *Understand the basic concepts and principles of Revit 2021*
- *Understand various terms used in Revit*
- *Describe the parametric behavior of Revit*
- *Start the Revit 2021 program*
- *Understand the interface of Revit*
- *Explain the concept of Worksharing using Revit Server*
- *Understand the linking of Analytical Model to Analysis Software*
- *Access the Revit 2021 Help*

INTRODUCTION TO Autodesk Revit for Structure

Welcome to the realm of Autodesk Revit, a powerful software for structural engineering that provides purpose-built tools for structural design, engineering, and analysis.

Autodesk Revit software provides the Engineers and Designers with tools for structural analysis and design. Revit is a BIM software that helps the users in a project to coordinate the documentation of structural design with other disciplines of engineering. Its integrated parametric modeling technology is used to create the information model of a project and to collect and coordinate information across all its representations. In Autodesk Revit, drawing sheets, 2D views, 3D views, and schedules directly represent the same building information model (BIM). In this software, the physical model is associated with an analytical model. As a result, the model created in Revit is ready to be analyzed in a compatible structural analysis software, such as Autodesk Robot Structural Analysis. Using its parametric change engine, you can modify a design at any stage of its creation. The change in the project is automatically made and represented in all its views resulting in the development of better designs along with an improved coordination. The use of Autodesk Revit provides a competitive advantage and a higher profitability to structural engineers and building industry professionals.

Autodesk Revit AS A BUILDING INFORMATION MODELER

The history of computer aided design and documentation dates back to the early 1980s when architects and engineers began using this technology for documenting their projects. Realizing its advantages, information sharing capabilities were developed especially to share data with other consultants. This led to the development of object-based CAD systems in the early 1990s. Before the development of these systems, objects such as structural walls, beams, columns, and slabs were stored as a non-graphical data with the assigned graphics. These systems arranged the information logically but were unable to optimize its usage in a building project. Realizing the advantages of the solid modeling tools, the mechanical and manufacturing industry professionals began using the information modeling CAD technology. This technology enabled them to extract data based on the relationship between model elements.

In 1997, a group of mechanical CAD technologists began working on a new software for building industry. The Building Information Modeling (BIM) provided an alternative approach to building design, construction, and management. This approach, however, required a suitable technology to implement so as to reap its benefits. In such a situation, the use of parametric technology with the Building Information Modeling approach was envisaged as an ideal combination. They developed a software that was suitable for creating building projects. This led to the development of Autodesk Revit.

Autodesk Revit provides powerful tools for structural design and documentation, in which a digital structural model is created using the parametric elements such as structural walls, beams, columns and so on. All building elements have inherent relationship with one another, which can be tracked, managed, and maintained by the computer.

BASIC CONCEPTS AND PRINCIPLES

Autodesk Revit enables you to envisage and develop a structural model with actual 3D parametric structural elements. It provides a new approach to the structural design and the implementation process. It replicates the way structural engineers conceive the structure of a building. The

2D CAD platforms, such as AutoCAD, mostly use lines to represent the elements, as shown in Figure 1-1. However, in Autodesk Revit, you can create the structural model of a building project using 3D elements such as structural floors, columns, beams, and so on, as shown in Figure 1-2.

Figure 1-1 *The project created using 2D lines*

Figure 1-2 *A structural project created using parametric structural elements*

Using these 3D elements, you can visualize the structural project with respect to its scale, volume, and proportions. This enables you to study design alternatives and develop superior quality design solutions. Autodesk Revit automates routine drafting and coordination tasks and assists in reducing errors in documentation. This in turn saves time, improves the speed of documentation, and lowers the cost for users.

Understanding the Parametric Building Modeling Technology

A project in Autodesk Revit is created using the inbuilt parametric building elements. The term 'parametric' refers to the parameters that relate to various building elements. Some relationships are made by Autodesk Revit itself and others by the user. For example, doors, which have an inherent parametric relationship with the structural walls cannot be created without first creating a host wall. A door always moves with the host wall. Similarly, floors too are parametrically linked to walls. When you move structural walls, the structural floor extents are also modified automatically. Each structural element has inbuilt bidirectional associativity with many other elements in the project.

A building information model is created using different interdependent parametric building elements such as structural walls, beams, columns, structural floors, foundations, and so on. As they are bidirectionally associated elements, any change made in one element is automatically adopted by others. The integrated building information model created contains all data for a project. You can then create project presentation views such as structural plans, sections, elevations, and so on for documentation. As you modify the model while working in certain views, Autodesk Revit's parametric change engine automatically updates other views. This capability is, therefore, the underlying concept in Autodesk Revit.

Autodesk Revit's parametric change engine enables you to modify design elements at any stage of the project development. As changes are made immediately and automatically, it saves the time and effort of coordinating them in all other associated views, which, for most projects, is an inevitable part of the design process. Autodesk Revit's capability to coordinate between various aspects of the building design provides immense flexibility in the design and development process along with an error-free documentation.

Autodesk Revit also provides a variety of in-built parametric element libraries that can be selected and used to create a building model. It also provides you with the flexibility to modify the properties of these elements or to create your own parametric elements, based on the project requirement.

Terms Used in Autodesk Revit for Structure

Before using Autodesk Revit, it is important to understand the basic terms used for creating a building model. Various terms used in Autodesk Revit for Structure such as project, level, category, family, type, and instance are described next.

Autodesk Revit Project

A project in Autodesk Revit is similar to an actual structural project. In an actual project, the entire documentation such as drawings, 3D views, specifications, schedules, cost estimates, and so on are inherently linked and read together. Similarly, in Autodesk Revit, a project not only includes the digital 3D building model but also its parametrically associated documentation. Thus, all components such as the building model, its standard views, structural drawings, and schedules combine together to form a complete project. A project file contains all project information such as building elements used in a project, drawing sheets, schedules, cost estimates, 3D views, renderings, and so on. A project file also stores various settings such as environment, lighting, and so on. As data is stored in the same file, so it becomes easier for Autodesk Revit to coordinate the entire database.

Levels in a Building Model

In Autodesk Revit, a building model is divided into various levels. These levels may be understood as infinite horizontal planes that act as hosts for different elements such as roof, floor, ceiling, and so on. The defined levels in a building model can, in most cases, relate to different floor levels, or stories of the building project. Each element that you create belongs to a particular level.

Subdivisions of Elements into Categories and Subcategories

Apart from building elements, Autodesk Revit project also contains other associated elements such as annotations, imported files, links, and so on. These elements have been divided into the following categories:

Model Category : Consists of various structural elements used in creating a building model such as structural walls, structural floors, foundations, beams, braces, and columns.

Annotation Category : Consists of annotations such as dimensions, text notes, tags, symbols, and so on

Datum Category : Consists of datums such as levels, grids, reference planes, and so on

View Category : Consists of interactive project views such as structural floor plans, elevations, sections, 3D views, and renderings

In addition to these four categories, other categories such as **Imported**, **Workset**, **Filter**, and **Revit Categories** can also exist if the project has imported files, enabled worksets, or linked Autodesk Revit projects, respectively.

Families in Autodesk Revit

Another powerful concept in Autodesk Revit is family. A family is described as a set of elements of the same category that can be grouped together based on certain common parameters or characteristics. Elements of the same family may have different properties, but they all have common characteristics. For example, **Concrete-Rectangular-Column** is a concrete column family, but it contains different sizes of columns. Family files have the *.rfa* extension. You can load additional building component families from the libraries provided in Autodesk Revit package.

Families are further divided into certain types. Type or family type, as it is called, is a specific size or style of a family. For example, **Concrete-Rectangular-Column: 12 x 18** is a column type in Imperial system and **M_Concrete-Rectangular-Column: 300 x 450mm** in Metric system. All uses of the same family type in a project have the same properties. Family and family types can also be used to create new families using the **Family Editor**.

Instances are the actual usage of model elements in a building model or annotations in a drawing sheet. A family type created in a new location is identified as an instance of the family type. All instances of the same family type have the same properties. Therefore, when you modify the properties of a family type, the properties of all its instances also get modified. The family categorization of Revit elements is given below:

Model Category   : Column
Family   : **Concrete-Rectangular-Column** in Imperial
                             M_Concrete-Rectangular-Column in Metric
Family type   : 12 x 18 (300 x 450mm)
Instance   : Particular usage of a family type

The hierarchy of building elements in Autodesk Revit plays an important role in providing the flexibility and ease of managing a change in a building model. Figure 1-3 shows the hierarchy of categories and families in a typical Autodesk Revit project.

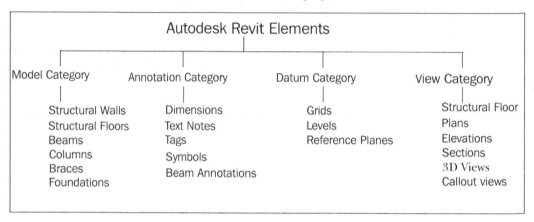

Figure 1-3 *Hierarchy of Autodesk Revit categories and families*

Creating a Structural Model Using Parametric Building Elements

Another classification of categories of elements followed in Autodesk Revit is based on their usage. Autodesk Revit uses five classes of elements: Host, component, annotation, view, and datum. Hosts are the element categories that form the basic structure of a building model and include model elements such as structural walls and floors. Components are the elements that are added to the host elements or act as stand-alone elements such as doors, windows, and foundations. Annotations are the 2D, view-specific elements that add content to the project documentation such as dimensions, tags, text notes, and so on. Views represent various orientations of a building model such as plans, elevations, sections, 3D views, and so on. Datum refers to the reference elements that assist you in creating a building model. The reference elements which include grids, levels, reference planes, and so on.

There is no specific methodology available for creating a building model in Autodesk Revit. It provides you with the flexibility of generating the building geometry based on the project requirement, design complexity, and other factors. However, the following steps describe a general procedure that may be followed for creating an architectural building model using the built-in parametric elements provided in Autodesk Revit.

The first step is to define the levels of the structural model based on the story height of the building and then create grids for inserting columns and foundation at the lowest level. Next, add columns, foundation slab, structural wall, and foundations in that level. You can also link the control height of the structural walls and columns to the levels. Next, create framing members and floors using the defined levels. You can add loads to the model and define load conditions and various analytical settings for the model.

After creating the structural analytical model, you will transfer it to Autodesk Robot Structural Analysis software and analyze the structural entities based on the loads applied to it. After performing the analysis and retrieving the design detail of the model, you will import the structural model from the analysis software into Autodesk Revit. Next, you will create drawing sheets with the desired views for its presentation. You can also add reinforcements to the concrete elements in the structural model. Autodesk Revit also provides tools to create rendered 3D views and walkthroughs. Figure 1-4 shows an example of a building elevation with various structural elements.

Figure 1-4 Building section showing building elements and levels

Visibility/Graphics Overrides, Scale, and Detail Level

Autodesk Revit enables you to control the display and graphic representation of a single element or the element category of various elements in project views by using the visibility and graphics overrides tools. You can select a model category and modify its linetype and detail level. This can also be done for various annotation category elements and imported files. These settings can be done for each project view based on its desired representation. You can also hide an element or an element category in a view using the **Hide in view** and **Isolate** tools. You can override the graphic representation of an element or an element category in any view using the **Visibility/ Graphics** tool.

The scale is an important concept in a Revit project. You can set the scale from the available list of standard scales such as 1/16"=1'0", 1/4"=1'0", 1"=1'0", 1/2"=1'0" (for Imperial) and

1:1, 1:2, 1:3, 1:4, 1:5, 1:10 (for Metric). As you set a scale, Autodesk Revit automatically sets the detail level that is appropriate for it. There are three detail levels provided in an Autodesk Revit project: **Coarse**, **Medium**, and **Fine**. You can also set the detail level manually for each project view. Each detail level has an associated linetype and the detail lines associated with it. The details of annotations such as dimensions, tags, and so on, are also defined by the selected scale.

Extracting Project Information
A single integrated building information is used to create and represent a building project. You can extract project information from a building model and create area schemes, schedule, and cost estimates, and then add them to the project presentation.

Autodesk Revit also enables you to export the extracted database to the industry standard Open Database Connectivity (ODBC) compliant relational database tables. The use of the building information model to extract database information eliminates the error-prone method of measuring building spaces individually.

Creating a Structural Drawing Set
After creating the building model, you can easily arrange the project views by plotting them on the drawing sheets. Drawing sheets can also be organized in a project file based on the established CAD standards followed by the firm. In this manner, the project documentation can easily be transformed from the conceptual design stage to the design development stage and finally to the construction document stage. The project view on a drawing sheet is only a graphical representation of the building information model. Therefore, any modification made in it is immediately updated in all the associated project views, thereby keeping the drawing sets updated.

Creating an Unusual Building Geometry
Autodesk Revit also helps you conceptualize a building project in terms of its volume, shape, and proportions before working with actual building elements. This is possible by using the Massing tool, which enables you to create quick 3D models of buildings and conduct volumetric and proportion study on overall masses. It also enables you to visualize and create an unusual building geometry. The same massing model can then be converted into a building model with individual parametric building elements. It provides continuity in the generation of building model right from sketch design to its development.

Flexibility of Creating Special Elements
Autodesk Revit provides a large number of in-built family types of various model elements and annotations. Each parametric element has the associated properties that can be modified based on the project requirement.

Autodesk Revit also enables you to create the elements that are designed specifically for a particular location. The in-built family editor enables you to create new elements using family templates. This provides you with the flexibility of using in-built elements for creating your own elements. For example, using the furniture template, you can create a reception desk that is suitable for a particular location in the design.

Creating Structural Layouts

Autodesk Revit's structural tools enable you to add structural elements to a building model. An extensive in-built library of structural elements has been provided in Autodesk Revit. You can add structural columns, beams, walls, braces, and so on to the project. Thus, structural consultants can also incorporate their elements in the basic architectural building model and check for inconsistency, if any.

Working on Large Projects

In Autodesk Revit, you can work on large projects by linking different building projects together. For a large project that consists of a number of buildings, you can create individual buildings as separate projects and then link all of them into a single base file. The database recognizes the linked projects and includes them in the project representation of the base file.

For example, while working on a large educational institution campus, you can create separate project files for academic building, administration area, gymnasium, cafeteria, computer centre, and so on, and then link them into the base site plan file. In this manner, large projects can be subdivided and worked upon simultaneously.

Working in Large Teams and Coordinating with Consultants

Worksets, in Autodesk Revit, enable the division of the building model into small editable set of elements. The worksets can be assigned to different teams working on the same project and then their work can easily be coordinated in the central file location. The effort required to coordinate, collaborate, and communicate the changes between various worksets is taken care of by computer. Various consultants working on a project can be assigned a workset with a set of editable elements. They can then incorporate their services and modify the associated elements.

For example, a high rise commercial building project can be divided into different worksets with independent teams working on exterior skin, interior walls, building core, toilet details, finishes, and so on. The structural consultants can be assigned the exterior skin and the core workset, in which they can incorporate structural elements. Similarly, the rest of the teams can work independently on different worksets.

STARTING Autodesk Revit 2021

Enhanced

You can start Autodesk Revit by double-clicking on its shortcut icon on the desktop. Alternatively, you can start Autodesk Revit 2021 from the taskbar. To do so, choose the **Start** button; a menu is displayed. Choose **Autodesk > Revit 2021**, as shown in Figure 1-5; the interface will be displayed, as shown in Figure 1-6. (For Windows 10)

Figure 1-5 *Starting Autodesk Revit 2021 using the taskbar*

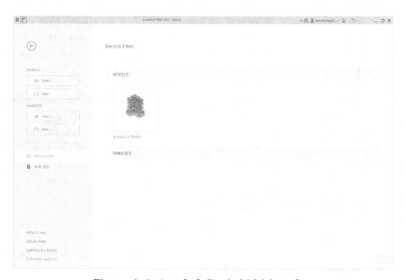

Figure 1-6 *Autodesk Revit 2021 interface*

 Note
The path for starting Autodesk Revit depends on the operating system being used.

The interface screen has four sections: **MODELS**, **FAMILIES**, **LEARN**, and **BIM 360**. The options in the **Models** section are used to open an existing model, a new model, and an existing template. The options in the **Families** section are used to open a new or an existing family. You can also invoke the Conceptual Mass environment from this section to create a conceptual mass model.

In the **Learn** section, you can choose the **What's New?** option to get information about the new tools and features in Revit 2021.

When you click on the **What's New?** option, you are directed to the **Autodesk Revit 2021** page that has a list of videos of newly added features in Revit. You can click on a link to view the corresponding video.

You can choose the **Essential Skills Videos** and **Getting Started Video** options to view the videos related to basic, advance concepts, and modelling in Revit 2021. These videos and their associated information help you to learn about different features and capabilities of the software. Moreover, you can choose the **Autodesk App Store** option from the **InfoCenter** to access various add-ons that can be used to enhance the productivity of Revit. On choosing this option, the **Autodesk App Store** page will be displayed. In this page, various links are available as add-ons which can be used in Revit applications. In the **Revit Community** option of the **InfoCenter** section, you can access information related to various communities and their contribution in the form of articles, tutorials, and videos.

In addition, you can choose the **Help** option from the **InfoCenter** to get help on various tools. When you choose this option, you will be directed to https://help.autodesk.com/view/RVT/2021/ENU/. Also, the Autodesk Revit 2021 page with the **Welcome to Revit 2021** Learning area will be displayed. To access information related to additions and enhancements in **Revit 2021** release, you can expand the **What's New** node from the left pane and then click on the **What's New** link. On doing so, the **What's New** page will be displayed with various links. You can visit the links to learn about enhancements in Revit 2021.

The new interface screen of Autodesk Revit 2021 has been enhanced to provide better experience of navigating BIM 360 projects. Now, you can access your projects stored in BIM 360 directly from the interface screen of Revit 2021 by clicking on the **BIM 360** button.

Some new features are also added to the interface screen of Autodesk Revit 2021. These includes the **Community Forum** and **Customer Support** options. When you click on the **Community Forum** option, Revit 2021 directs you to *https://forums.autodesk.com/t5/revit-products/ct-p/2003* page. On this page, you can access Autodesk's Revit Forums to share your knowledge, ask questions, collaborate on ideas, and explore popular Revit topics. When you click on the **Customer Support** option, you are directed to *https://knowledge.autodesk.com/contact-support* page. This page provides you the information on purchasing, downloading, installing and troubleshooting of various software. This page also assists you in managing your Autodesk account and your software license.

In the **Models** section, choose the **Open** option; the **Open** dialog box will be displayed. Browse to the desired location in the dialog box and select the file. Now, choose the **Open** button to open the file.

To open a new project file, choose the **New** option from the **Models** section. Alternatively, choose **New > Project** from the **File** menu; the **New Project** dialog box will be displayed. In this dialog box, you can select the desired template from the **Template file** drop-down or you can browse the other template files by using the **Browse** button from the **Template File** area. When you choose the **Browse** button, the **Choose Template** dialog box will be displayed. In this dialog box, make sure the **Project** radio button is selected, and then choose the **OK** button; a new project file will open and the interface screen will be activated.

To create a new project template file, choose the **New** option from the **Projects** section; The **New Project** dialog box will be displayed. In this dialog box, select the base template from the **Template file** drop-down list and make sure that the **Project template** radio button is selected. Choose the **OK** button; a new project template file will open with the interface screen.

USER INTERFACE

In Autodesk Revit, the user interface consists of the ribbon, Drawing Area, **Properties** palette, Status Bar, and the **View Control Bar**, as shown in Figure 1-7. In Autodesk Revit, ribbon is an interface from where you can invoke tools. The ribbon, which contains task-based tabs and panels, streamlines the structural workflow and optimizes the project delivery time. In Autodesk Revit, when you select an element in the Drawing area, the ribbon displays a contextual tab that comprises of tools corresponding to the selected element. The interface of Autodesk Revit is similar to the interfaces of many other Microsoft Windows-based programs. The main parts in the Revit interface are discussed next.

Figure 1-7 *The Autodesk Revit 2021 user interface*

Title Bar

The Title Bar is displayed on the top portion in the user interface, displays the program's logo, name of the current project, and the view opened in the viewing area.

Ribbon

The ribbon, as shown in Figure 1-8, is an interface that is used to invoke tools. When you open a file, the ribbon is displayed at the top in the screen. It comprises task-based tabs and panels, refer to Figure 1-8, which provide all the tools necessary for creating a project. The tabs and panels in the ribbon can be customized according to the need of the user. This can be done by moving the panels and changing the view states of the ribbon (the method of changing the ribbon view state is discussed later in this chapter). The ribbon contains buttons, drop-downs, panels, tabs, and tools. These buttons and the tools can be selected from the corresponding panels.

Figure 1-8 Different components of a ribbon

Tip
Tooltips appear when you place the cursor over any of the tool icons in the ribbon. The name of the tool appears in a box helping you in identifying the tool icon.

In the ribbon, you can move a panel and place it anywhere on the screen. To do so, press and hold the left mouse button on the panel label in the ribbon, and then drag the panel to a desired place on the screen. Next, use the tools of the moved panel and place the panel back in the ribbon. To do so, place the cursor on the moved panel and choose the **Return Panels to Ribbon** button from the upper right corner of this panel, as shown in Figure 1-9; the panel will return to the ribbon.

*Figure 1-9 Choosing the **Return Panels to Ribbon** button*

Changing the View States of the Ribbon

The ribbon can be displayed in three view states by selecting any of the following four options: **Minimize to Tabs**, **Minimize to Panel Titles**, **Minimize to Panel Buttons**, and **Cycle through All**. To use these options, place the cursor over the second arrow on the right of the **Modify** tab in the ribbon, refer to Figure 1-10; the arrow will be highlighted. Next, click on the down arrow; a flyout will be displayed, as shown in Figure 1-10. From this flyout, you can choose the **Minimize to Tabs** option to display the only tabs in the ribbon. If you choose the **Minimize to Panel Titles** option, the ribbon will display the titles of the panels along with the tabs. You can choose the **Minimize to Panel Buttons** option to display panels as buttons in the ribbon along with tabs.

Figure 1-10 Various options in the flyout for changing the view state of the ribbon

Note
*If the ribbon is changed to a different view state, then on placing the cursor over the first arrow on the right of the **Modify** tab, the **Show Full Ribbon** tooltip will be displayed. Click on the arrow; the full ribbon will be displayed.*

The table given next describes the tabs in the ribbon and their functions.

Tab	Description
Architecture	Contains tools for creating architectural elements for a project
Structure	Contains tools for creating structural elements in a project
Steel	Contains tools for creating steel structure and their connections details in a project
Precast	Contains tools to create precast assemblies and drawings
Systems	Contains tools for creating mechanical elements in a project
Insert	Contains tools to insert, link, and manage secondary files such as raster image files, CAD files or PDFs
Annotate	Contains tools for documenting a building model such as adding texts and dimensions
Analyze	Contains tools for energy analysis of the project
Massing & Site	Contains tools for modeling and modifying conceptual mass and site elements
Collaborate	Contains tools for collaborating the project with other team members (internal and external)
View	Contains tools used for managing and modifying the current view and also for switching views
Manage	Contains tools for specifying the project and system parameters and project settings
Add-Ins	Contains all the installed Add- Ins (Plug-Ins)
Modify	Contains tools for editing elements in the model

Contextual Tabs in the Ribbon

These tabs are displayed when you choose certain tools or select elements. They contain a set of tools or buttons that relate only to a particular tool or element.

For example, when you invoke the **Beam** tool, the **Modify | Place Beam** contextual tab is displayed. This tab has the following panels: **Select**, **Properties**, **Clipboard**, **Geometry**, **Modify**, **View**, **Measure**, **Create**, **Mode**, **Draw**, **Multiple**, and **Tag**. The **Select** panel contains the **Modify** tool. The **Properties** panel contains the **Properties** button and the **Type Properties** tool. The **Mode** panel has some necessary tools that are used to load model families or to create the model of a window in a drawing. The other panels, apart from those discussed above, contain the tools that are contextual and are used to edit elements when they are placed in a drawing or selected from a drawing for modification.

Application Frame

The application frame helps you manage projects in Autodesk Revit. It consists of the **File** menu, Quick Access Toolbar, InfoCenter, and Status Bar. These options are discussed next.

File Menu

The **File** menu contains tools that provide access to many common file actions such as **Open**, **Close**, and **Save**. To display this menu, choose **File** menu in the ribbon, refer to Figure 1-11. Alternatively, press ALT+F to display tools in the **File** menu.

*Figure 1-11 The **File** menu*

Quick Access Toolbar

The **Quick Access Toolbar**, shown in Figure 1-12, contains the options to undo and redo changes, open and save a file, create a new file, and so on.

*Figure 1-12 The **Quick Access Toolbar***

By default, the **Quick Access Toolbar** contains the options such as **Open, Home, Save, Redo, Undo**, and so on. You can customize the display of the **Quick Access Toolbar** by adding more tools and removing the unwanted tools. To add a tool or a button from the panel of the ribbon to the **Quick Access Toolbar**, place the cursor over the button; the button will be highlighted. Next, right-click; a flyout will be displayed. Choose **Add to Quick Access Toolbar** from the flyout displayed; the highlighted button will be added to the **Quick Access Toolbar**. The **Quick Access Toolbar** can be customized to reorder the tools displayed in it. To do so, choose the down arrow next to the **Switch Windows** drop-down, refer to Figure 1-12; a flyout will be displayed. Choose the **Customize Quick Access Toolbar** option located at the bottom of the flyout; the **Customize Quick Access Toolbar** dialog box will be displayed. Use various options in this dialog box and choose the **OK** button; the **Customize Quick Access Toolbar** dialog box will close and the tools in the **Quick Access Toolbar** will be reordered.

InfoCenter

You can use **InfoCenter** to search for information related to Revit (Help) to display the **Subscription Center** panel for subscription services and product updates, and to display the **Favorites** panel to access saved topics. Figure 1-13 displays various tools in **InfoCenter**.

Figure 1-13 The InfoCenter

Status Bar

The Status Bar is located at the bottom of the interface screen. When the cursor is placed over an element or a component, the Status Bar displays the name of the family and type of the corresponding element or components. It also displays prompts and messages to help you use the selected tools.

View Control Bar

The **View Control Bar** is located at the lower left corner of the drawing window, as shown in Figure 1-14. It can be used to access various view-related tools. The **Scale** button shows the scale of the current view. You can choose this button to display a flyout that contains standard drawing scales. From this flyout, you can then select the scale for the current view. The **Detail Level** button is used to set the detail level of a view. You can select the required detail level as **Coarse, Medium**, and **Fine**. Similarly, the **Visual Style** button enables you to set the display style. The options for setting the display style are: **Wireframe, Hidden Line, Shaded, Consistent Colors, Realistic**, and **Raytrace**.

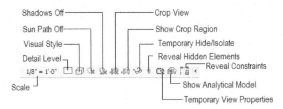

*Figure 1-14 The **View Control Bar***

Options Bar

The **Options Bar** provides information about the common parameters of a component type. It also displays options for creating or editing them. The options displayed in the **Options Bar** depend on the type of component being created and selected for editing. Figure 1-15 displays the options in the **Options Bar** to create a structural column.

*Figure 1-15 The **Options Bar** with different options to create a structural column*

Type Selector

The **Type Selector** drop-down list is located in the **Properties** palette for the currently invoked tool. On invoking the **Beam** tool, the properties of the beam will be displayed in the **Properties** palette. In this palette, you can use the **Type Selector** drop-down list to select the required type of the beam. The content in the **Type Selector** drop-down list keep changing, depending upon the current function of the tool or the elements selected. The **Type Selector** drop-down list can also be used to specify the type of the element or component while placing an element or a component in a drawing. You can also use this drop-down list to change the type of a selected element.

Drawing Area

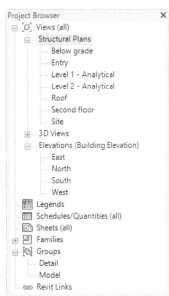

The Drawing Area is the actual modeling area where you can create and view the building model. It covers the major portion of the interface screen. You can draw building components in this area. The position of the pointing device is represented by the cursor. The Drawing Area also has the standard Microsoft Windows functions and buttons such as close, minimize, maximize, scroll bar, and so on. These buttons have the same function as that of the other Microsoft Windows-based programs.

PROJECT BROWSER

The **Project Browser** is located below the ribbon. It displays project views, schedules, sheets, families, and groups in a logical tree-like structure, as shown in Figure 1-16 and helps you open and manage them. To open a view, double-click

*Figure 1-16 The **Project Browser***

on the name of the view, or drag and drop the view in the Drawing Area. You can close the **Project Browser** or dock it anywhere in the Drawing Area.

Note
*If the **Project Browser** is not displayed on the screen, choose the **View** tab from the ribbon and then select the **Project Browser** check box from **View > Windows > User Interface** drop-down.*

The **Project Browser** can be organized to group the views and sheets based on the project requirement. For example, while working on a large project with a number of sheets, you can organize the **Project Browser** to view and access specific sheets.

Note
*In the **Project Browser**, you can expand or collapse the view listing by selecting the '+' or '-' sign, respectively. The current view in the drawing window is highlighted in bold letters. The default project file has a set of preloaded views.*

Keyboard Accelerators

In Autodesk Revit, accelerator keys have been assigned to some of the frequently used tools. These keys are shortcuts that you can type through the keyboard to invoke the corresponding tool. Accelerator keys corresponding to a tool appear as a tooltip when you move the cursor over the tool.

Tip
*As you become accustomed to use Autodesk Revit, you will find these **Keyboard Accelerators** quite useful because they save the effort of browsing through the menus.*

Properties Palette

The **Properties** palette, as shown in Figure 1-17, is a modeless interface, which displays the type and element properties of various elements and views in a drawing. The **Properties** palette is dockable and resizable, and it supports multiple monitor configurations. The **Properties** palette is displayed in the Revit interface by default and it shows the instance properties of an active view. When you select an element from a drawing, the **Properties** palette displays its instance properties. You can also access the type properties of the selected element from the **Properties** palette. To do so, choose the **Edit Type** button from the palette; the **Type Properties** dialog box will be displayed. In this dialog box, you can change the type properties of the selected element.

In the **Properties** palette, you can assign a type to a selected element in a drawing from the **Type Selector** drop-down list. In Revit, you can toggle the display of the **Properties** palette in its interface. Choose the

***Figure 1-17** The **Properties** palette*

Properties button in the **Properties** panel of the **Modify** tab to hide it. Similarly, you can choose the **Properties** button to display the palette if it is not visible in the interface.

DIALOG BOXES

Some Autodesk Revit tools, when invoked, display a dialog box. A dialog box is an interface for accessing, specifying, and modifying the parameters related to that tool. For example, when you choose **Save As > Project** from the **Application Menu**, the **Save As** dialog box is displayed, as shown in Figure 1-18. A dialog box consists of various parts such as dialog label, radio buttons, text or edit boxes, check boxes, slider bars, image box, buttons, and tools, which are similar to other windows-based programs. Some dialog boxes contain the [**...**] button, which displays another related dialog box. There are certain buttons such as **OK**, **Cancel**, and **Help**, which appear at the bottom of most of the dialog boxes. The names of the buttons imply their respective functions. The button with a dark border is the default button.

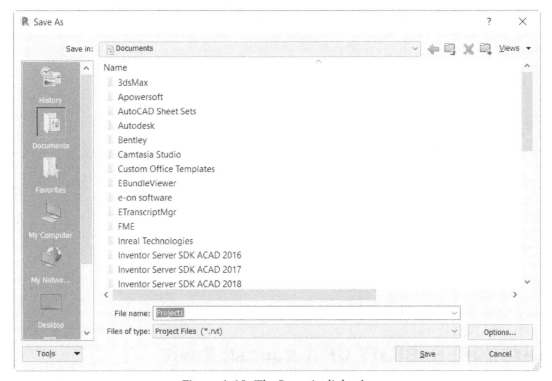

Figure 1-18 *The Save As dialog box*

MULTIPLE DOCUMENT ENVIRONMENT

The multiple document environment feature allows you to open more than one project at a time in a single Autodesk Revit session. This is very useful when you want to work on different projects simultaneously and make changes with reference to each other.

Sometimes, you may need to incorporate certain features from one project into the other. With the help of multiple document environment feature, you can open multiple projects and then use the **Cut**, **Copy** and **Paste** tools from the **Clipboard** panel of the **Modify (type of element)** tab to transfer the required components from one project to another. These editing tools can also be invoked by using the CTRL+C and CTRL+V keyboard shortcuts.

To access the opened projects, click on the **Switch Windows** drop-down arrow in the **Windows** panel of the **View** tab; the options for the names of different opened project files will be displayed, as shown in Figure 1-19. Like other Microsoft Windows-based programs, you can select and view the opened projects using the **Tile Views** tools from the **Windows** panel of the **View** tab. The tile views of a project is shown in Figure 1-20.

*Figure 1-19 Selecting an option from the **Switch Windows** drop-down list*

*Figure 1-20 The **Tile Views** tool for project*

INTEROPERABILITY OF Autodesk Revit

The models or geometries created in Autodesk Revit can be easily exported to AutoCAD and AutoCAD Architecture in the DWG file format. This enables structural engineers to collaborate with Architects.

One of the important aspects of the job of a structural engineer is to collaborate and share information with the rest of the design team including the architect. To facilitate this requirement, Revit follows a wide range of industry standards and supports various CAD file formats such as DWF, DGN, DWG, DGN, IFC, SKP, and SAT. For image files, it supports JPG, TIFF, BMP, PNG, AVI, PAN, IVR, and TGA file formats. Besides these, the formats that are supported by Revit include ODBC, HTML, TXT, XML, XLS, and MDB. Autodesk Revit is compatible with any CAD system that supports the DWG, DXF, or DGN file format. Revit can import the models and geometries as ACIS solids. This enables engineers to import models from AutoCAD Architecture and AutoCAD MEP (Mechanical, Electrical, and Plumbing) software and to link and import 3D information to Revit. This feature makes Autodesk Revit 2021 an efficient, user-friendly, and compatible software.

BUILDING INFORMATION MODELING AND Autodesk Revit

Building Information Modeling (BIM) is defined as a design technology that involves the creation and use of coordinated, internally consistent, and computable information about a building project in design and construction.

Using BIM, you can demonstrate the entire life cycle of a building project starting from the process of construction, facility operation, and information about quantities and shared properties of elements. BIM enables the circulation of virtual information model from the design team to contractors and then to the owner, thereby adding changes and their knowledge to update the model at each stage of transfer. The ability to keep information up-to-date and make it available in an integrated digital environment enables the architects, owners, builders, and engineers to have clear vision of the project before the commencement of actual construction. It also enables them to make better and faster decisions to improve the quality and profitability of projects. Autodesk Revit is a specially designed platform based on BIM.

In Revit, the analytical and physical representations of a structural model are created simultaneously. These representations are just different views of a computable building model that contains necessary information for a third-party analysis application. Revit provides a common modeling interface for third-party analysis applications. You can use Revit API to move data directly from the Revit building information model to the analysis software. You can further bring back the analysis while keeping the analysis, design, and documentation synchronized.

Revit's parametric model represents a building as an integrated database of coordinated information. In Revit, change anywhere is change everywhere. A change made in your project at any stage is reflected in the entire project, and also, due to the parametric behavior of elements, the project is updated automatically. Also, the integration of Revit with the available in-built commercial tools such as solar studies, material takeoffs, and so on greatly simplifies the project design and reduces the time consumed by these analyses, thereby enabling faster decision making.

WORKSHARING USING REVIT SERVER

Worksharing is a method of distributing work among people involved in a project, and accomplishing it within the stipulated period of time. In worksharing, each person involved in the project is assigned a task that has to be accomplished through proper planning and by coordinating with the other members of the team.

In a large scale building project, worksharing helps in finishing a project in time and meeting the quality requirements that are set during the process. Generally, in a large scale building project, worksharing is based on the specialization of work. The professionals such as structural engineers, architects, interior architects, and MEP engineers are involved in their respective fields to accomplish the project. So, the distribution of work at the primary stage is made on the basis of the area of specialization. Each professional has his own set of work to perform for the accomplishment of the project. Therefore, worksharing is an important process that is required to be implemented efficiently to complete the project in time.

In Autodesk Revit, you can apply server-based worksharing with the help of Revit Server, which is a server application. Revit Server uses a central server and multiple local servers for collaborating across a Wide Area Network (WAN). The central server hosts the central model of a workshared project and remains accessible to all team members over the Wide Area Network. Similarly, the local server is accessible to all team members in a Local Area Network (LAN). The local server hosts a local updated copy of the central model. In the Worksharing environment, the team members are not aware of the local server as it is transparent in their daily operations. Refer to Figure 1-21 for the network model of Revit Server.

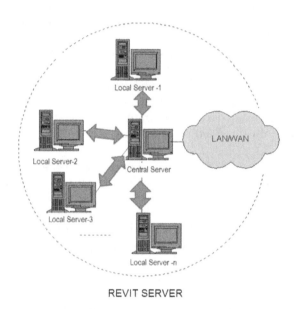

Figure 1-21 *The Network Model of Revit Server*

In Worksharing environment, a team member starts working on the local model of the central model. The local model will be saved in the computer of the team member. As the team member works, the local server requests updated information from the central model on the central server, using available network capacity to transfer the data over the WAN. The updated version of the model is stored on the local server, so the updates are readily available when a team member requests them.

LINKING ANALYTICAL MODEL FOR ANALYSIS

In Autodesk Revit, the physical model represents the physical layout that consists of structural walls, beams, columns, footings, and so on. The analytical model is created along with the physical model. The analytical model is the engineering description of a structural physical model.

The following elements have analytical model associated with them: Structural Columns, Structural Framing elements (such as beams and braces), Structural Floors, Structural Footings, and Structural Walls. The analytical model is a 3D model that is used for structural analysis. In this model, you can add loads and material properties that are required for analysis. To analyze the analytical model, transfer it into a third-party analysis software. You can link the analytical model via application programming interface (API) to several leading industry applications for building analysis, such as ADAPT-Builder, RISA 3D, Fastrack, ROBOT Millennium, Sofistik, and others. After the analysis has been performed, the results of the analysis are returned to the building model (physical and analytical) in Revit. The results that are returned to Revit, dynamically update the building model and the documentation associated with it.

Autodesk Revit HELP

Autodesk Revit 2021 helps you to easily understand the tools and methods used in a project. In Autodesk Revit 2021, you can access online help documentation (Autodesk WikiHelp) as well as local (offline) help documentation.

To access the help feature, click on the **Help** down arrow on the right of the **InfoCenter**; a flyout with various help options will be displayed. The options to access the help are discussed next.

Using the Revit 2021 Help

To access the local Revit 2021 help, choose the **Help** tool from **InfoCenter**; the **Autodesk Revit 2021** page will be displayed, as shown in Figure 1-22. You can also display the **Autodesk Revit 2021** page by pressing the F1 key. In this page, different areas such as **Learn about Revit**, **Resources**, and others are displayed. You can click on the required link from these areas to get the related information. In the **Learn about Revit** area, various help options related to Autodesk Revit are available. You can click on the required option to display the help page corresponding to the option. The **Resources** area contains various learning resources. You can click on the desired option in this area to get the information related to it.

Figure 1-22 *The local* **Revit Help** *page*

Self-Evaluation Test

Answer the following questions and then compare them to those given at the end of this chapter:

1. You cannot add template file under the **Projects** head. (T/F)

2. You can create analytical model in Revit. (T/F)

3. Worksharing method is used only to hide elements in Revit. (T/F)

4. You can work on four detail levels in Revit. (T/F)

5. Elements of the same family may have different properties. (T/F)

Answers to Self-Evaluation Test
1. T, 2. T, 3. F, 4. F, 5. T

Chapter 2

Getting Started with a Structural Project

Learning Objectives

After completing this chapter, you will be able to:
- *Start a new structural project*
- *Set the units of various measurement parameters for a project*
- *Understand the concept of snaps, dimensions, and object snaps*
- *Save a project*
- *Close a project and exit Revit 2021*
- *Open an existing project*

In this chapter, you will learn how to create a new structural project. Also, you will learn the methods of creating initial setups such as units and snaps.

STARTING A NEW STRUCTURAL PROJECT

File Menu: New > Project
Shortcut Key: CTRL+N

In Revit, a structural project is considered as a single database containing information related to a building design. This means that the project file created will contain all the information related to building design, from geometry to construction documentation. Generally, this information include the details of the components used to design building models (like walls, doors, windows, beams, columns, and other relevant information about the building design), different views of the model, working drawings created from model, and documentation related to design of the model.

In Revit, you can create different views such as plan, elevation, and sections from a single model created for a building project. These views are associated with each other. This means, when you change the building design in one view, it is propagated throughout the project.

In Revit, a new project file uses the default settings that are defined in the project template.

To start a new project, choose **New > Project** from the **File** menu, as shown in Figure 2-1; the **New Project** dialog box will be displayed, refer to Figure 2-2. In this dialog box, the **Imperial-Construction Template** is selected by default in the **Template file** drop-down list. As a result, the new project will adopt the settings of the template file. A template file has various project parameters saved in it such as units, views, and so on. When you apply the template file on a new project, it will adopt the same parameters as the template file. The difference between a template file format and a project file format is that the former has a *.rte* extension, whereas the latter has a *.rvt* extension. You can either select any of the template files provided in Revit or create your own template file.

Figure 2-1 *Choosing the* **Project** *option from* **File** *menu*

*Figure 2-2 The **New Project** dialog box*

You can also save any project file as a template file. You can select a file as template by first choosing the **Browse** button in the **Template file** area of the **New Project** dialog box and then selecting the required file from appropriate location. To create a new project, select the **Project** radio button and to create a template, select the **Project template** radio button in the **New Project** dialog box.

Note
*If you select the **None** option from the **New Template** drop-down list in the **New Project** dialog box, a new project file will be created without a template file but with the default settings of Revit.*

SETTING PROJECT UNITS

Ribbon:	Manage > Settings > Project Units
Shortcut Key:	UN

Units are important parameters of a project as they provide a standard for measurement of different entities. While installing Revit, you are prompted to set the Imperial (feet and inches) or Metric (meter and millimeter) unit as default. Setting a default unit system helps you to start your project with a specific type of unit as per the conventions followed in the industry. To set units, choose the **Project Units** tool from the **Settings** panel of the **Manage** tab; the **Project Units** dialog box will be displayed, as shown in Figure 2-3. Alternatively, type **UN** to display the **Project Units** dialog box. Under the **Units** column in this dialog box, you can specify various units that are relevant to the building project. In the **Project Units** dialog box, units are grouped into seven disciplines: **Common**, **Structural**, **HVAC**, **Electrical**, **Piping**, **Energy**, and **Infrastructure**. Each discipline has a set of measurement parameters. You can select any of these disciplines from the **Discipline** drop-down list in the **Project Units** dialog box. The **Format** column in this dialog box displays the current unit format for the corresponding parameter in the **Units** column. You can preview and select the possible digit grouping and decimal separators from the **Decimal symbol/digit grouping** drop-down list, which is at the lower left corner of the dialog box. Different types of units and their parameters are discussed next.

Note
*The values displayed in the **Format** column of the **Project Units** dialog box may differ depending upon the type of unit system, Imperial or Metric, selected for the project. In this textbook, the Imperial and Metric unit systems have been used in tutorials and illustrations.*

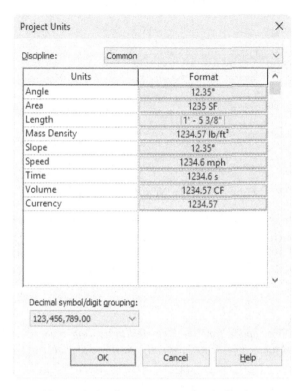

Figure 2-3 *The **Project Units** dialog box*

Common Unit Type

The **Common** unit type used in a structural project includes parameters such as **angle, area**, **length, mass density, slope, speed, time, volume**, and **currency.** In the **Project Units** dialog box, the **Common** option is selected by default in the **Discipline** drop-down list, refer to Figure 2-3. The **Common** unit type used in Revit is similar to those used in other Revit platforms. Moreover, the settings of the parameters of common units are similar to those used in other CAD programs. The methods of setting various parameters under the **Common** unit type are discussed next.

Setting Length Units

In a structural project, you can assign a unit for the measurement of length. To do so, click on the field corresponding to the **Length** parameter in the **Format** column of the **Project Units** dialog box; the **Format** dialog box will be displayed. This dialog box displays the units of length and their settings, as shown in Figure 2-4. Select the required unit from the **Units** drop-down list in the dialog box. The options that can be selected from this drop-down list are **Feet, Feet and fractional inches, US survey feet, Fractional inches, Meters, Decimeters, Centimeters, Millimeters**, and **Meters and centimeters**. By default, the **Feet and fractional inches** option is selected in this drop-down list if the **Imperial** is selected as the unit system at the time of installing Revit. But, if you have selected **Metric** as the unit system then the **Millimeters** option is selected in this drop-down list by default. The settings for rounding increment for the length unit can be made from their respective drop-down lists and edit boxes. To do so, select the desired option from the **Rounding** drop-down list. For certain units, you can specify custom rounding value using the **Rounding increment** edit box which is placed next to the **Rounding** drop-down list. This edit box is inactive by default. To make it active, first select any option from the **Units** drop-down list and then the **Custom** option from the **Rounding** drop-down list. Once the **Rounding increment** edit box is active, you can specify the desired rounding value in it for the selected unit (the **Custom** option remains inactive for the **Feet and fractional inches**, **Fractional inches**, and **Meters and Centimeters** options of the **Units** drop-down list).

 Note
*The **Rounding increment** edit box is not available for the **Meters and Centimeters**, **Feet and fractional inches**, and **Fractional inches** options.*

*Figure 2-4 The **Format** dialog box*

The **Unit symbol** drop-down list will be inactive if any of the **Feet and fractional inches**, **Fractional inches**, and **Meters and centimeters** options is selected in the **Units** drop-down list.

Once you make the **Unit symbol** drop-down list active, you can select the desired option from it to specify the measurement symbol to be used along with the unit of length in a project. For example, to use the symbol 'm' after all metric length measurements, you can select **m** option from the **Unit symbol** drop-down list as the measurement symbol. You can select the **Suppress spaces** check box to remove all spaces around the dash from the length strings. For example, you can remove spaces around the dash when a length string is expressed in feet and fractional inches to denote a particular measurement.

 Note
*The **Suppress spaces** is only active when **Feet and Fractional inches** is selected in the **Units** drop down.*

Setting the Area and Volume Units
In the **Project Units** dialog box, you can assign a unit for the measurements of areas. To do so, click on the field corresponding to the **Area** parameter in the **Format** column of the **Project Units** dialog box; the **Format** dialog box will be displayed. In this dialog box, you can set the unit for measuring the area by using the options in the **Units** drop-down list. This drop-down

list contains various options for the units of area such as **Square feet, Square meters, Square inches, Square centimeters, Square millimeters, Acres** and **Hectares**. By default, the **Square feet** option is selected in this drop-down list, if you had selected the **Imperial** units at the time of installing Revit. But, if you have selected the **Metric** units then the **Square meters** option is selected in this drop-down list by default. The settings for rounding increment and unit symbol for the area units can be made from their respective drop-down lists.

Similar to set the units for the area, you can set the units for volume. To set unit for the volume measurement, click in the field of the **Format** column corresponding to the **Volume** parameter in the **Project Units** dialog box; the **Format** dialog box will be displayed. In this dialog box, click in the **Units** drop-down list and select: **Cubic yards, Cubic feet, Cubic meters, Cubic millimeters,** or **Liters** and so on. After selecting a suitable option from the **Units** drop-down list, choose the **OK** button; the **Format** dialog box will be closed and the selected unit for the volume measurement will be displayed in the field of the **Format** column corresponding to the **Volume** parameter in the **Project Units** dialog box.

Setting Angle Units

In the **Project Units** dialog box, you can assign a unit for the measurement of angle. To do so, click on the field corresponding to angle parameter in **Format** column of the **Project Units** dialog box. The **Format** dialog box will be displayed. You can specify the unit for the angle by selecting the required option from the **Units** drop-down list in the **Format** dialog box for the **Angle** parameter. You can select **Degrees, Degrees minutes seconds, Radians,** or **Gradians** from the **Units** drop-down list to specify the unit for the angular measurement. By default, the **Decimal degrees** option is selected in this drop-down list, if Imperial is selected as a unit system at the time of installing Revit. Similarly, **12.35°** option is selected for Metric unit. The settings for rounding increment for the angle unit can be made from their respective drop-down list and edit box.

Setting Slope Units

In the **Project Units** dialog box, you can assign a unit for the measurement of slope. To do so, click on the field corresponding to angle parameter in the **Format** column of the **Project Units** dialog box. The **Format** dialog box will be displayed. You can specify the unit for the slope by selecting the required option from the **Units** drop-down list in the **Format** dialog box for the **Slope** parameter. You can select options such as **1 : Ratio, Ratio : 1, Ratio : 12, Ratio : 10, Rise / 12", Rise / 1'- 0", Rise / 1000 mm, Degrees,** or **Percentage** for the slope measurement from the **Units** drop-down list to specify the unit for the slope measurement. By default, the **Decimal degrees** option is selected in this drop-down list as the unit system while installing Revit. The settings for rounding increment for the slope unit can be made from their respective drop-down list and edit box.

Setting the Currency Units

In Revit, you can set the unit for the currency as well. To do so, click on the corresponding field for the **Currency** parameter in the **Project Units** dialog box; the **Format** dialog box will be displayed. In this dialog box, select appropriate currency symbols and rounding values from the **Unit symbol** and **Rounding** drop-down lists, respectively.

Setting the Mass Density Units

In Revit, you can set the unit for mass density. To do so, click on the corresponding field for the **Mass Density** parameter in the Format column in the **Project Units** dialog box; the **Format** dialog box will be displayed. In this dialog box, you can specify the desired unit by selecting it from the **Units** drop-down list. The **Units** drop-down list contains options such as **Kilograms per cubic meter** and **Pounds mass per cubic foot** for mass density measurement. By default, the **Pound per cubic foot** option is selected in this drop-down list for the **Imperial** unit system and **Kilograms per cubic meter** option is selected for the **Metric** unit system. The settings for the parameters of the rounding, rounding increment, and units symbol can be set by selecting the required option from the respective drop-down lists.

Setting the Time Units

To specify the unit for time, click in the **Format** column corresponding to the **Time** parameter; the **Format** dialog box will be displayed. In this dialog box, you can select the desired unit of time from the **Units** drop-down list. This drop-down list contains various options such as **Milliseconds**, **Seconds**, **Minutes**, and **Hours**.

Setting the Speed Units

To specify the unit for speed, click in the **Format** column corresponding to the **Speed** parameter; the **Format** dialog box will be displayed. In this dialog box, you can select the desired unit of speed from the **Units** drop-down list. This drop-down list contains various options such as **Feet per minute**, **Meters per second**, **Feet per second**, **Kilometers per hour**, and **Miles per hour**.

 Note
*You can format only the display of units on the screen or for printout using the **Project Units** dialog box. The actual values for these units in the project may be different. For example, if you set the wall length rounding to the nearest value 1', the wall may show this rounded value, but the actual length of the wall might be in fractional feet. Similarly, for Metric, if you set the wall length rounding to the nearest value 10, the wall may show this rounded value, but the actual length of the wall might be different.*

Structural Unit Type

Structural units include the settings such as Force, Moment, Stress, Unit Weight, and so on. In Revit, you can set the structural units in the **Project Units** dialog box. To do so, invoke the **Project Units** dialog box and then select the **Structural** option from the **Discipline** drop-down list. Figure 2-5 displays the **Project Units** dialog box with the **Structural** option selected in the **Discipline** drop-down list. Some of the structural units are discussed next.

*Figure 2-5   The **Project Units** dialog box with the **Structural** option selected from the **Discipline** drop-down list*

Setting the Unit for Force

To specify the unit for the concentrated forces that act on the structural model, click on the field corresponding to the **Force** parameter in the **Format** column; the **Format** dialog box will be displayed. In this dialog box, specify a unit by selecting the required option from the **Units** drop-down list. The **Units** drop-down list contains the options such as **Newtons**, **Dekanewtons**, **Kilonewtons**, **Meganewtons**, **Kips**, **Kilograms force**, **Pounds force**, and **Tonnes force**. For the Imperial unit system, **Kips** is the default option selected in the drop-down list. For the Metric unit system, **Kilonewtons** is the default option selected. The settings for rounding increment and unit symbol for the force units can be made from their respective drop-down list.

Setting the Unit for Linear Force

The linear force implies a uniformly distributed load that you can apply to any structural member. To specify unit for the linear force, click on the field corresponding to the **Linear Force** parameter in the **Format** column of the **Project Units** dialog box; the **Format** dialog box will be displayed. In this dialog box, specify the desired unit for the linear force by selecting an option from the **Units** drop-down list. The **Units** drop-down list contains options such as **Newtons per meter**, **Dekanewtons per meter**, **Kilonewtons per meter**, **Meganewtons per meter**, **Kips per foot**, **Kilograms force per meter**, **Pounds force per foot**, and **Tonnes force per meter**. The default unit selected for the **Imperial** unit system in is **Kips per foot**. The default unit selected for the **Metric** unit system in the drop-down list is **Kilonewtons per meter**.

Tip
*While selecting a rounding value from the **Rounding** drop-down list in the **Format** dialog box, you should consider the extent of detailing that may be required for the project, and then select it. For projects that require too much detailing, a lower rounding value may be set. This parameter, however, can be modified at any time during the project development.*

Setting the Unit for Area Force

Area forces denote the pressure forces that you can apply to any structural element (beams, columns, slabs, and so on). To specify unit for the area force, click on the field corresponding to the **Area Force** parameter in the **Format** column of the **Project Units** dialog box; the **Format** dialog box will be displayed. In this dialog box, specify the desired unit for the area force by selecting an option from the **Units** drop-down list. In the **Units** drop-down list, you can select various options such as **Newtons per square meter**, **Dekanewtons per square meter**, **Kilonewtons per square meter**, **Meganewtons per square meter**, **Kips per square foot**, **Kilograms force per square meter**, and so on. The default unit selected for the Imperial unit system in the drop-down list is **Kips per square foot** and for the Metric unit system is **Kilonewtons per square meter.**

Setting the Unit for Mass per Unit Area

The **Mass per Unit Area** parameter specifies the density that you can apply on any structural elements such as rebars, structural steel, and so on. To specify a unit for the mass per unit area, click on the field corresponding to the **Mass per Unit Area** parameter in the **Format** column of the **Project Units** dialog box; the **Format** dialog box will be displayed. In this dialog box, specify the desired unit for the mass per unit area by selecting an option from the **Units** drop-down list. In the **Units** drop-down list, you can select options such as **Kilograms per square meter** and **Pounds per square foot**. The default unit selected in the Imperial unit system for this parameter is **Pound per square foot** and in the Metric unit system is **Kilograms per square meter**.

Similarly, you can set the units for the other options of different discipline types.

STRUCTURAL SETTINGS

Ribbon: Manage > Settings > Structural Settings

In Autodesk Revit, you can specify various structural settings of a project such as settings of the symbolic representation of structural framing components, settings of various load cases to be applied to structural model, settings for the analysis to be performed on model, and settings for providing supports to structural model. You can specify all these settings by using the **Structural Settings** dialog box. The **Structural Settings** dialog box can be invoked by choosing the **Structural Settings** tool from the **Settings** panel of the **Manage** tab, as shown in Figure 2-6. This dialog box contains five tabs, namely **Symbolic Representation Settings**, **Load Cases**, **Load Combinations**, **Analytical Model Settings**, and **Boundary Conditions Settings**. In this dialog box, the **Symbolic Representation Settings** tab is chosen by default, refer to Figure 2-7.

Figure 2-6 *Choosing the **Structural Settings** tool*

Figure 2-7 *The **Symbolic Representation Settings** tab chosen in the*
***Structural Settings** dialog box*

The settings that you specify in the tabs of the **Structural Settings** dialog box pertain to the appearance of the structural members. In the **Structural Settings** dialog box, you can also specify the load cases, boundary conditions, and the settings for the analytical model. In this chapter, you will learn about various options in the **Symbolic Representation Settings** tab. This will help you adjust the symbolic representation of various structural elements for documentation output.

Symbolic Representation Settings Tab

Whenever you invoke the **Structural Settings** dialog box, the **Symbolic Representation Settings** tab is chosen by default, refer to Figure 2-7. The options in this tab control the display and symbology of different structural conditions in plans, sections, and schedules of steel shapes. These options determine how certain elements of an object will display or allow you to use a symbol of your choice in different conditions. In this tab, there are three areas: **Symbolic Cutback Distance**, **Brace Symbols**, and **Connection Symbols**. The options in these areas are discussed next.

Symbolic Cutback Distance Area

The **Symbolic Cutback Distance** area, refer to Figure 2-7, contains three edit boxes: **Brace**, **Beam/Truss**, and **Column**. The values in these edit boxes control the cutback distances of the structural symbolic lines that represent beams, columns, and braces at a coarse detailed level of a structural project. These values are global settings that affect all beams, trusses, braces, and steel columns in a project.

In the **Symbolic Cutback Distance** area, you can enter a numeric value in the **Brace** edit box to control the symbolic cutback distance between a structural steel beam or column and a structural steel brace at a coarse detail level. In the Imperial unit system, the default value in this edit box is 3/32" whereas in Metric unit system, the default value in the edit box is 2.5000 mm. Figure 2-8 shows the symbolic cutback distance between a brace and a column at a coarse detail level.

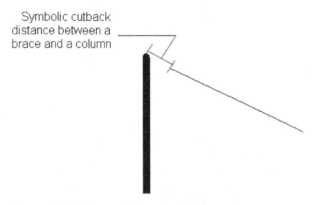

Figure 2-8 *The symbolic cutback distance between a column and brace*

In the **Beam/Truss** edit box of the **Symbolic Cutback Distance** area, you can enter any numeric value to control the symbolic cutback distance between beams and columns, or between beams, trusses, and columns. In the Imperial unit system, the default value in this edit box is 3/32" whereas in Metric unit system, the default value in the edit box is 2.5000mm. Figure 2-9 shows the symbolic cutback distance between two beams and a column.

Figure 2-9 *The symbolic cutback distance between beams and column at coarse detail level*

The value in the **Column** edit box is used to increase or decrease the gap between the symbolic representations of joined columns in an elevation view. This gap will be visible in a coarse detail elevation view only if the **Top Connection Symbol** instance parameter of the bottom column is set to a value other than **None**. The default value in the **Column** edit box is 1/16" for Imperial unit system and in Metric system, the default value is 1.5875 mm. Figure 2-10 shows the symbolic cutback distance between columns in an elevation view.

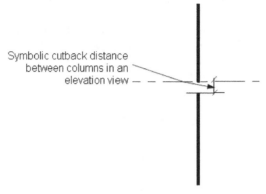

Figure 2-10 The symbolic cutback distance between columns in an elevation view at a coarse detail level

The Brace Symbols Area

The settings in the **Brace Symbols** area are used to control the symbolic display of bracing and kicker bracings that exist in a project. Figure 2-11 shows the settings in the **Brace Symbols** area in the **Symbolic Representation Settings** tab of the **Structural Settings** dialog box. The **Plan representation** drop-down list in this area contains two options: **Parallel Line** and **Line with Angle**. The **Parallel Line** option is selected by default. As a result, the symbolic representation of braces in a plan view is displayed with an offset and a line parallel to the actual brace. You can control the offset distance of this parallel line by entering a suitable value in the **Parallel line offset** edit box.

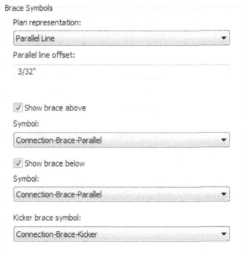

*Figure 2-11 Settings in the **Brace Symbols** area*

In the Imperial unit system, 3/32" is set as the default value in the **Parallel line offset** edit box and in the Metric unit system, default value is 2.3813 mm. Figure 2-12 shows the symbolic representation of a brace in a plan view with default offset distance. On selecting the **Line with Angle** option from the **Plan representation** drop-down list, the symbolic representations of braces in a plan view are displayed with an angled line. The angled line originates from the point of intersection of a brace and level line, if they intersect, or from the closest point to the level line on the brace. The angled line goes upward from the point of origin for the portion of the brace which is above the level or it goes downward for the portion of the brace which is below the level. Figure 2-13 shows a bracing symbol as an angled line.

Figure 2-12 *The symbolic representation of a brace in a plan view*

Figure 2-13 *The symbolic representation of a brace as an angled line*

The **Show brace above** check box in the **Brace Symbols** area is selected by default. As a result, the brace symbols representing the braces placed above the current view are displayed. When you select the **Show brace above** check box, the **Symbol** drop-down list below the check box gets activated. From this drop-down list, you can select an option depending upon the option selected from the **Plan representation** drop-down list. You can select the **Connection-Brace -Parallel** option from the **Symbol** drop-down list, if the **Parallel Line** option is selected in the **Plan representation** drop-down list. Similarly, if the **Line with Angle** option is selected in the **Plan representation** drop-down list, you can select the **Connection-Brace-Angle** from the **Symbol** drop-down list. On clearing the **Show brace above** check box, the brace option placed above the current view will not be displayed.

Similar to the **Show brace above** check box, the **Show brace below** check box is selected by default. As a result, the brace symbols representing the braces placed below the current view are displayed. The **Symbol** drop-down list below the **Show brace below** check box becomes active when the **Show brace below** check box is selected. The options in the **Symbol** drop-down list located below the **Show brace below** check box are similar to those of the **Symbol** check box located below the **Show brace above** check box.

In the **Kicker brace symbol** drop-down list, the **Connection-Brace-Kicker** option is selected by default. As a result, the symbolic representation of a kicker brace will be a connection-brace in a plan view.

Note

*A normal bracing can be converted into a kicker bracing if the **Structural Usage** instance parameter in the **Properties** palette of the bracing is set to **Kicker Bracing**, refer to Figure 2-14.*

Figure 2-14 *Partial view of the **Properties** palette displaying the* **Structural Usage** *parameter set to **Kicker Bracing***

Connection Symbols Area

The options in the **Connection Symbols** area, as shown in Figure 2-15, can be used to control the symbolic display of moment and shear connections for beams, braces, and columns that exist throughout the project. To select the type of framing member for which you want to modify the symbolic display for moment and shear connections, click on the **Display Symbols** drop-down list and then select any of the three options: **Beams and Braces**, **Column Base**, and **Column Top**. In the **Display Symbols** drop-down list, the **Beams and Braces** option is selected by default. As a result, the settings for this option will be displayed in a table located below the **Display Symbols** drop-down list, refer to Figure 2-15. In this table, you will notice two columns: **Connection Type** and **Annotation Symbol**. In the **Connection Type** column, two parameters are displayed: **Moment Frame** and **Cantilever Moment**.

Figure 2-15 *The options in the* **Connection Symbols** *area*

The parameters displayed in the **Connection Type** column may vary depending on the option selected from the **Display Symbols** drop-down list. The values for these parameters are displayed in their corresponding fields in the **Annotation Symbol** column. To specify the annotation symbol for a beam or brace of **Moment Frame** parameter, click on the **Annotation Symbol** column corresponding to the **Moment Frame** parameter and select any of the three options: **None**, **Connection-Moment-Filled**, and **Connection-Moment-Not Filled**. Similarly, you can specify an option for **Cantilever Moment** parameter. To add a connection type parameter (for beams and braces) in the table, choose the **Add a connection type** button (first button from the left) displayed below the table, refer to Figure 2-15. On doing so, the **New Connection Type** dialog box will be displayed. In the **Connection Type** edit box of the **New Connection Type** dialog box, enter a name for the new connection type. Next, click in the **Annotation Symbol** drop-down list and select an option to assign an annotation symbol for the connection type. Optionally, in the **New Connection Type** dialog box, you can choose the **Load Symbol** button to load a symbol (with file format *.rfa* or *.adsk)* for the new connection type. Now, choose the **OK** button; the new connection type will be added as parameter in the table. Next, rename, delete, and create a duplicate for the connection type displayed in the table.

In the **Connection Symbols** area, you can specify the base plate symbol for the column. To do so, select the **Column Base** option from the **Display Symbols** drop-down list and specify a symbol for the base plate from the table displayed below the **Display Symbols** drop-down list. Similarly, to assign a symbol to the base plate of a column base, you can specify symbols for shear column connection and moment column connection by selecting the **Column Top** option from the **Display Symbols** drop-down list. Figure 2-16 shows a moment connection and cantilever connection symbols for a steel member.

Figure 2-16 *The moment connection and cantilever connection symbols*

CONNECTION SETTINGS

Ribbon: Manage > Settings > Structural Settings drop-down > Connection Settings

In Autodesk Revit, you can specify various connection settings for structural connections such as the **Beam end to end**, **Column - Beam**, **General bracings**, and so on. You can load different sets of connection in the project by using the **Structural Connection Settings** dialog box. The **Structural Connection Settings** dialog box can be invoked by choosing the **Connection Settings** tool from the **Settings** panel of the **Manage** tab, as shown in Figure 2-17.

Figure 2-17 *Choosing the* **Connection Settings** *tool*

This dialog box contains two tabs, namely **Connections** and **Parameters**. In this dialog box, the **Connections** tab is chosen by default, as shown in Figure 2-18.

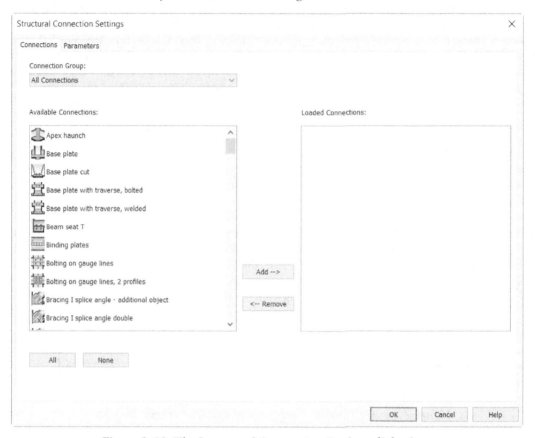

*Figure 2-18 The **Structural Connection Settings** dialog box*

In the **Connections** tab of the **Structural Connection Settings** dialog box, the **All Connections** option is selected by default in the **Connection Group** drop-down list. In the **Available Connections** area, some of the possible connections between different structural members are displayed. To load any of the connection types in the project, select the desired connection type from the **Available Connection** area and choose the **Add** button; the selected type of connection is added to the **Loaded Connections** area. To load more than one connection type in the project from the **Available Connections** area, select desired connections while holding the **Ctrl** key and choose the **Add** button.

You can select different types of connection groups from the **Connection Group** drop-down list. The connection groups available in the **Available Connections** area depends on the type of connection selected in the **Connection** Group drop-down list. Some of the **Connection Groups** available in this drop-down list are **Beam end to end**, **Column-Beam**, **General bracings**, and so on.

Once connections are added in the **Loaded Connections** area, choose the **OK** button, the **Structural Connection Settings** dialog box is closed and the type of connections is loaded in the project.

Now, to set a connection between the structural members, invoke the **Connection** tool from the **Connection** panel of the **Structure** tab. Select the type of connection from the **Type Selector** drop-down list in the **Properties** panel and select the structural member between which the connection is to be created. The connection loaded from the **Type Selector** drop-down list is displayed between the member in the 3D view. If the connection type is not displayed in the 3D view, choose the **Visibility/Graphics** option from the **Graphics** panel of the **View** tab; the **Visibility/Graphic Overrides for <View>** will be displayed. Select all the options available in the **Structural Connections** head from the **Visibility** column of the **Model Categories** tab in the displayed dialog box, as shown in Figure 2-19.

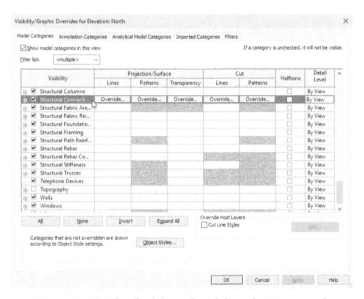

Figure 2-19 *The check box selected from the **Structural Connection** head*

SNAPS TOOL

Ribbon: Manage > Settings > Snaps

The **Snaps** tool is one of the important tools used for creating and editing elements in a structural model. This tool is used to make the cursor snap or jump depending on the preset increments or specific object properties of elements such as endpoint, midpoint, and so on. Invoke the **Snaps** tool from the **Settings** panel of the **Manage** tab; the **Snaps** dialog box will be displayed, as shown in Figure 2-20. This dialog box has three areas, **Dimension Snaps**, **Object Snaps**, and **Temporary Overrides**. These areas are discussed next.

Note
The settings specified in this dialog box will be applied to all the projects opened in the session and will not be saved.

*Figure 2-20 The **Snaps** dialog box*

Tip
*The **Snaps** tool is used frequently not only while creating various building elements but also while editing and placing them. Besides making the modeling simpler, by using this feature efficiently, you can also improve the performance and accuracy of your project.*

Dimension Snaps Area

In the **Dimension Snaps** area, you can set the length and angle dimension snap increments for placing various elements and components in a project. The dimension snap determines the increment by which the cursor will jump/snap along with length or angular dimension while placing elements and components in a project.

The **Length dimension snap increments** check box is selected by default. As a result, you can set the snap increment for the length dimension. On selecting the **Length dimension snap increments** check box, you can enter suitable value(s) in the edit box to set the snap value for length. The default values in this edit box are: 4' ; 0' 6" ; 0' 1" ; 0' 0 1/4", if the **English-Imperial** template is selected. On selecting the **English-Metric** template, the default values in this edit box are: 1000 ; 100 ; 20 ; 5. Note that every incremental value is separated by a semicolon (;).

You can also set increments by typing the values that are separated by a semicolon. For example, to create an interior layout plan in which the length of the partitions is in 5' (1524mm) modules, counter top width is 2' (610mm), and thickness of partitions is 4" (100mm), you can enter the values for the dimension snaps as **5'; 2';4"** (English-Imperial) and **1524; 610; 100** (English-Metric). This will enable the cursor to move in these increments and help to create the layout with relative ease. Similarly, you can set the angular dimension snap increments. However, ensure that the **Angular dimension snap increments** check box is selected and then enter suitable value(s) in the edit box below it. This parameter is quite useful for the projects that have radial geometry. To restore the default setting, choose the **Restore Defaults** button from the **Snaps** dialog box.

Note
The reason for specifying multiple length and angle snap increment values in the edit boxes is that the priority of increments may change on changing the zoom level of the drawing. Therefore, when you zoom in the drawing, Revit will use smaller increment values, whereas on zooming out, the larger increment values will be used.

Object Snaps Area

Object Snaps refer to the cursor's ability to snap to geometric points on an element such as its endpoint, midpoint, perpendicular, and so on. In the **Object Snaps** area of the **Snaps** dialog box, you can use various options to snap points of elements or objects in a project. The advantage of using these options is that you do not need to specify the exact point in a drawing. When object snaps are enabled, the suitable object snap is displayed as the cursor is moved close to an element. For example, it is virtually impossible to pick the exact endpoint to start a wall from the endpoint of an existing wall. But when you enable the endpoint object snap, the cursor automatically jumps or snaps to the endpoint of this wall. This helps to start the new wall from the endpoint. This, besides making the drawing accurate, later helps add dimensions to the project.

Tip
*The **Dimension Snaps** parameter should be set based on the scale and the amount of detailing required for the project. You may set smaller increments for working on a detailed or small portion of a building.*

Note
The object snaps tool works only with the objects that are visible on the screen. A tooltip, with the same name as the object snap is also displayed when you bring the cursor close to a snap point.

In a structural model, you can use various **Object Snaps** modes such as **Endpoints**, **Midpoints**, **Nearest**, **Work Plane Grid**, **Quadrants**, **Intersections**, **Centers**, **Perpendicular**, **Tangents**, **Points**, **Snap to Point Clouds**, and **Snap to Remote Objects**.

The name of each object snap option resembles its usage in the project. For example, the **Work Plane Grid** snap option helps you snap the intersection points of grid lines in a work plane grid that is displayed for the current work plane.

Each object snap mode is represented by a geometrical shaped marker to identify it from other object snaps. For example, the endpoint object snap is represented by a square, midpoint by a triangle, nearest by a cross, and so on. To use an object snap mode, move the cursor on the object. As you move it close to the snap point, a marker appears. To select the appropriate snap point, click when the corresponding marker or tooltip is displayed.

In Revit, all enabled object snaps work simultaneously. You can turn off all snap options, including dimension snaps and object snaps by selecting the **Snaps Off** check box located at the top of the **Snaps** dialog box. Alternatively, you can type **SO** on the keyboard to turn them off and on while using a tool. The **Check All** and **Check None** buttons are used to select or clear all check boxes (except the **Snap to Remote Objects** and **Snap to point Clouds**) in the **Object Snaps** area.

Temporary Overrides Area

The options in the **Temporary Overrides** area provide you with an alternative of overriding snaps setting for a single use only. For example, if you have not selected the **Endpoints** check box in the **Snaps** dialog box and you want to use this option while working with a tool, you do not need to open the **Snaps** dialog box to select this option. Instead, you can type the shortcut, **SE** in this case, to temporarily activate the endpoint object snap. Once you have used this object snap option, snapping to the endpoint is automatically turned off.

Using overrides, you can toggle between various object snap options available at the same location. To do so, press the TAB key while snapping the points in the drawing. You can also use other overrides like pressing the SHIFT key to create elements vertically or horizontally. This restricts the movement of the cursor in the orthogonal directions only. Once you release the SHIFT key, the cursor resumes its movement in all directions. You can select the **Snaps Off** check box to disable all types of snapping.

OPTIONS DIALOG BOX

In Autodesk Revit, you can configure global settings by using the **Options** dialog box. This dialog box can be invoked by choosing the **Options** button from the **File** menu. The **Options** dialog box, as shown in Figure 2-21, contains ten tabs: **General**, **Graphics**, **Hardware**, **File Locations**, **Rendering**, **Check Spelling**, **SteeringWheels**, **ViewCube**, **User Interface**, and **Macros**. These tabs are discussed next.

General Tab

The **General** tab is chosen by default and contains five areas: **Notifications**, **Username**, **Journal file cleanup**, **Worksharing update frequency**, and **View options**. These areas are discussed next.

Notifications Area

Revit provides an option for setting reminders to save a work at regular intervals. To do so, select the desired option from the **Save reminder interval** drop-down list in the **Notifications** area. By default, 30 minutes is selected in this drop-down list. If you do not want a reminder to save your work in the project, select the **No reminders** option from this drop-down list. Similarly, you can select a value in the **Synchronize with Central reminder interval** drop-down list.

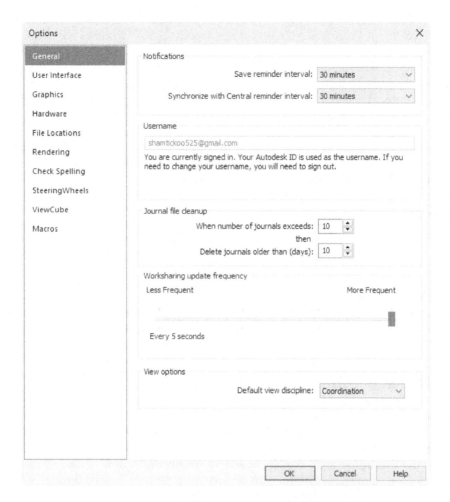

Figure 2-21 *Setting the file options using the **Options** dialog box*

Username Area

In Autodesk Revit, if you are not signed in as a user of Autodesk account, then the username will not be displayed. To enter a name in the **Username** area, you need to sign in to Autodesk 360. When you sign in, your Autodesk ID will be used as a username.

Note
If you are not logged into an Autodesk account, system username will be taken as the default username.

Journal File Cleanup Area

Journal files are the text files that are used to resolve the technical problems which occur during the Revit session. These files record every step during the session. Whenever you encounter a technical problem with the software, you can run this file to detect the problem or recover the lost files or to know the steps that may have caused the problem. In Autodesk Revit, these files are saved at the following default location: *C:\Users\<Username>\AppData\Local\Autodesk*

Revit\Autodesk Revit 2021\Journals for Windows 10, Windows 7 or Window Vista users and *C:\ Documents and Settings\<Username>\Local Settings\Application* for Windows XP users. These files are saved each time you close the Revit session. Therefore, the number of these files keeps on increasing until you remove these files from their location. However to remove these files while retaining some of them, you can use the **Journal file cleanup** area in the **General** tab of the **Options** dialog box. This area contains two spinners: **When number of journal exceeds** and **Delete journals older than (days)**. You can set the required values in these spinners to retain the recently created files. The default value in both the edit boxes is 10. If you want to delete journal files if their number exceeds 15 and if they were created before 30 days, then in such a situation, set the value in the **When number of journals exceeds** spinner to **15** and the value in the **Delete journals older than (days)** spinner to **30**.

Worksharing Update Frequency Area

In this area, you can set the update frequency that indicates the time interval for updating the project in a worksharing environment. To set the limits for worksharing, you can set the slider between the **Less Frequent** and **More Frequent** limits.

View Options Area

In the **View options** area, you can specify the default view discipline to be used in the Revit project. To do so, select an option from the **Default view discipline** drop-down list in this area. In this drop-down list, the **Coordination** option is selected by default.

User Interface Tab

The **User Interface** tab contains three areas: **Configure**, **Ribbon tab switching behavior** and **Visual experience**. In the **Configure** area, you can use different options such as **Keyboard Shortcuts**, **Double-click Options**, and **Tooltip assistance** to change the appearance and operational settings. If you choose the **Customize** button corresponding to the **Keyboard Shortcuts** in the **Configure** area, the **Keyboard Shortcuts** dialog box will be displayed. In this dialog box, various commands with their respective shortcut keys are displayed. You can use the **Assign** and **Remove** buttons to add and remove the shortcut keys.

If you choose the **Customize** button corresponding to the **Double-click Options** parameter; the **Customize Double-click Settings** dialog box will be displayed. In this dialog box, you can specify the double-click action response for an element. To do so, select the option in the **Double-click Action** coloumn corresponding to desired element displayed under the **Element Type** column; a drop-down list will be displayed. Select an option from the drop-down list for the required double-clicking response for the element; double-click response of the element will change to the newly chosen option.

 In the **Configure** area, you can select an option from the **Tooltip assistance** drop-down list to set the required level of assistance that a tool tip will display when a cursor is placed over a tool or an element in the project view. From the drop-down list, you can select any of the following options: **Normal**, **None**, **Minimal**, and **High**. By default, the **Normal** option is selected in the **Tooltip assistance** drop-down list.

In the **Ribbon tab switching behavior** area, you can specify the tab to be displayed once you clear a selection or exit a tool. In this area, the **Project Environment** drop-down list contains two options: **Stay on the Modify tab** and **Return to the previous tab**. Select the **Stay on the Modify tab** option to display the options in the **Modify** tab after exiting a tool or clearing a selection. Alternatively, you can select the **Return to the previous tab** option to display the last used tab after exiting a tool or clearing a selection. Similarly, you can use the settings in the **Family Editor** heading to specify the display behavior of the family editor mode. In the **Ribbon tab switching behavior** area, the **Display the contextual tab on selection** check box is selected by default. As a result, the contextual tab is displayed once you select a tool from the Revit interface.

To change the theme of Revit interface, choose the desired option from the **Active theme** drop-down list of the **Visual experience** area. There are two themes available in the **Active theme** drop down list: **Light** and **Dark**. **Light** theme is selected by default. To accelerate the graphical speed of any operation in software, select the **Use hardware graphics acceleration if available** check box from the **Visual experience** area in the **User Interface** tab.

Graphics Tab

You can use this tab to assign colors to selections, highlights, and alerts, and to enable anti-aliasing for 3D views. In the **View navigation performance** area, the **Allow navigation during redraw** check box is selected by default. The selection of the check box allows you to navigate the model in a 2D view or a 3D view, and also pan, zoom and orbit while sketching the drawing. On clearing the check box, you will not be able to perform any of the above actions before the completion of drawing. In this area, the **Simplify display during view navigation** check box is cleared by default. If you select this check box, it will suspend various graphic effects and details such as fill and line, shadows, hidden lines, underlays, etc during camera manipulation. In the **Graphics mode** area, you can select the **Smooth line with anti-aliasing** check box to improve the quality of lines in 3D views. In the **Colors** area of the **Graphics** tab, choose the button corresponding to the **Background** parameter to change the color of the background. The **Selection** parameter refers to a color that an element acquires when it is selected. The default color is **RGB 000-059-189**. To use any other color, click the button on the right of the **Selection** parameter and select the desired color from the **Color** dialog box. The **Pre-selection** parameter is used to specify the color of the highlighted elements. To use any other color, click the button on the right of the **Selection** parameter to display the **Color** dialog box and then select the desired color from this dialog box. Revit uses the **Alert** button to highlight elements when an error occurs. In the **Colors** area, you can select the **Semi-transparent** check box to make the selected elements semi-transparent. Semi-transparency of a selected element allows you to view the elements behind it. In the **Temporary dimension text appearance** area, you can select an option from the **Size** drop-down list to specify the size of temporary dimension text. You can also set the background of the temporary dimensions text. To do so, select the **Opaque** or **Transparent** option from the **Background** drop-down list. **Transparent** is selected by default.

Hardware Tab

The options in the **Hardware** tab enables you to view information related to hardware setup and change related information for better navigation and rendering view. In the **Hardware setup** area of this tab, the **Use hardware acceleration** check box is selected by default. As a result, the hardware accelerators are enabled. Hardware accelerators help display the larger models faster on refreshing the views. In addition, the hardware accelerators help you speed up the process of switching between the windows of views.

File Locations Tab

By using the **File Locations** tab, you can set the path for various files and directories that are accessed frequently, refer to Figure 2-22. The path for these files is set while installing Revit. However, you can modify the location of a file by choosing the corresponding **Browse** button and specify a new location. You can also change the default template file location, in case, you wish to use a custom made template file for your projects. In Revit, the default path to save or open a project can be specified in the **Default path for user files** edit box. You can also specify the default path for family template files and for the point clouds by using the corresponding **Browse** button.

*Figure 2-22 The **File Locations** tab of the **Options** dialog box*

In Autodesk Revit 2021, you can add a new template file used for the workflows for system analysis. To do so, click the **Add Value** button under the **System analysis workflows**: area and specify the desired path for the new template file in the **Browse for System Analysis Workflow** dialog box. To modify the path of the default template file, click on the path given under the **Path** column corresponding to the desired workflow; the **Browse** button will be activated. Now, click on the **Browse** button; the **Browse for System Analysis Workflow** dialog box will be displayed. In this dialog box, specify the desired path for the template file.

Rendering Tab

Autodesk Revit uses the mental ray rendering engine for its rendering process. The mental ray has its own library, Render Appearance Library. This library stores information about render appearances for materials, default RPC contents in the software, and other information relevant to the rendering process. The Render Appearance Library is a read-only library and is loaded into the following default location while installing the Revit software: *C:\Program Files (x86)\ Common Files\Autodesk Shared\Materials\2021\assetlibrary_base.fbm*.

In addition to the default Render Appearance Library location, you can also specify paths for the additional image files defining texture, bump map, and custom color for the render appearance that you can use in the project. These image files are not present in the software and therefore, you need to specify their paths to use them. To do so, choose the **Add Value** button in the **Additional render appearance paths** area and specify the required path in the displayed field or choose the **Browse** button; the **Browse For Folder** dialog box will be displayed. In this dialog box, select the desired path and choose the **Open** button to add the path in the field.

Check Spelling Tab

Revit provides you with the option to run spell check to find out spelling errors in text and then rectify them. You can choose the **Check Spelling** tab from the **Options** dialog box to display its options. Figure 2-23 shows various options in the **Check Spelling** tab. In the **Settings** list box of this tab, you can specify various self-explanatory settings by selecting their respective check boxes. In the **Main Dictionary** area, you can select the type of dictionary to be used as main dictionary for the spell check from the **Autodesk Revit** drop-down list. Apart from the main dictionary, you can also use additional dictionaries available in this dialog box such as the personal and building industry dictionaries. This facilitates the use of various personal and industrial terms in the text. There are many words that are not included in the main dictionary but are frequently used in the building industry. For example, the abbreviation 'conc' for the word concrete is not available in the main dictionary. The additional building industry dictionary has many such words and abbreviations that can be used in the text of the project and therefore, it does not prompt you to check for spelling errors when it finds such terms/words. You can also add or remove words from your personal and building industry dictionary. To do so, choose the **Edit** button next to the required option in the **Additional dictionaries** area to view the list of words and then enter or remove any word from these lists by using the cursor and keyboard. To run spell check in your drawing, choose the **Check Spelling** tool from the **Text** panel of the **Annotate** tab; the **Spelling** dialog box will be displayed, wherein you can rectify spelling errors in the text by selecting the correct spelling and then choosing the **Change** button in the dialog box. Alternatively, you can press the F7 key to display the **Check Spelling** dialog box.

Figure 2-23 The Check Spelling tab of the Options dialog box

SteeringWheels Tab

The **SteeringWheels** tab in the **Options** dialog box has options to control the visibility, appearance, and operational tools of different types of SteeringWheels. This tab has seven different areas, as shown in Figure 2-24. These areas are discussed next.

Text Visibility Area

You can control the display of tool messages, tooltips, and tool cursor of SteeringWheels by using the options in the **Text visibility** area of the **SteeringWheels** tab. You need to select the **Show tool messages** check box to enable the visibility of tool messages in SteeringWheels. To display tooltips along with SteeringWheels, select the **Show tooltips** check box in this area. Similarly, to control the display of the cursor text when a tool is active, select the **Show tool cursor text** check box.

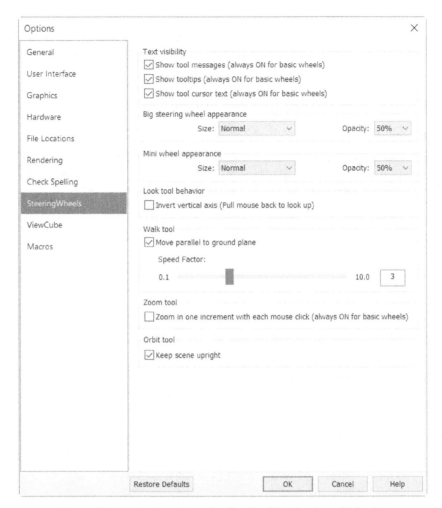

*Figure 2-24 The **SteeringWheels** tab of the **Options** dialog box*

Big Steering Wheel Appearance and Mini Wheel Appearance Areas

The options in these areas are used to set the size and transparency of the SteeringWheels. To set the size of SteeringWheels, select the required option from the **Size** drop-down list in the corresponding areas and set its size to small, normal, or large. Similarly, you can set the transparency of SteeringWheels by selecting the required option from the **Opacity** drop-down list.

Look Tool Behavior and Walk Tool Areas

In the **Look tool behavior** area of the **SteeringWheels** tab, select the **Invert vertical axis** check box to change the vertical axis movement of the view. Selecting this check box enables the view to move in the same direction as the cursor does in the vertical axis.

The **Speed Factor** slider in the **Walk tool** area is used to change the speed of walk while using the **Walk** tool of the SteeringWheels. You can also select the **Move parallel to ground plane** check box in the **Walk tool** area to constrain the angular movement of the walk to ground plane.

Zoom Tool and Orbit Tool Areas

Select the **Zoom in one increment with each mouse click** check box in the **Zoom tool** area to enable the zooming operation with a single click.

In the **Orbit tool** area, select the **Keep scene upright** check box to maintain perpendicularity between the sides of the model and the ground plane while using the **Orbit** tool.

ViewCube Tab

The **ViewCube** tab in the **Options** dialog box is used to edit various settings of the ViewCube. It has four different areas: **ViewCube appearance**, **When dragging the ViewCube**, **When clicking on the ViewCube**, and **Compass**, as shown in Figure 2-25. These areas are discussed next.

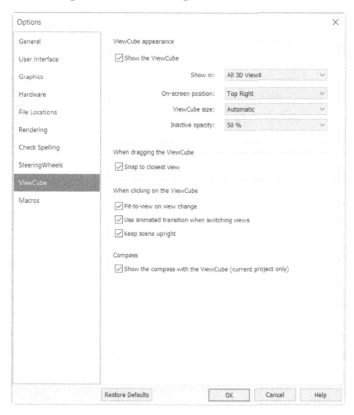

*Figure 2-25 The **ViewCube** tab of the **Options** dialog box*

ViewCube Appearance Area

This area is used to control the appearance and display of the **ViewCube**. In this area, the **Show the ViewCube** check box is selected by default. As a result, the ViewCube will be visible. If you clear this check box, the ViewCube will disappear and all options in the **ViewCube** tab will be deactivated. In the **ViewCube appearance** area, you can use various drop-down lists to align, resize, and change the transparency of the ViewCube.

Select the options from the **On-screen position** drop-down list to align the ViewCube on the screen. Similarly, if you want to resize the ViewCube, select the required option from the **ViewCube size** drop-down list. You can also set the opacity of the inactive ViewCube by selecting an option from the **Inactive opacity** drop-down list.

When Dragging the ViewCube Area

Select the **Snap to closest view** check box in this area to enable the snap to select the closest view in the ViewCube.

When Clicking on the ViewCube Area

Select the **Fit-to-view on view change** check box in the **When clicking on the ViewCube** area to fit the view on the screen while changing the viewing direction. In this area, the **Use animated transition when switching views** check box is selected by default. As a result, the animated transition occurs while switching the views. If you clear this check box, the animated transition will not occur while using the ViewCube. Select the **Keep scene upright** check box to keep the sides of ViewCube and the sides of the view perpendicular to the ground plane. Clear the check box to turn around the model in full 360-degree swing. Clearing this check box can be useful when you are editing a family.

Compass Area

In this area, the **Show the compass with the ViewCube** check box is selected by default. As a result, the compass along with the ViewCube is visible in the drawing. In the **ViewCube** tab, you can choose the **Restore Defaults** button to restore the default settings that were changed in its different areas.

Macros Tab

Revit provides you with the option to run macros within the projectI and then rectify the problems occurred. To do so, choose the **Macros** tab from the **Options** dialog box; various options will be displayed in the window, refer to Figure 2-26. The options in the **Macros** tab can be used to set the security level for the macros used in the project. There are two options in this area, **Application macro security settings** and **Document macro security settings**, which are discussed next.

Application Macro Security Settings Area

In this area, the **Enable application macros** radio button is selected by default. As a result, the application macros in the project are enabled. To disable the application macros, select the **Disable application macros** radio button from the **Application macro security settings** area.

Document Macro Security Settings Area

In this area, the **Ask before enabling document macros** radio button is selected by default. As a result, the document macros are disabled but you will be prompted to enable them whenever you open a project that contains a macro. To enable the document macros, select the **Enable document macros** radio button. Similarly, to disable a document macros in the project, select the **Disable document macros** radio button in the **Document macro security settings** area.

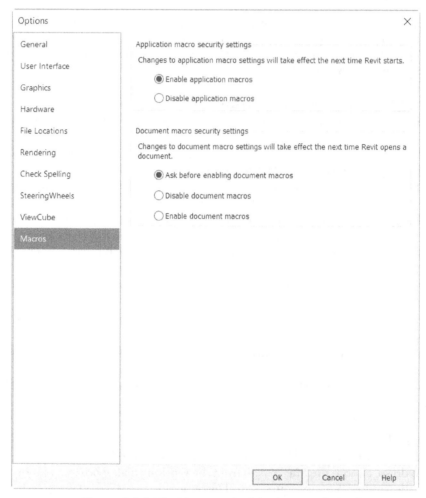

Figure 2-26 *The **Macros** tab of the **Options** dialog box*

SAVING A PROJECT

Before you close or exit a Revit session, it is recommended to save the project file. You can save a project file in a permanent storage device, such as a hard disk or a removable storage device like CD or USB. Also, you must save your work at regular intervals to avoid data loss due to any error in the computer's hardware or software.

Using the Save As Tool

Application Menu: Save As > Project

In Revit, you can save your project file at the desired location. To do so, choose the **File** menu and then choose **Save As > Project**; the **Save As** dialog box will be displayed, refer to Figure 2-27. Alternatively, you can save the project file by choosing the **Save** button from the **Quick Access Toolbar.**

Figure 2-27 The Save As dialog box

In the **Save As** dialog box, the **Save in** drop-down list displays the current drive and path in which the project file will be saved. The list box below the **Save in** drop-down list shows all folders available in the current directory. The **File name** edit box is used to specify the name of the file to be assigned to the project. The **Places List** area on the left of the **Save As** dialog box contains shortcuts for the folders that are frequently used.

You can use different file saving features by choosing the **Options** button from the **Save As** dialog box. On choosing this button, the **File Save Options** dialog box will be displayed, as shown in Figure 2-28. Using the **Maximum** edit box from this dialog box, you can specify the maximum number of backup files that you need to store for a project. In Autodesk Revit, the non-workshared projects have three backup files and the workshared projects have twenty backup files by default. The options in the **Worksharing** area are inactive for non-workshared projects. You can use the options in this area to make the current workshared file central compact and select the default workset. The options in the **Thumbnail Preview** area enable you to specify the image to be used as the preview of the project file. This image is used at the time of opening a project file. You can specify a view of the model as a preview image by selecting the corresponding option from the **Source** drop-down list in the **Thumbnail Preview** area of the **File Save Options** dialog box. By default, the **Active view/sheet** option is selected in the **Source** drop-down list of the **Thumbnail Preview** area for the preview of a project file. For example, to make **Structural Plan: Level 1** as the preview image, select it from the drop-down list. As a result, when you invoke the **Open** dialog box and select a file to open, the view displayed in the **Preview** area will correspond to the selection that is made from the **Source** drop-down list in the **File Save Options** dialog box.

*Figure 2-28 The **File Save Options** dialog box*

In the **File Save Options** dialog box, you can select the **Regenerate if view/sheet is not up-to-date** check box to see the preview with the latest modifications. On selecting this check box, the preview image will be updated when you close the project file.

Note
*Revit updates the preview image continuously. Therefore, selecting the **Regenerate if view/sheet is not up-to-date** check box can consume considerable resources.*

Using the Save Tool

Once a project has been saved using the **Save As** tool, you do not need to re-enter file parameters to save it again. To save a project to the hard disk, choose the **File** menu button and then choose the **Save** option from **File Menu**. If you are saving the project for the first time, the **Save As** dialog box will be displayed, even if you invoke the **Save** tool.

Tip
*By default, the preview of a file is the last active view or sheet at the time it was last saved. You can set the preview to a particular view using the **Options** button in the **Save As** dialog box.*

Alternatively, you can save your project by choosing the **Save** button from the **Quick Access Toolbar**. As you save your project file, Revit updates it automatically without prompting you to re-enter the file name and path.

CLOSING A STRUCTURAL PROJECT

To close a project, choose the **File** menu button and then select the **Close** option. If you have already saved the latest changes, the project file will be closed. Otherwise, Revit will prompt you to save the changes through the **Save File** dialog box. You can save the changes by choosing the **Yes** button or discard them by choosing the **No** button. You can also choose the **Cancel** button to return to the interface and continue working on the project file. You can also use the **Close** button (X) in the drawing area to close the project.

EXITING A STRUCTURAL PROJECT

To exit a Revit session, choose the **Exit Revit** button from **File** menu. Even if the project is open, you can choose the **Exit Revit** button to close the file and exit Revit. If the project has not been saved once, the **Save File** dialog box will be displayed on choosing the **Exit Revit** button. In this dialog box, if you choose the **No** button, all unsaved changes will be lost. You can also use the **Close** button (**X**) in the main Revit window (in the title bar) to end the Revit session.

OPENING AN EXISTING STRUCTURAL PROJECT

Application Menu:	Open > Project
Shortcut Keys:	CTRL+O

In Autodesk Revit, there are several options available to open an existing project. These options are discussed next.

Opening an Existing Project Using the Open Tool

To open an existing project file, choose **Open > Project** from **File Menu**, as shown in Figure 2-29. Alternatively, you can open the project file by choosing the **Open** button from the **Quick Access Toolbar** or by pressing the CTRL+O keys. On invoking the **Open** tool, the **Open** dialog box will be displayed, as shown in Figure 2-30. Using the **Look in** drop-down list in this dialog box, you can access the desired folder and open the desired file.

*Figure 2-29 Choosing the **Project** option from the **File** menu*

Figure 2-30 The **Open** dialog box

The **Preview** area of the **Open** dialog box shows the preview of the selected project file. It helps you select a particular file by viewing its contents, even if you are not sure about the name of the file. The window icons such as the **Views** menu, placed on the right of the **Look in** drop-down list, helps you select a project file based on its size, type, or date when it was last saved. On choosing the **Thumbnails** option from the **Views** menu, you can preview the contents of the project files inside the selected folder in the file list area. In the **Open** dialog box, you can browse to important locations from the **Places** list. The **Places** list is located on the left side of the **Open** dialog box. In this list, you can add or remove folders as per your requirement. To do so, first close the **Open** dialog box and then choose the **Options** button from **File** menu; the **Options** dialog box will be displayed. In this dialog box, choose the **File Locations** tab and then the **Places** button from it; the **Places** dialog box will be displayed, as shown in Figure 2-31. The **Places** dialog box contains two columns: **Library Name** and **Library Path**.

Figure 2-31 The **Places** dialog box

You can add or remove folders in the libraries list to create a list of frequently accessed folders. The four buttons on the left side of the **Places** dialog box can be used to create or delete a library, or move it up and down in the list. To create a new library, choose the **Add Value** button, which is the third button from the top; a new library will be added to the defined path. By default, the name of the new library in the **Library Name** section will be **New Library1**. Change the name of the new library and then click in the **Library Path** column to display the **Browse** button. Choose the **Browse** button and select the folder to be added in the libraries list by using the **Browse For Folder** dialog box. Next, choose the **Open** button; the new folder will get added to the list. If required, choose the upward arrow button from the **Places** dialog box to move the folder up to the top of the list. Similarly, you can choose the down arrow button to move it down. To delete a library, select it and choose the **Remove Value** button. Choose the **OK** button in the **Places** dialog box to exit, and then close the **Options** dialog box. When you invoke the **Open** tool next time, the new folder icon will be displayed in the places list.

Once the file to be opened has been selected, its name will be displayed in the **File Name** edit box of the **Open** dialog box and its preview will be displayed in the **Preview** area.

Note
*If you try opening an already opened file that has been modified in the Revit session, a message box appears, prompting you to close the file first and then reopen it. In case, you open a file that has been created using an older version of Revit, the **Program Upgrade** message box is displayed. This message box informs that the file is being upgraded to the latest file format and that this is a onetime process. Once the file is opened, choose the **Save** button from the **Application** menu to save it to upgraded Autodesk Revit version.*

Using the Windows Explorer to Open an Existing Project
Apart from using the **Open** tool from the Revit interface to open a file, you can also open files directly from the **Windows Explorer** by using the methods discussed next. A file can be opened by double-clicking on its icon in the **Windows Explorer**. It opens the project file in the latest Revit session. If Revit is not running, double-click on the file icon to start Revit and then open the file.

Another method of opening a project file is by dragging the project file icon from the **Windows Explorer** and dropping it in the drawing window of the Revit interface. You can also select, drag, and drop more than one file in the drawing window. In this case, Revit prompts you to open the files in separate windows. Choose the **OK** button to open all files in the same Revit session.

TUTORIALS

In this tutorial, you will create two structural projects as tutorials: a commercial project of a concrete structure and an industrial project of steel and concrete structure. These tutorials will be created in a sequence according to the topics discussed in the chapter.

Tutorial 1	Commercial Complex

In this tutorial, you will create a revit file for the *Commercial Complex* project with the following parameters and project specifications: **(Expected time: 15 min)**

1.   Template file:
     For Imperial   **English-Imperial > Structural Analysis-Default.rte**
     For Metric   **English-Metric > Structural Analysis-DefaultMetric.rte**

2.   Project Units:
     For Imperial   **Feet and fractional inches**, Rounding- **To the nearest 1/2"**
     For Metric   **Millimeters**, Rounding- **To the nearest 10**

3.   Length dimension snap increment:
     For Imperial   **5'; 2' 6"; 0' 3"; 0' 01/2"**
     For Metric   **1500; 70; 70; 10**

4.   File name to be assigned:
     For Imperial   *c02_Commercial-Complex_tut1.rvt*
     For Metric   *M_ c02_Commercial-Complex_tut1.rvt*

The following steps are required to complete this tutorial:

a.   Start a Revit session.

b.   Open a new project.

c.   Use the template file for the project.
     For Imperial   **Structural Analysis-Default.rte**.
     For Metric   **Structural Analysis-DefaultMetric.rte**

d.   Select project units.

e.   Set **Endpoint, Midpoint, Nearest, Perpendicular, Work Plane Grid**, and **Intersections** as the object snaps in the **Snaps** dialog box for both the systems (Imperial & Metric).

f.   Save the project by using the **Save** tool.
     For Imperial   *c02_Commercial-Complex_tut1.rvt*
     For Metric   *M_c02_Commercial-Complex_tut1.rvt*

g.   Close the project by using the **Close** tool.

Starting Autodesk Revit 2021

1. Start Autodesk Revit by choosing **Start > All Programs > Autodesk > Revit 2021**. On doing so, the Revit interface window is displayed.

Opening a New Project

1. Choose **New > Project** from menu; the **New Project** dialog box is displayed.

Selecting the Template File

To select the template file for the project, you need to access the appropriate folder and select the required template file from it.

1. In the **New Project** dialog box, choose the **Browse** button from the **Template file** area; the **Choose Template** dialog box is displayed. This dialog box shows a list of template files available in the **English-Imperial** folder if **Imperial** unit system is selected at the time of Revit installation. (On selecting **Metric** unit system, list of metric template is displayed).

2. In the **Choose Template** dialog box, the template file named **Structural Analysis-Default. rte**, as shown in Figure 2-32, is selected as the default template file in the **English-Imperial** folder. In **English-Metric** folder, default template file is **Structural Analysis-DefaultMetric. rte**. Choose the **Open** button to assign the selected template file to the **New Project** dialog box.

3. Select the **Project** radio button (default) to create a project file and then choose the **OK** button; the selected template file of selected unit system is loaded. Note that the **Project Browser** shows different levels and views that have already been created in the selected template file.

*Figure 2-32 The **Choose Template** dialog box*

Setting Project Units

1. To set units for the project, choose the **Project Units** tool from the **Settings** panel of the **Manage** tab; the **Project Units** dialog box is displayed.

2. Make sure that the **Common** option is selected in the **Discipline** drop-down list of the **Project Units** dialog box. Now, click in the **Format** column corresponding to the **Length** unit; the **Format** dialog box is displayed.

3. In this dialog box, select the option by clicking on the **Units** drop-down list.
    For Imperial   **Feet and fractional inches**
    For Metric   **Millimeters**

4. Select the option from the **Rounding** drop-down list.
    For Imperial   **To the nearest 1/2"**
    For Metric   **To the nearest 10**

5. Choose the **OK** button in the **Format** dialog box and then in the **Project Units** dialog box to close them.

Setting Dimension and Object Snaps

You need to set dimension snaps and object snaps by using the **Snaps** tool. These settings are based on the type of the project and the amount of detailing required.

1. Choose the **Snaps** tool from the **Settings** panel of the **Manage** tab; the **Snaps** dialog box is displayed, as shown in Figure 2-33.

2. In the **Dimension Snaps** area of this dialog box, ensure that the **Length dimension snap increments** check box is selected.

3. Now, click in the edit box below the **Length dimension snap increments** check box and enter new values as given next.

                 For Imperial   **5'; 2' 6"; 0' 3"; 0' 0 1/2"**
                 For Metric   **1500; 700; 70; 10**

Figure 2-33 shows the value entered for length snaps increment.

4. In the **Object Snaps** area, clear the **Quadrants**, **Centers**, **Tangents**, and **Points** check boxes to disable them. Leave rest of the check boxes enabled, refer to Figure 2-33. Choose the **OK** button to apply settings and to close the **Snaps** dialog box.

*Figure 2-33 The **Snaps** dialog box*

Saving the Project

The project parameters set in the previous steps are the global settings of the project file. To save this project file, use the **Save As** tool.

1. Choose the **Save** option from the **File** menu. As you are saving the project for the first time, the **Save As** dialog box is displayed.

2. In this dialog box, browse to the *C* drive and then create a folder with the name **rst_2021**.

3. Open the *rst_2021* folder and then create a sub-folder with the name *c02_rst_2021_tut*. Next, open the created folder and save the file with the name *c02_Commercial-Complex_tut1.rvt* (For Imperial), refer to Figure 2-34. For Metric, save the file with the name *M_c02_Commercial-Complex_tut1.rvt*.

4. Choose the **Save** button; the **Save As** dialog box closes and the project file is saved.

Figure 2-34 The Save As dialog box

Closing the Project

1. Choose the **Close** option from **File** menu in the Ribbon.

Tutorial 2   Industrial Complex

In this tutorial, you will create a new project file for the *Industrial Complex* project by using the following parameters and project specifications.   **(Expected time: 15 min)**

1. Template file:

       For Imperial   **English-Imperial > Structural Analysis-Default.rte**
       For Metric   **English-Metric > Structural Analysis-DefaultMetric.rte**

2. Project Units:

          For Imperial   **Feet and fractional inches,** Rounding- **To the nearest 1/4"**

          For Metric   **Millimeters,** Rounding- **To the nearest 10**

3. Length dimension snap increment:

          For Imperial   **10'; 2'6"; 1'; 0'3"**

          For Metric   **3000; 760; 300; 70**

4. Object snaps to be set- all available object snaps.

5. File name to be assigned:

          For Imperial   *c02_Industrial-Complex_tut2.rvt*

          For Metric   *M_c02_Industrial-Complex_tut2.rvt*

The following steps are required to complete this tutorial:

a. Start the Revit session.

b. Open a new project.

c. Use the template file.

          For Imperial   *Structural Analysis-Default.rte*

          For Metric   *Structural Analysis-DefaultMetric.rte*

d. Set the project units by using the **Project Units** dialog box.

          For Imperial   **Feet and fractional inches**

          For Metric   **Millimeters**

e. Set the length dimension snap increment in the **Snaps** dialog box.

          For Imperial   **10'; 2'6"; 1'; 0'3"**

          For Metric   **3000; 760; 300; 70**

f. Enable all object snaps using the **Snaps** dialog box.

g. Save the project by using the **Save As** tool.

          For Imperial   *c02_Industrial-Complex_tut2.rvt*

          For Metric   *M_c02_Industrial-Complex_tut2.rvt*

h. Close the project by using the **Close** tool.

Starting Revit and Opening a New Project

1. Start a new Revit session by double-clicking on the Revit 2021 shortcut icon on the desktop. The program is loaded and the user interface screen is displayed. If the Revit session is already running, you can ignore the step and open the project file directly.

2. Choose **New > Project** from the **File** menu; the **New Project** dialog box is displayed.

Using the Template File

As given in the project parameters, you need to use the template file for this project. You can select this template file from the **New Project** dialog box.

1. In the **New Project** dialog box, choose the **Browse** button in the **Template file** area; the **Choose Template** dialog box is displayed. Select the **Structural Analysis-Default.rte** template file from the **English-Imperial** folder or the **Structural Analysis-DefaultMetric. rte** template file from the **English-Metric** folder and then choose the **Open** button; the **Choose Template** dialog box is closed. Make sure that the **Project** radio button is selected in the **Create new** area. Next, choose **OK** to exit the **New Project** dialog box; the template file is loaded for this project.

Setting Project Units

You can set units for various measurement parameters by using the **Project Units** dialog box.

1. Choose the **Project Units** tool from the **Settings** panel of the **Manage** tab; the **Project Units** dialog box is displayed.

2. Click in the **Format** column corresponding to the **Length** unit; the **Format** dialog box is displayed. In this dialog box, select the option from the **Units** drop-down list.

        For Imperial   **Feet and fractional inches**
        For Metric   **Millimeters**

3. Click on the **Rounding** drop-down list and select the desired option, as shown in Figure 2-35.

        For Imperial   **To the nearest 1/4"**
        For Metric   **To the nearest 10**

*Figure 2-35 The **Format** dialog box*

4. Choose **OK** to return to the **Project Units** dialog box. Next, choose the **OK** button; the dialog box is closed and the user interface screen is displayed.

Setting Dimensions and Object Snaps

Next, you need to access and modify settings in the **Snaps** dialog box. You need to specify the dimension snap increment and enable all object snap options.

1.   Choose the **Snaps** tool from the **Settings** panel of the **Manage** tab; the **Snaps** dialog box is displayed.

2.   In this dialog box, enter values in the edit box below the **Length dimension snap increments** check box in the **Dimension Snaps** area.

        For Imperial   **10'; 2'6"; 1'; 0'3"**
        For Metric   **3000; 760; 300; 70**

3.   In the **Object Snaps** area, ensure that all the object snaps options are selected and then choose the **OK** button to apply settings and exit the **Snaps** dialog box.

Saving the Project

In this section, you need to save the project and the settings using the **Save As** tool.

1.   Choose **Save As > Project** from the **File** menu. The **Save As** dialog box is displayed.

2.   Browse to the *C:\rst_2021\c02_rst_2021_tut* and for imperial enter **c02_Industrial-Complex_tut2** in the **File name** edit box (for Metric enter **M_c02_Industrial-Complex_tut2**). Notice that in the **File of type** drop-down list, the **Project Files (*.rvt)** option is selected by default.

3.   Choose the **Save** button to save the project as *c02_Industrial-Complex_tut2.rvt* for Imperial *(M_c02_Industrial-Complex_tut2.rvt* for Metric). The project is saved at the specified location.

Closing the Project

1.   Choose the **Close** option from the **File** menu; the project gets closed.

Self-Evaluation Test

Answer the following questions and then compare them to those given at the end of this chapter:

1.   The options in the _____ drop-down list are used to control the symbolic display of moment connections for cantilever framing that exists throughout a project.

2.   The _____ drop-down list in the **Structural Settings** dialog box contains two options: **Parallel Line** and **Line with Angle**.

3.   In Autodesk Revit, you can set the symbolic representation of structural framing components by using the _____ dialog box.

4.   To specify the location of the default template file, you can use the _____ tab in the **Options** dialog box.

5. The _____ button in the **Save As** dialog box can be used to specify the maximum numbers of backup(s) for a project file.

6. The _____ option of Revit enables you to override snap settings for a single pick only.

7. You can add folders to the _____ in the **Save As** dialog box to access the frequently used folders directly.

8. You can open only one Revit project at a time. (T/F)

9. In Revit, all enabled object snaps work together. (T/F)

10. A project file can be opened by double-clicking on its file name in the Windows Explorer. (T/F).

Review Questions

Answer the following questions:

1. Which of the following options is not an object snap option?

    a) **Endpoints**   b) **Work Plane Grid**
    c) **Dimension**   d) **Centers**

2. Which of the following keys is used to toggle between the object snap options available at the same point?

    a) TAB   b) CTRL
    c) ALT   d) F3

3. You can specify the settings for **ViewCube** and **SteeringWheels** in the _____ dialog box.

4. You can select any of the three options, namely **Beams and Braces**, **Column Base**, and **Column Top** from the _____ drop-down list.

5. You can modify the project unit settings anytime during a project. (T/F)

6. The name and path of a project file should be specified each time you save the project. (T/F)

7. You cannot control the visibility of the tooltip assistant. (T/F)

8. The **Save reminder interval** drop-down list available in the **General** tab of the **Options** dialog box is used to specify the time interval between reminder prompts to save a project file. (T/F)

9. If you choose the **Close** button without saving the changes made in a project file, Revit will prompt you to save the changes before closing it. (T/F).

10. You can add words to additional dictionaries for checking spelling errors. (T/F)

EXERCISES

Exercise 1   Academic Institution

In this exercise, you will create a new project file for the *Academic Institution* project with the following parameters.   **(Expected time: 15 min)**

1. Template file-
For Imperial	**English-Imperial > Structural-Analysis Default.rte**
For Metric	**English-Metric > Structural-Analysis DefaultMetric.rte**

2. Project Units-
For Imperial	**Feet and fractional inches**
For Metric	**Millimeters**

3. File name to be assigned:
For Imperial	*c02_Academic-Institution_exer1.rvt*
For Metric	*M_c02_Academic-Institution_exer1.rvt*

Exercise 2   Factory Shed

In this exercise, you will create a new project file for the *Factory Shed* project by using the following parameters.   **(Expected time: 15 min)**

1. Template file:
For Imperial	**English-Imperial > Structural-Analysis Default.rte**
For Metric	**English-Metric > Structural-Analysis DefaultMetric.rte**

2. Project Units:
For Imperial	**Feet and fractional inches**
For Metric	**Millimeters**

3. File name to be assigned:
For Imperial	*c02_Factory-Shed_exer2.rvt*
For Metric	*M_c02_Factory-Shed_exer2.rvt*

Answers to Self-Evaluation Test

1. Cantilever connection, 2. Plan representation, 3. Structural Settings, 4. File Locations,
5. Options, 6. Temporary Overrides, 7. Places list, 8. F, 9. T, 10. T

Chapter 3

Setting up a Structural Project

Learning Objectives

After completing this chapter, you will be able to:
- *Create project templates*
- *Understand and create grids*
- *Understand and create levels*
- *Understand and create work planes*
- *Sketch reference planes*
- *Create scope box*

In the previous chapter, you learned to open a new file and create initial setups. Now, after opening a new file and creating initial setups such as units and snaps, you need to learn about creating advanced setups such as creating the project templates, levels, and grids for your project. These advance setups help you to start your project more efficiently and accurately.

In this chapter, you will learn to create a project template, save the project template and then create structural grids and levels for a structural project. Further, you will learn the use of Work Planes and Reference Planes in a project.

PROJECT TEMPLATE

Project templates are files that can be opened while starting a new project. These files, commonly known as template files, contains predefined settings for project, display of annotations, display of graphics, and so on. Similarly, for the display of graphics, the template files contain predefined settings for materials, line styles, line weights, line patterns, and structural symbols.

Project templates provide initial conditions for a project. In Autodesk Revit, you will find in-built templates that are saved with *.rte* file extension when you install the software. You can also create your own template based on the project requirement. In Revit, any new template-based project inherits all families, settings (such as units, fill patterns, line styles, line weights, and view scales), and geometry from the template.

Template files carry project-specific information. You may have different project template files for different types of projects. For example, for a concrete structure, you may not use steel members for your design purpose. For this kind of project, you may require a template that carries families with more concrete sections and less steel members. A template file can also carry predefined levels and grids and thus saves a lot of time while starting up a new project. Schedules for footings, columns, piers, and other structural elements can also be a part of a project template.

In the next sections, you will learn how to create custom templates and use them in a structural project.

Creating a Custom Project Template

In Autodesk Revit, there are various methods to create a custom project template. The common method is to open an existing template file and modify its settings based on the project requirement and then save it as a different template file. You can also create a custom project template by starting a blank project file, defining all settings such as naming the viewports, creating levels, adding grids, and others, and then saving it as a template (.rte) file. For certain projects, you can create a template file which includes geometry that can be used repeatedly as a base for the new projects. For example, if you have defined geometry for a shopping complex and want to include this geometry whenever you start a new project, you can save the file that includes this geometry as a template. Each time you open a project with this template, the geometry is included.

Creating a New Template from a Blank Project File

File Menu: New > Project

In Revit, you can create a new template file from a blank project file or use the default template file (*Imperial-Structural Analysis.rte* for Imperial and *Metric-Structural Analysis.rte* for Metric). To create a template file from a blank project file, choose **New > Project** from the **File** menu; the **New Project** dialog box will be displayed. In the **Template file** area of this dialog box, select the **<None>** option from the drop-down list. Next, select the **Project template** radio button in the **Create new** area and choose the **OK** button; the **Undefined System of Measurement** dialog box will be displayed, as shown in Figure 3-1. This dialog box prompts you to select a system of measurement for your project.

*Figure 3-1 The Undefined System of Measurement
dialog box*

You can choose the **Imperial** or **Metric** option from this dialog box. If you choose the **Imperial** option, a template file containing all default unit settings in Imperial unit system will open. Similarly, if you choose the **Metric** option, the template file containing default units in the Metric unit system will open. After opening the template file, you can modify its existing settings based on your project environment and then save the modified file as a template file. To do so, choose **Save As > Template** from the **File** menu; the **Save As** dialog box will be displayed. In this dialog box, select a folder from the **Save in** drop-down list and enter a name for the template file in the **File name** edit box. Note that the **Template Files (*.rte)** option is selected from the **Files of type** drop-down list. After entering the file name, choose the **Save** button; the template file will be saved with the settings defined in the blank project file.

Note
*You can also select the template file, Structural Analysis-Default.rte for Imperial and Structural Analysis-DefaultMetric.rte for Metric, to create a new template file from a blank project. To do so, select the **Structural Template** option from the drop-down list in the **Template file** area of the **New Project** dialog box, and then choose the **OK** button.*

Tip
*You can change the default template file displayed in the **New Project** dialog box. To do so, invoke the **Options** dialog box by choosing the **Options** button from the **File** menu. Next, in the **Project template** area of the **File Locations** tab, click in the **Path** column corresponding to the **Structural Template** name; a browse button will be displayed. Choose the browse button; the **Browse For Template File** dialog box will be invoked. In this dialog box, select the file that is to be made default template file and then choose the **Open** button. Next click the **OK** button to save changes.*

Creating a New Project Template from an Existing Project Template

To speed up your project, you may be required to use predefined template files. These template files contain predefined information or settings pertaining to the project you need to start. To use these template files, choose **New>Project** from the **File** menu; the **New Project** dialog box will be displayed. In this dialog box, ensure that the **Project template** radio button in the **Create new** area is selected. Now, to select the desired template file for your project, choose the **Browse** button; the **Choose Template** dialog box will be displayed, as shown in Figure 3-2. In this dialog box, browse to the desired folder to locate the template file. Next, select the template file from the folder and choose the **Open** button; the **Choose Template** dialog box will close and the **New Project** dialog box will be displayed again. In this dialog box, keep the default setting and choose the **OK** button; a new project file will open, which inherits all project settings from the selected template file.

*Figure 3-2 The **Choose Template** dialog box*

Settings for the Project Template

While creating a project template, you can predefine certain settings based on your project requirement. To start a new project template, you need to fill in the information specific to the project. The information includes the name of the project, project number, client's name, and so on. These information are useful while publishing or plotting the drawing. Next, you need to enter the project settings. These settings include units, snaps, the line styles for components and lines, fill patterns for materials, and more. Some of the settings such as units and snaps have already been discussed in Chapter 2.

After modifying the project settings, you can create settings for families. The families in a project template can be system families and loaded families. While defining the settings for the project template, you can modify or duplicate system families (for example, walls) as required for the project. You can also load the commonly used families, user-defined families, and title blocks.

After setting families in the project template, you can modify or create settings for project views. These settings include plan views (Structural Plans), levels, schedules, sheets, and so on. There are other settings that can be made for the project template other than those discussed. These are visibility/graphics settings, and the plot (Print) settings. The settings for the project information are discussed in the next section.

Setting the Project Information

When you create a project template, you can also set the project information. To do so, choose the **Project Information** tool from the **Settings** panel of the **Manage** tab; the **Project Information** dialog box will be displayed, refer to Figure 3-3. In this dialog box, you can specify various settings related to the project information displayed in the **Instance Parameters** area. To enter information regarding the **Organization Name**, **Organization Description**, **Building Name**, and **Author** of the project, click on the **Value** fields of their corresponding parameters and enter appropriate values in them. Similarly, to edit the energy settings of the project, choose the **Edit** button in the **Value** field of the **Energy Settings** parameter; the **Energy Settings** dialog box will be displayed. In this dialog box, you can specify various settings related to the type of the building, site location of the building, and the level that will represent the ground plane of the site. To do so, click on the **Value** fields corresponding to the **Project Phase**, **Mode**, and **Ground Plane** and so on parameters and specify the desired values in them. You can also choose the **Edit** button corresponding to the **Other Options** parameter from the **Advanced** area of the **Project Information** dialog box. On doing so, the **Advanced Energy Settings** dialog box will be displayed. You can specify various advance settings like HVAC system, building type, building operating schedule and so on from the **Advanced Energy Settings** dialog box. Choose the **OK** button twice; the settings will be applied and the **Energy Settings** dialog box will be closed and the **Project Information** dialog box will be displayed.

*Figure 3-3 Partial view of the **Project Information** dialog box used for setting the project information*

In the **Project Information** dialog box, you can enter the information regarding the start or issue date of the project. To do so, click on the **Value** field of the **Project Issue Date** parameter and enter a valid date in the **Project Information** dialog box. Similarly, to specify the status of the project, click on the **Value** field of the **Project Status** parameter and specify a valid status of the project.

To enter the address of location of the project, choose the browse button in the **Value** field of the **Project Address** parameter; the **Edit Text** dialog box will be displayed. In the text area of this dialog box, enter a suitable address and choose the **OK** button; the address of the project will be updated.

Next, specify the name and number of the project in the **Value** fields of the **Project Name** and **Project Number** parameters, respectively. After entering the appropriate information in the **Project Information** dialog box, choose the **OK** button; the **Project Information** dialog box will be closed and the project information entered will be updated.

In addition to the parameters discussed in the **Project Information** dialog box, you can add more parameters for entering project information. To do so, choose the **Project Parameters** tool from the **Settings** panel of the **Manage** tab; the **Project Parameters** dialog box will be displayed. Choose the **Add** button from this dialog box; the **Parameter Properties** dialog box will be displayed, as shown Figure 3-4. Ensure that the **Project parameter** radio button is selected in the **Parameter Type** area of this dialog box. Next, select the **Project Information** check box from the **Categories** area. In the **Parameter Data** area, enter the name of the parameter data in the **Name** edit box. For example, you can specify **Engineer's Name** as the name of the parameter. Next, you need to assign a discipline for the new parameter. To do so, select an appropriate option from the **Discipline** drop-down list. For example, to assign a discipline for the **Engineer's Name** parameter, ensure that the **Common** option is selected in the **Discipline** drop-down list.

Figure 3-4 *The* **Parameter Properties** *dialog box*

To assign type and group for the **Engineer's Name** parameter, select the **Text** options from both the **Type of Parameter** and **Group parameter under** drop-down lists. Next, choose the **OK** button; the **Project Parameters** dialog box will be displayed with the added parameter displayed in the list box. Choose the **OK** button from this dialog box; the newly created project parameter will be added in the **Project Information** dialog box. Figure 3-5 shows partial view of the **Project Information** dialog box for the project information with **Engineer's Name** as the added parameter.

Figure 3-5 *The* ***Project Information*** *dialog box displaying the newly added parameter*

Setting the Project Location

For each project in Autodesk Revit, you need to define a location with respect to a coordinate system. This definition includes the geographical location (azimuth) of a project, which needs the latitude and longitude of the nearest city and the coordinate system of the host model and the linked model (if present).

To define the geographical location of a project, choose the **Location** tool from the **Project Location** panel of the **Manage** tab; the **Location Weather and Site** dialog box will be displayed, refer to in Figure 3-6. This dialog box contains three tabs: **Location**, **Weather**, and **Site**. The **Location** tab is chosen by default. In the **Define Location by** drop-down list of this tab, the **Internet Mapping Service** option is selected by default. As a result, you can use the bing map service to find out the geographical location of a desired place. To find out the geographical location, type it in the **Project Address** edit box and then choose the **Search** button; the location searched will be displayed in a map.

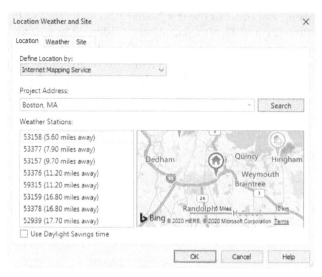

Figure 3-6 *The options in the **Location** tab of
the **Location Weather and Site** dialog box*

Alternatively, you can select the **Default City List** option from the **Define Location by** drop-down list. This option is selected to specify a city nearest to the project location and to define the latitude and longitude of the location. To specify the nearest city, select an option from the **City** drop-down list; the **Latitude** and **Longitude** edit boxes will display the corresponding values for the latitude and longitude of the selected city. If the name of a city is not available in the **City** drop-down list, then enter the values of latitude and longitude in the **Latitude** and **Longitude** edit boxes, respectively. You can choose the **Site** tab in the **Location Weather and Site** dialog box to name the current setting of the location. The options in the **Site** tab are shown in Figure 3-7. In this tab, the name(s) of location(s) is (are) displayed in the **Sites defined in this project** list box. By default, the **Internal (current)** location is listed and selected in the list box.

To define a different location for the project, choose the **Duplicate** button from the **Location Weather and Site** dialog box; the **Name** dialog box will be displayed. Enter a name in the **Name** edit box and choose the **OK** button; the **Name** dialog box will be closed and the name of the new location will be listed in the **Sites defined in this project** list box. After you have added a location, you will notice that the **Delete** and **Make Current** buttons are active. You can choose the **Delete** button to delete location(s) apart from the current location. A current location is a location being currently used. To make a location current, select the location from the **Sites defined in this project** list box and choose the **Make Current** button. Note that after you have made a location current, the name of the location is suffixed with the word **(current)**.

Figure 3-7 *The options in the* **Site** *tab of the* **Location Weather** *and* **Site** *dialog box*

Transferring Project Standards

Ribbon: Manage > Settings > Transfer Project Standards

When you create a template file, you can copy project standards from another project to the current file. These standards include various project settings such as Family Types (only system families, not loaded families), Line Weight, Line Styles, Line Patterns, Materials, and View Templates. To transfer project standards to the template file (target file), open the source file from which standards are to be copied. Next, choose the **Transfer Project Standards** tool from the **Settings** panel of the **Manage** tab; the **Select Items To Copy** dialog box will be displayed, as shown in Figure 3-8.

Figure 3-8 *The* **Select Items To Copy** *dialog box*

In the **Select Items To Copy** dialog box, click on **Copy from** drop-down list; the list of opened projects will be displayed in the drop-down list. Next, select any of the projects from which you want to copy standards. Note that when you select a source project from this list, the standards included in the project along with their respective check boxes are displayed. By default, all check boxes in the list box are selected. You can keep the check boxes selected for the standards you want to copy to the template file and clear rest of them. If you want to clear all check boxes for fresh selection, you can choose the **Check None** button located on the right of the list box. Similarly, to select all check boxes, you can choose the **Check All** button. After selecting the check boxes for the standards that you want to transfer, choose the **OK** button; the **Select Items To Copy** dialog box will be closed. Note that if the selected standards are already present in the template file, the **Duplicate Types** message box will appear, refer to Figure 3-9. You can choose the **Overwrite** button from this message box to overwrite the common standards or choose the **New Only** button to transfer the standards that are present in the template file. After you have chosen the required options, the selected standards will be copied to the destination file.

*Figure 3-9 The **Duplicate Types** message box*

Setting the Browser Organization

While creating a project template, you can organize the **Project Browser**. To do so, choose the **Browser Organization** tool from **View > Windows > User Interface** drop-down; the **Browser Organization** dialog box will be displayed, as shown in Figure 3-10.

This dialog box contains three tabs: **Views, Sheets** and **Schedules**. The **Views** tab is chosen by default. The options in this tab are used to select, edit, or create a browser organization for the views present in the project. In the list box of the **Views** tab, the list of default browser organizations is displayed with their respective check boxes. You can edit the settings of the check boxes displayed. To do so, click on the name of the browser organization whose settings you want to change, and then choose the **Edit** button; the **Browser Organization Properties** dialog box will be displayed, refer to Figure 3-11. This dialog box contains two tabs: **Filtering** and **Grouping and Sorting**. The **Filtering** tab is chosen by default. The options in the **Grouping and Sorting** tab are used to create group by sorting the project views, refer to Figure 3-11. After specifying the options in the **Grouping and Sorting** tab, you can choose the **Filtering** tab to apply a filter to the project views.

Figure 3-10 *The* **Browser Organization** *dialog box*

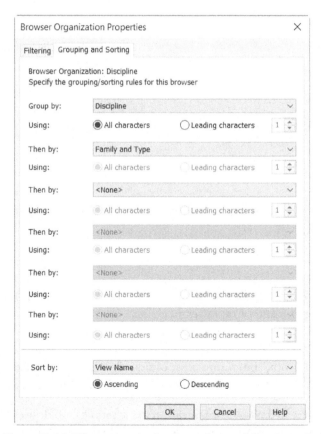

Figure 3-11 *The options in the* **Grouping and Sorting** *tab of the* **Browser Organization Properties** *dialog box*

In the **Filter by** area of this tab, you can specify view property, filter operator, and filter value, refer to Figure 3-12. After specifying options in the **Filtering** and **Grouping and Sorting** tabs, choose the **OK** button from this dialog box; the **Browser Organization Properties** dialog box will close and the settings of the selected browser organization will be edited. Similarly, you can also create a new browser organization for the project views. To do so, ensure that the **Views** tab is chosen from the **Browser Organization** dialog box and then choose the **New** button from it; the **Create New Browser Organization** dialog box will be displayed. In this dialog box, you can enter the name of the new browser organization in the **Name** edit box and then choose the **OK** button; the **Browser Organization Properties** dialog box will be displayed. The options in this dialog box have already been discussed.

Figure 3-12 The options in the Filtering tab of the Browser Organization Properties dialog box

As you created browser organization for project view, you can also create browser organization for sheets. To do so, choose the **Sheets** tab from the **Browser Organization** dialog box. The **Sheets** tab displays a list box containing a list of default browser organizations for sheets. The options in this tab are similar to those discussed for the **Views** tab.

Similarly you can also create browser organization for schedules. To do so, choose the **Schedules** tab from the **Browser Organization** dialog box. The **Schedules** tab displays the **all** check box which is selected by default.

USING LEVELS

Creating levels is one of the important tasks in a BIM project. In any structural model of a building project, levels define horizontal planes for placing the level-hosted elements, such as walls, roofs, foundations, floors, slabs, beams, columns, and ceilings.

In Revit, you can use the **Level** tool to add new levels by sketching the required level lines in the elevation or section views. By default, all level lines have associated labels that display the name and elevation of the level. There are two types of level that you can create: story and nonstory. The procedure to create these levels is discussed later in this chapter. A story level defines a floor, roof, or ceiling of a building. You can create a level for each known story in a structural model. The main characteristic of story levels is that they have corresponding plan views. In a project view, the bubble for a story level will be displayed in blue.

On the other hand, a nonstory level does not hold any plan view but can act as host for placing objects and information. The examples of a nonstory level are top of wall, top of foundation, top of column, etc. The bubble for a nonstory level is displayed in black. Figure 3-13 shows both types of levels in the **East** elevation view of a structural model. In this figure, the **T.O. Column** and **Column Splice** levels are nonstory levels and the rest of the levels are story levels.

Figure 3-13 *Different types of level in the **East** elevation view*

In Autodesk Revit, when you use the default template file for creating a new project file, it loads two predefined levels: **Level 1** and **Level 2**. These levels are displayed in the elevation or section view. You can view any of the elevations or section views using the **Project Browser**. Levels can be added, renamed, and modified at any time during the project development. In the following sections, you will learn more about properties of levels, creating levels, modifying levels, and working with levels.

Understanding Controls in a Level

A typical level is represented by a level line, level bubble, level name, level elevation, and so on, as shown in Figure 3-14. You can modify the appearance of a level by using these controls and parameters. The level name is an editable parameter which refers to different levels.

The level elevation is the distance of the level from the base level. The visibility of level bubble on either sides of the level line can be controlled by using the bubble display control. The length alignment control can be used to align level lines. Autodesk Revit provides the 2D or 3D extent control for datums when you select them. As a result, you can change their extents in one or multiple views in which they are visible. When a datum is in the 3D mode, any modification made in the 3D view is propagated in all views of the structural model. On the other hand, the 2D mode can be used to modify the datum in a specific view, thereby making it view-specific. In the next section, you will learn about adding levels in your project.

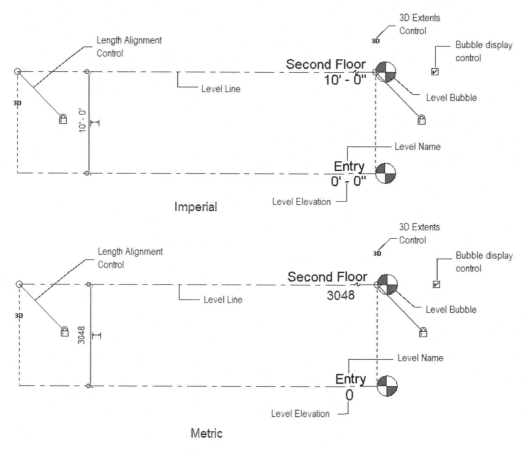

Figure 3-14 Various controls of a typical level

Adding Levels

Ribbon: Structure > Datum > Level
Shortcut Keys: LL

In Autodesk Revit, you can create multiple levels in an elevation or a section view. To create a level, invoke the **Level** tool from the **Datum** panel of the **Structure** tab, as shown in Figure 3-15; the **Modify | Place Level** contextual tab will be displayed. In this tab, choose any of the sketching options displayed in the **Draw** panel to create levels in your project. Alternatively, you can invoke the **Level** tool by pressing **LL**. After invoking the **Level** tool, you can select a level type from the **Type Selector** drop-down list in the **Properties** palette. There are three options in this drop-down list: **Level: 1/4" Head**, **Level: Story Level**, and **Level: Story Level - no head** in the **Imperial** unit system and **Level: 8mm Head** option for the **Metric** unit system. If you select the **Level: 1/4" Head** option of **Imperial** or **Level: 8mm Head** of **Metric** from the **Type Selector** drop-down list, level lines will be added as dashed lines along with the level bubbles. If you select the **Level: Story Level** option from the drop-down list, level lines will be added with continuous line along with the level bubbles. Similarly, by selecting the **Level: Story Level-no head** option, you can add level lines as continuous lines without level bubbles.

Figure 3-15 Invoking the Level tool

You can choose the **Line** (default) or **Pick Lines** tool from the **Draw** panel of the **Modify | Place Level** contextual tab to sketch the level line. Notice that the **Make Plan View** check box is selected in the **Options Bar**. This implies that when a level is added, Autodesk Revit treats it as a story level under the **Structural Plans** head in **Project Browser**. As a result, the level created will be displayed under the **Structural Plans** head in **Project Browser**. While working with the **Level** tool if you clear the **Make Plan View** check box from the **Options Bar**, a nonstory level will be created. Choose the **Plan View Types** button in the **Options Bar**; the **Plan View Types** dialog box will be displayed. In this dialog box, **Ceiling Plan**, **Floor Plan** and **Structural Plan** views will be displayed. All the views are selected by default. Press the **OK** button to create all the views. You can click and deselect the view you do not want to create. The created view can be invoked from the **Project Browser**. Note that the **Plan View Types** button will be active only if the **Make Plan View** check box is selected. The **Offset** edit box in the **Options Bar** can be used to add a level at a specified distance from the selected point or element.

To add a level, invoke the **Level** tool and move the cursor near the existing level line. The temporary dimension displayed indicates the perpendicular distance between the nearest level and the cursor. To add a level at the specified distance from the existing level line, enter the perpendicular distance value in the **Imperial** and **Metric** template, as shown in Figure 3-16. Next, click to specify the first point and move the cursor to left or right. You will notice that the level line, level name, and elevation appear and move with the cursor. On moving the cursor above the endpoint of the existing level line, a dashed alignment line appears, indicating its alignment with the existing level, as shown in Figure 3-17. When the alignment line appears, click to specify the endpoint of the level line.

Imperial   Metric

Figure 3-16 Entering the perpendicular distance value

Figure 3-17 *The appearance of a dashed alignment line along with the cursor*

 Note

Although levels are infinite horizontal planes, you are required to specify the start point and endpoint of level line. However, the placement of a level line can be useful in elevation and section views.

The recently added level when selected will be highlighted and a square box on either side of the level will be displayed, as shown in Figure 3-18 in both **Imperial** and **Metric** unit system. These boxes are used to control the visibility of the level bubble. They can be checked or cleared to make the bubble visible or invisible, respectively, at the desired side(s). The two small circles representing the drag controls for the level line can be used to increase or decrease its length. The padlocks act as the length alignment control for the alignment of all level lines. When the padlock is locked, if you change the length of a level line, all level lines aligned to it will increase or decrease simultaneously. To modify the length of a single level line, unlock the control and then modify its length.

Figure 3-18 *The selected level displaying check boxes on its right and left in both the **Imperial** and **Metric** template files*

Instance and Type Properties of a Level

Like other structural and building elements used in Autodesk Revit project, levels also have associated types and instance properties. To view and modify the instance properties of a level, select the level from the drawing; the instance properties of the selected level will be displayed in the **Properties** palette, as shown in Figure 3-19. You can use this palette to view and modify the type properties of the selected level. To do so, choose the **Edit Type** button; the **Type Properties** dialog box will be displayed. Alternatively, you can display this dialog box by choosing the **Type Properties** tool from the **Properties** panel of the **Modify | Levels** contextual tab. You can use the **Type Properties** dialog box to modify and view the type properties of the level selected from the drawing. The parameters in the **Properties** palette and the **Type Properties** dialog box are discussed next.

Figure 3-19 The instance properties of a level displayed in the **Properties** palette

Instance Properties of a Level

When you change the instance property of a selected level, the properties of the selected instance are changed. Different instance properties of a level are described in the following table:

Parameter Name	Description
Elevation	Specifies to the vertical height of a level from the elevation base.
Story Above	Specifies the building story above the current level. By default, the next highest level will be specified for this parameter. To change the value of this parameter, click on the value field corresponding to this parameter; a drop-down list will be displayed. The drop-down list will display all the levels above the current level. You can select any of these levels to specify it as the story above the current level.

Computation Height	Specifies the computation height for a level. This value is entered to calculate the area, perimeter, and volume of a room.
Name	Specifies the name assigned to the selected level in the model.
Structural	Specifies that the current level is a structural level. To specify this parameter, select the check box displayed in the value field corresponding to this parameter.
Building Story	Specifies whether the current level will be a building story or not. A building story is a floor level such as first, second, third, and more. By default, the check box corresponding to this parameter is selected; As a result, the current level will become a building story.
Scope Box	Specifies to the scope box assigned to the level that controls its visibility in different views.

Type Properties of a Level

The type properties of a level can be viewed and modified in the **Type Properties** dialog box, refer to Figure 3-20.

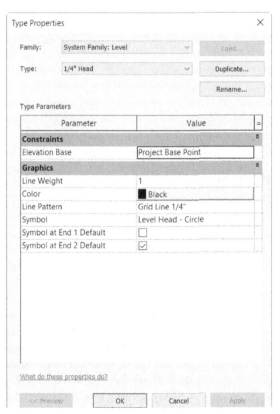

*Figure 3-20 The **Type Properties** dialog box of the selected level*

When you change the type properties of a level, all instances of the level are modified. In the **Type Properties** dialog box, you can modify the value of a parameter by clicking on its **Value** field and selecting a new value from the drop-down list or entering a new value in the field. Different level type properties are described in the table given next.

Parameter Name	Value and Description
Elevation Base	Describes the elevation base value with respect to project or the shared origin.
Line Weight	Refers to the weight of a line defining the level. It can be selected from the drop-down list.
Color	Refers to the color of a level line and can be selected from the available colors. The default color is black.
Line Pattern	Used to set the linetype of a level line.
Symbol	Refers to the symbol indicating level and can be selected from the drop-down list. The **None** option can be selected if the level head is not required.
Symbol at End 1 Default	Check box is used if a bubble is required at the left end of a level line.
Symbol at End 2 Default	Check box is used if a bubble is required at the right end of a level line.

Tip
It is recommended that you name the building story level according to the floor such as first floor, second floor, or roof. This helps in referring to their corresponding plan views. This will also help in editing the level-hosted elements. The names assigned to the levels are also reflected in the schedules created for the project.

Changing the Level Parameters

While working in a structural project, you may need to change various parameters of a level based on your project requirement. The type and instance parameters can be changed by using the **Properties** palette and the **Type Properties** dialog box. The options in this dialog box have already been discussed in the previous sections. Further, you can change the level type by selecting a level and then selecting a different level type from the **Type Selector** drop-down list. In Revit, some of the parameters can also be modified by clicking on the level element in the drawing window and entering a new value. For example, after selecting a level, you can click on its name. On doing so, an edit box will appear with the present name highlighted. Remove the present name, type a new name, and then click again or press ENTER. Note that if you are renaming the level for the first time, Autodesk Revit will prompt you to specify whether you want to rename all the corresponding views. If you choose to rename the views, the name of the associated views will also be changed in the **Project Browser**. Similarly, you can also modify the elevation of a level by selecting the elevation value below the elevation name and entering a new elevation value in the edit box displayed on clicking it, as shown in Figure 3-21. When you enter a new value, the level automatically moves to the specified elevation.

Alternatively, you can move levels by simply dragging them to the desired location. To do so, select a level line and drag it to the desired location. As you drag the level line, the elevation level changes dynamically with respect to the cursor location.

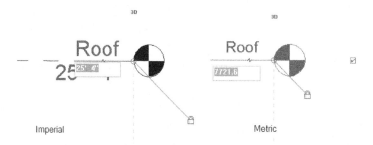

Figure 3-21 *Entering a value for the new elevation in the edit box*

It is recommended to hold the SHIFT key to constrain the cursor to move vertically. After dragging the level line to the desired location, release the mouse button; the level will be relocated to a new position. While working on a project, you may need to quickly view the structural plan of a level that is displayed in the elevation. To do so, open an elevation view and move the cursor near a level line until it gets highlighted. Next, right-click on the highlighted level line; a shortcut menu will be displayed. From the shortcut menu, choose the **Go to Floor Plan** option to open the corresponding floor plan for the level, as shown in Figure 3-22.

Figure 3-22 *Choosing the **Go to Floor Plan** option from the shortcut menu*

Tip
When you select a level, its distance from the adjacent levels is displayed. Click on the corresponding temporary dimension and enter a new value to move the level to a new location.

To move a level bubble, select the corresponding level; a break control also called elbow appears below the level name. The elbow can be used to break the level line and move the level bubble away from level line. On clicking the elbow, you will notice that the level name and the level bubble are also moved to the new location and an extension line is created. Figure 3-23 illustrates the appearance of the bubble dots after they are moved. Notice that as the bubble is moved, it appears with two blue dots or drag points. You can use these drag points to place the level bubble at an appropriate location.

Figure 3-23 *The level bubble after its relocation*

Controlling the Visibility of Levels

While working in an elevation view or a section view, sometimes you may need to hide some or all level lines to avoid congestion of construction lines. This helps in viewing the detail lines for sections and elevations properly. To do so, in the elevation view or section view, select the level line that you need to hide, and then right-click; a shortcut menu will be displayed. From this shortcut menu, choose **Hide in View > Elements**, as shown in Figure 3-24; the selected level line will be hidden.

Figure 3-24 *Choosing the Elements option from the shortcut menu*

If you need the hidden level line to be visible, choose the **Reveal Hidden Elements** button from the **View Control Bar**; the hidden level line will appear red in the drawing area. Next, right-click on the level appearing in red color in the drawing area; a shortcut menu will be displayed. Choose **Unhide in View > Element** from the shortcut menu. Next, choose the **Close Reveal Hidden Elements** button from **View Control Bar**; the hidden level will appear.

Similar to hiding a single level line, you can also hide all levels that are displayed in an elevation or a section view. To do so, select any level from the view and right-click; a shortcut menu will be displayed. Choose **Hide in View > Category** from the shortcut menu; all levels in the view will hide.

GRIDS

Grids are the essential features that will help you to align and place structural elements such as columns, beams, and walls in a structural plan. With grids, you can easily trace the exact location of a desired column or any other structural elements. Grids are definite vertical planes represented as lineworks in the plan, elevation, and section views.

You can add grids as lines or arcs. You can also create them from existing lines, or link/import them from other software such as AutoCAD Architecture, Revit Architecture, and AutoCAD and then convert them to revit grids. In the following sections, you will learn how to create, modify, and understand the grids.

Creating Grids

Ribbon:	Structure > Datum > Grid
Shortcut Key:	GR

To create a grid, invoke the **Grid** tool from the **Datum** panel of the **Structure** tab; the **Modify | Place Grid** contextual tab will be displayed, as shown in Figure 3-25. The options in the **Modify | Place Grid** contextual tab can be used to assign and change the element properties (instance and type) of the grid, to select a type for grid, and to draw grid in the desired plan or elevation.

Figure 3-25 The options in the **Modify | Place Grid** *contextual tab*

Before you start sketching grids, you need to assign their element properties (instance or type) using the **Properties** palette. To do so, invoke the **Grid** tool; the **Properties** palette will display the parameters that can be added to the grid. In the palette, you will notice that the value assigned to the **Scope Box** parameter is **None**, which implies that no scope box will be assigned to the grid to be added. Next, in the palette, choose the **Edit Type** button; the **Type Properties** dialog box will be invoked. In this dialog box, you can change the type parameters of grids, as discussed next.

Type Parameters of a Grid

Before sketching a grid, you can assign its type parameters. To do so, choose the **Type Properties** tool from the **Properties** panel in the **Modify | Place Grid** contextual tab; the **Type Properties** dialog box will be displayed. Figure 3-26 shows partial view of the dialog box. In this dialog box, you can change values for various type parameters, which are given in the following table:

Figure 3-26 The **Type Properties** *dialog box*

Parameter Name	Value and Description
Symbol	Refers to the display of symbol at the end grid.
Center Segment	Refers to the display type of the center segment of a grid line. You can select **Continuous**, **None**, or **Custom** from the drop-down list.
End Segment Weight	Refers to the line weight of a grid line, if the **Center Segment** parameter is set to **Continuous**, **None** or **Custom**.
End Segment Color	Refers to the color assigned to a grid line, if the **Center Segment** parameter is set to **Continuous**, **None** or **Custom**.
End Segment Pattern	Refers to the line type of the grid line if the **Center Segment** parameter is set to **Continuous**, **None** or **Custom**.
Plan View Symbols End 1 (Default)	Refers to the default visibility status of the symbol at end 1 of the grid line in the plan view. By default, the check box is cleared. If you select the check box, the visibility of the symbol at end 1 in the plan view will be turned on.
Plan View Symbols End 2 (Default)	Refers to the default visibility status of the symbol at end 2 of grid line in the plan views. By default, the check box is selected. If you clear the check box, the visibility of symbol at end 2 in the plan view will be turned off.
Non-Plan View Symbols (Default)	Refers to the default visibility status of the grid line in sections and elevations other than in the plan views. You can control the visibility of the symbol at the top and bottom of grid line by selecting various options from the drop-down list.

Sketching the Grids

After assigning the type parameters in the **Type Properties** dialog box, you can now start sketching the grid line. To sketch the grid line, invoke any of the sketching tools from the **Draw** panel of the **Modify | Place Grid** contextual tab. The **Draw** panel of the **Modify | Place Grid** contextual tab contains four tools: **Line**, **Start-End-Radius Arc**, **Center-ends Arc**, and **Pick Lines**, as shown in Figure 3-27. The use of these sketching tools is discussed next.

Figure 3-27 *The sketching tools in the **Draw** panel*

Sketching a Grid Using the Line Tool

The **Line** tool in the **Draw** panel of the **Modify | Place Grid** contextual tab is invoked by default. To start sketching the grid line, click at the desired location in the drawing area to specify its start point. Notice that as you move the cursor, a grid line with one end fixed at the specified point and the other end attached to the cursor is created. A temporary angular dimension, indicating the angle of the grid line with the horizontal axis is also displayed, as shown in Figure 3-28. Click to specify the endpoint of the grid line when the appropriate angular dimension is displayed. You can also sketch an arbitrary inclined grid line and then click on the angular dimension to enter a new value of the angle. To draw orthogonal grids, hold the SHIFT key and restrain the movement of the cursor to the horizontal and vertical axes.

Figure 3-28 Temporary angular dimension displayed while sketching the grid

When you click to specify the endpoint, a grid is created and its controls are highlighted, as shown in Figure 3-29. Also, the recently added grid is highlighted and displays one square box on either side. These boxes are used to control the visibility of grid bubble. They can be selected or cleared to make the grid bubble visible or invisible on the desired side(s), respectively. The two circles on the start point and the endpoint can be dragged to extend or reduce the extent of the grid line.

Figure 3-29 The highlighted controls of the grid created

Similarly, when you sketch a new grid line near an existing one, a temporary dimension indicating the distance between them is displayed. You can enter a value in the edit box to specify the distance, as shown in Figure 3-30. Alternatively, you can move the cursor to the desired location using the temporary dimensions and click to specify the start point of the second grid line. Then, move the cursor horizontally to the right, and when the alignment line appears, click to specify the endpoint of the grid line.

Tip
*It is recommended that you draw grid lines with the endpoints aligned to each other. You can use the alignment line that is displayed when the cursor is moved to its proximity. The **Lock** constraints can be used to drag the extents of the single or multiple grid line.*

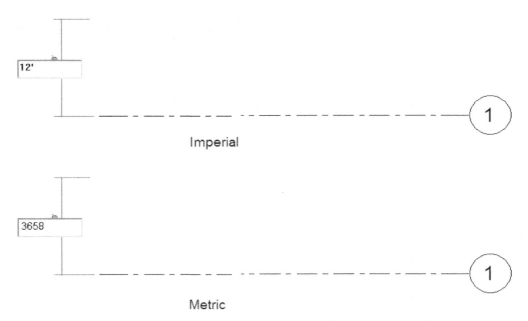

Imperial

Metric

Figure 3-30 *Distance value entered in the edit box for another grid*

On doing so, the second grid line will be created. Notice that the name of this grid is 2. Autodesk Revit automatically numbers the grid lines in ascending order as they are created. Similarly, you can draw more parallel grid lines. The **Offset** edit box in the **Options Bar** is used to specify the offset distance of a grid line from the desired point. To create vertical grid lines, specify the start point below the first grid line. Next, move the cursor vertically upward and click below the last horizontal grid line to specify the endpoint. You can create multiple vertical grid lines by using the method used for creating multiple horizontal lines.

You can also create a rectangular grid pattern that is aligned at a given angle to the horizontal axis. You can also specify different angles for grid lines and create grid patterns based on your project requirement.

Sketching a Curve Grid
You can sketch curved or radial grid patterns based on your project requirement. To do so, invoke the **Start-End-Radius Arc** or **Center-ends Arc** tools from the **Draw** panel of the **Modify | Place Grid** contextual tab.

After you have invoked the **Start-End-Radius Arc** tool, click at a point in the drawing area to specify the start point of the curved grid. Next, click at an appropriate location to locate the endpoint of the grid. On doing so, the curved grid will emerge with the temporary dimension displayed for the radius. Enter a suitable value for the radius or click in the drawing area; the curved grid will be created. Alternatively, after invoking the **Start-End-Radius Arc** tool, you can create multiple curved grids by selecting the **Radius** check box from the **Options Bar**. To do so, enter a suitable value in the edit box next to the **Radius** check box and then pick the start point and endpoint in the drawing to create an arc. You can also use the **Center-ends Arc** tool to create arcs by defining its center point, start point, and endpoint.

While sketching a structural grid, generally a combination of radial and linear grid patterns is used. Figure 3-31 shows a grid pattern created by using both the line and arc tools.

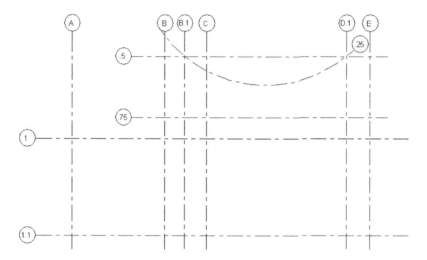

Figure 3-31 *An example of a grid pattern created using arc and straight grid lines*

Tip
You can also use different editing tools such as ***Copy***, ***Array***, ***Mirror***, ***Move***, *and so on to create grid patterns. Autodesk Revit numbers grids intuitively. For example, if you create an array of a grid named A, the new grids will sequentially be named as B, C, D, E, and so on.*

Creating Grids Using the Pick Lines Tool
The **Pick line** tool is useful for creating grid lines that are aligned to existing elements. When you choose this tool from the **Draw** panel of the **Modify | Place Grid** contextual tab and move the cursor near an existing element, the cursor snaps to certain object properties such as the interior face of walls, centerlines of columns, and so on. Click when the desired property of the element is highlighted; Autodesk Revit automatically creates a grid line along the specified alignment of element.

For example, to create grid lines for the structural wall profile, invoke the **Pick Lines** tool from the **Draw** panel and move the cursor near the curved exterior wall. As you move the cursor over the wall, it will snap to the interior and exterior faces. Click when the interior face is highlighted, as shown in Figure 3-32; a grid line aligned with the interior face of the wall will be displayed, as shown in Figure 3-33. Similarly, you can click on the other wall segments to create a grid pattern required for the building.

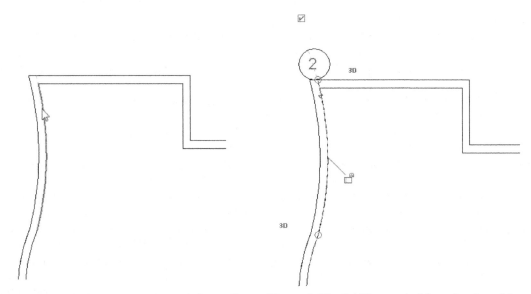

Figure 3-32 *The interior face of the wall highlighted*

Figure 3-33 *Grid line created from the edge of the interior face of the wall*

If the cursor does not snap to the centerline of the wall, you can align the grid lines along the center of the wall by specifying the distance value of the centerline from the interior face in the **Offset** edit box and then use the **Pick Lines** tool to select the interior face.

Creating Multi-Segmented Grids

In Autodesk Revit, you can create grids having more than one segment. To create a multi-segmented grid, choose the **Grid** tool from the **Datum** panel of the **Structure** tab; the **Modify | Place Grid** contextual tab will be displayed. In the **Draw** panel of this tab, choose the **Multi-Segment** tool; the **Modify | Edit Sketch** contextual tab will be displayed. In the **Draw** panel of the tab, the **Line** tool is chosen by default. As a result, the grid segment that you will draw will be a straight line. In the **Draw** panel, you can choose other sketching tools such as **Start-End-Radius Arc**, **Center-ends Arc**, **Tangent-end Arc**, and others depending on the requirement of the sketch of the grid lines in the project. In the **Options Bar**, the **Chain** check box is selected by default. As a result, the grid will be created from end-to-end in a chain. If you clear this check box, you need to specify start and end points for each grid segment that will be created. In the **Options Bar**, you can enter a suitable value in the **Offset** edit box to specify an offset distance by which the grid segment will be offset from the point you specify in the drawing area. In the **Options Bar**, the **Radius** check box is cleared by default. As a result, no fillet or curve will be created at the join of the grid segment. On selecting the **Radius** check box, the edit box next to it will be enabled. As a result, you can specify a suitable value in it to set the fillet radius of the curve that will be created at the join of two grid segments. Next, after specifying the desired options in the **Options Bar**, click in drawing area to start the multi-segment grid line. Now, click in the drawing area to specify the endpoint of the grid line.

Modifying Grids

Grids can be modified before or after they are created. To modify a grid, you need to select the grid and modify its properties using the **Properties** palette. Some of the parameters can also be modified by selecting the grid in the drawing window and entering the new values. For example, after selecting the grid, you can click on its name and assign it a new name. Similarly, you can modify the distance between the grids by selecting the temporary dimension and entering a new value. When you enter a new value, the grid automatically moves to the specified distance.

You can also move multiple grids by simply dragging them to the desired locations. To do so, click and select a single grid. Then, hold the CTRL key and click to select multiple grids. Next, you can drag the grid(s) to the desired location. Hold the SHIFT key to restrain the movement of the cursor in the orthogonal direction. When you move the cursor near a grid, it gets highlighted. At this stage, right-click and then choose the **Properties** option from the shortcut menu to display the **Properties** palette, if it is not displayed in the interface of Revit. You can also choose other options from the shortcut menu such as **Select Previous**, **Select All Instances**, and so on to select other grids. For certain grids, you may need to move or offset grid bubble to a different location. To do so, select a grid; a blue circle will appear on each of its endpoints. Also, the grid line break control will appear near the grid bubble. This control is used to create a grid bubble offset. You can click on this control and use the drag controls displayed to move the grid bubble to the desired location. The grid name also moves to the new location. Note that an extension line is also created along it.

Customizing the Grid Display

In Revit, you can customize the grid display. You can change the color, line weight, and line type of the entire grid line or part of the grid line such as center segment and end segment. You can also change the display of symbols at the end of the grid line.

Changing the Continuous Grid Line

A grid line is said to be continuous when the **Center Segment** parameter in the **Type Properties** dialog box is set to **Continuous**. You can change the line type, line weight, and color of the end segments using various options available in the **Type Properties** dialog box. Similarly, you can change the display of a symbol at the ends of a grid by using the other options available in the **Type Properties** dialog box.

Creating a Grid Line with Central Gap

You can create a grid line with central gap between its two end segments. To do so, select the **1/4" Bubble Custom Gap** or **1/4" Bubble Gap** option from the **Type Selector** drop-down list for Imperial unit system in the **Properties** palette. In Metric, you can select the option **6.5mm Bubble Custom Gap** or **6.5mm Bubble Gap** option from the **Type Selector** drop-down list. Then, set the **Center Segment** parameter in the **Type Properties** dialog box to **None**. Figure 3-34 shows a grid line with gap between the two segments. You can also change the display properties of the end segments, as discussed above.

Figure 3-34 *A grid line with a central gap*

Creating a Grid Line with Center Segment

You can create a grid line with the center and end segments containing different display properties such as line color, line weight, and line pattern. To do so, select the **1/4" Bubble Custom Gap** or **1/4" Bubble Gap** option from the **Type Selector** drop-down list in the **Properties** palette for the Imperial unit system. In Metric, you can select the option **6.5mm Bubble Custom Gap** or **6.5mm Bubble Gap** option from the **Type Selector** drop-down list. Then, set the **Center Segment** parameter in the **Type Properties** dialog box to **Custom**. You can change the display properties of the center segment and end segments using various options available in the **Type Properties** dialog box.

Controlling the Visibility of Grids

You can control the visibility of each grid or all grids in any of the project views. To do so, select a grid and right-click; a shortcut menu will be displayed. Choose **Hide in View > Category** from the shortcut menu; the grid category will be hidden in the current view. Similarly, you can also hide one particular grid by choosing **Hide in View > Elements** from the shortcut menu. On doing so, the selected grid will be hidden in the current view. However, the grid will be displayed in all the other views.

Alternatively, you can control the visibility of the grids by using the visibility/graphics feature of Autodesk Revit. To do so, select a grid from the drawing and choose the **Override by Category** tool from **Modify | Grids > View > Override Graphics in View > Override by Category** drop-down; the **View-Specific Category Graphics** dialog box will be displayed. Choose the **Open the Visibility Graphics dialog** button; the **Visibility/Graphic Overrides for Structural Plan: <view name>** dialog box for the current project view will be displayed. In the **Annotation Categories** tab of this dialog box, clear the check box for the visibility of grids; the visibility of all grids will turn off in the current view. You can also control the visibility of grids using the **Scope Box** feature.

WORKING WITH REFERENCE PLANES

Ribbon:	Structure > Work Plane > Ref Plane
Shortcut Keys:	RP

Ref Plane   Reference planes help sketching and adding structural elements to a design. They can be used as datum planes to act as guidelines to create elements. They can also be used for creating new family elements. To create a reference plane, invoke the **Ref Plane** tool from the **Work Plane** panel of the **Structure** tab. Alternatively, enter **RP**; the **Modify | Place Reference Plane** contextual tab will be displayed. In the **Draw** panel of this tab, the **Line** and **Pick Line** tools are present, the **Line** tool is invoked by default. You can use this tool to draw a straight line or a chain of connected line segments to represent a reference plane.

Before drawing a reference plane using the **Line** tool, you can use the **Offset** edit box in the **Options Bar** to specify a suitable offset distance for it. To draw a line for the reference plane, click at the desired location in the drawing window. Next, drag the cursor to a new location and release the left button to specify the endpoint of the reference line; the reference plane will be created. Select the reference plane and assign a name to it in the corresponding field of the **Name** parameter in the **Properties** palette.

Alternatively, you can draw a reference plane in your project view by selecting the edge of a wall, beam, column, or an existing model line in the drawing. To do so, invoke the **Ref Plane** tool as discussed earlier and then choose the **Pick Lines** option from the **Draw** panel of the **Modify|Place Reference Plane** contextual tab. On doing so, you will be prompted to select an edge or a line from the drawing. Move the cursor toward the desired edge of an element; the edge of the element will be highlighted. Click on the highlighted edge to add a reference plane aligned to it.

WORKING WITH WORK PLANES

A work plane is a plane which is used to sketch elements. In Autodesk Revit, you can create and edit only those elements that are in the current work plane. A work plane can be horizontal, vertical, or inclined at any specified angle. Each generated view has an associated work plane. This plane is automatically defined for some standard views such as floor plans. For others, such as sections, elevations, and 3D views, you can set the work plane based on the location of the elements to be created or edited. The concept of work planes is especially useful for creating elements in elevations, sections, or inclined planes. You will learn more about the work planes in the following sections.

Setting a Work Plane

Ribbon: Structure > Work Plane > Set

You can set a work plane based on your project requirement. To set a work plane, invoke the **Set** tool from the **Work Plane** panel of the **Structure** tab; the **Work Plane** dialog box will be displayed, as shown in Figure 3-35. This dialog box shows the current work plane. You can also specify parameters for setting a new work plane in this dialog box. In the **Specify a new Work Plane** area, you will notice drop-down list is available on the right of the **Name** radio button. This drop-down list contains the options that can be levels, grids, and named reference planes. Select an option from the drop-down list to set the current work plane.

The **Pick a plane** radio button can be used to set a work plane along an existing plane. To do so, select this radio button and then an existing plane in the drawing. You can select the **Pick a line and use the work plane it was sketched in** radio button to create a work plane that is coplanar with the plane on which the selected line was created.

Figure 3-35 *The* **Work Plane** *dialog box*

Controlling the Visibility of Work Planes

Ribbon: Structure > Work Plane > Show

You can control the visibility of the current work plane by invoking the **Show** tool from the **Work Plane** panel of the **Structure** tab. The work plane appears as a grid in the current view. To hide it, choose the **Show** tool again.

You can also set the grid spacing for a work plane. To do so, select a work plane from the drawing; the work plane will be highlighted. Specify the spacing by entering a new value in the **Spacing** edit box in the **Options Bar**. You can also enter the spacing in the corresponding value field of the **Work Plane Grid Spacing** parameter in the **Properties** palette. You can snap to the work plane grid using the object snap tools. These tools can be used to create basic locations for columns and footings in a project view.

Using the Workplane Viewer Window

While working on a project you may require to modify elements at a specified workplane. To do so, you can use the **Workplane Viewer** window. This window displays temporary views of models present in the Project Environment and helps in editing the profile in forms, sweeps, blends, and swept blends. You can invoke the **Workplane Viewer** window by choosing the **Viewer** tool from the **Workplane** panel of the **Structure** tab.

WORKING WITH PROJECT VIEWS

While working on a structural model, you may need to view its different exterior and interior portions in order to add or edit elements in the design. Autodesk Revit provides various features and techniques that can be used to view the structural model. In this section, you will learn about the tools that help in working with views.

Viewing a Building Model

The default template file has certain predefined standard project views displayed in the **Views (all)** head of the **Project Browser**, refer to Figure 3-36. These views include structural plans, 3d views, and elevations. To open a view, double-click on its name; the corresponding view will be displayed in the viewing area. In the Revit interface, you can hide or unhide the **Project Browser**. To do so, choose the **User Interface** tool from the **Windows** panel of the **View** tab; a cascading menu will be displayed. By default, the **Project Browser** check box is selected in this cascading menu, which indicates that the **Project Browser** is displayed in your drawing. Clear this check box to hide the **Project Browser** in your drawing.

Autodesk Revit also enables you to add elements to a building model by simply dragging and dropping them directly from the **Project Browser** instead of using the **Type Selector** drop-down list.

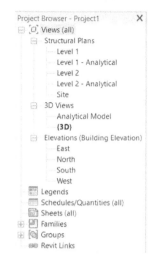

Figure 3-36 *The options displayed in the* ***Project Browser***

When you open a new project, the viewing area displays four inward arrow symbols in the floor plan view, which indicates the four-side elevations: North, East, South, and West. You can use these symbols to view appropriate building elevation by double-clicking on them.

Controlling the Visibility of Elements in Views

To control the visibility of certain categories of elements, select the element from the drawing; the contextual tab related to it will be displayed in the ribbon. From the **View** panel of the displayed contextual tab, choose the **Override Graphics in View** drop-down menu; a list of available override tool will be displayed. Next, select the **Override by Category** option from the list; the **View-Specific Category Graphics** dialog box will be displayed. Choose the **Open the Visibility Graphics dialog** button; the **Visibility/Graphic Overrides for Structural Plan: <Level name>** dialog box for the specific view will be displayed. You can use the various tabs in this dialog box to hide different categories of elements.

SCOPE BOX

Ribbon:	View > Create > Scope Box

The **Scope Box** tool helps you to control the visibility of the datum elements (grids, reference lines, and levels) in the project views. As described earlier in this chapter, these datum elements have infinite scope and they extend throughout the project. Using the **Scope Box** tool, you can create boundary limit for the visibility of these datum elements. You can also specify the views in which these datum elements become visible.

Creating a Scope Box

A scope box can be created in the plan view by invoking the **Scope Box** tool. You can invoke this tool from the **Create** panel of the **View** tab. Once this tool has been invoked, the **Options Bar** displays the **Name** and **Height** edit boxes. You can enter the name and height of the scope box in their respective edit boxes. To create a scope box, move the cursor in the viewing area; the cursor will change into a cross symbol and will prompt you to draw scope box in the plan view. To define the scope box, click on its upper left corner, move the cursor to the lower right corner, and then click to specify the diagonally opposite ends. Note that the rectangle should be drawn in such a way that the elements that need to be visible are enclosed in it. The scope box with the assigned name will be created. When you select the scope box, drag controls are visible on it, as shown in Figure 3-37. These drag controls can be used to resize the scope box.

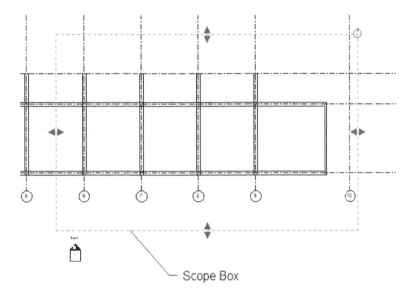

Figure 3-37 The scope box displayed in the drawing

Applying a Scope Box to Datum Elements

The visibility of datum elements can be controlled by associating them with a scope box. To associate the scope box created to the desired datum elements, select the scope box from the drawing; the properties of the selected scope box will be displayed in the **Properties** palette. Click on the value field corresponding to the **Scope Box** parameter and select the name of the scope box from the drop-down list. Next, choose the **Apply** button to apply property to the selected datum element. On doing so, you will notice that the datum elements that intersect the boundary of the assigned scope box will restrict its extent throughout the boundary of the scope box. Figures 3-38 and 3-39 illustrate the extent of the grid elements before and after applying the scope box to them.

Figure 3-38 *Grids before applying the scope box*   ***Figure 3-39*** *Grids after applying the scope box*

Controlling the Visibility of a Scope Box

A scope box can be resized to limit its visibility for certain views. Its visibility can also be controlled for each view. To do so, select a scope box, and then in the **Properties** palette, choose the **Edit** button displayed in the value field for the **Views Visible** parameter; the **Scope Box Views Visible** dialog box will be displayed. This dialog box lists all views types and view names available in the project. The **Automatic visibility** column shows the current visibility of scope boxes. You can click on the **Override** column for a specific view and select the **Visible** or **Invisible** option from the drop-down list displayed to override the automatic visibility setting, refer to Figure 3-40.

Figure 3-40 *Selecting an option from the drop-down list in the **Override** column*

TUTORIALS
Tutorial 1   Commercial Complex

In this tutorial, you will create various project settings such as project information, project location, and browser organization for the project created in Tutorial 1 of Chapter 2. Further, you will add levels and grids to the project file. Use the following project parameters and specifications:

(Expected time: 1 hr 15 min)

1. Rename Level 1 and Level 2 as **Below Grade** and **Entry**, respectively.

2. Specify the elevation of **Below Grade** and **Entry** levels as follows.
    For Imperial   **-4' 0"** and **0' 0"**
    For Metric   **-1219** mm and **0** mm

3. Levels to be added:
    For Imperial   **Second Floor - Elevation 12' 6"**
                     Roof - Elevation 25' 0"
    For Metric   **Second Floor - Elevation 3810 mm**
                     Roof - Elevation 7620 mm

4. File name to be assigned:
    For Imperial   *c03_Commercial-Complex_tut1.rvt*
    For Metric   *M_c03_Commercial-Complex_tut1.rvt*

    The following steps are required to complete this tutorial:

a. Open Tutorial 1 of Chapter 2.
b. Set the project information, project location, and browser organization.
c. Modify existing levels and add new levels.
d. Add grid lines.
e. Save the project using the **Save As** tool.
f. Close the project using the **Close** tool.

Opening an Existing Project
In this section, you will open the project file created in Tutorial 1 of Chapter 2.

1. Choose **Open > Project** from the **File** menu; the **Open** dialog box is displayed.

2. In this dialog box, browse to *C:\rst_2021\c02_rst_2021_tut* folder and then choose the *c02_Commercial-Complex_tut1.rvt* (for Imperial) or *M_c02_Commercial-Complex_tut1.rvt* (for Metric) project file. You can also download this file from *https://www.cadcim.com*. The path of the file is as follows: *Textbooks > Civil/GIS > Revit Structure > Exploring Autodesk Revit 2021 for Structure*

3. Choose the **Open** button from the **Open** dialog box to open the selected project file.

Setting the Project Information

In this section, you will add project information to the opened file. Further, you will define a parameter for the project information and add it to the project information of the project file.

1. Choose the **Project Information** tool from the **Settings** panel of the **Manage** tab; the **Project Information** dialog box is displayed.

2. In this dialog box, specify the project parameters as follows:

Parameter	Value
Project Issue Date	**01/01/2020**
Project Status	**Started**
Client Name	**Tickoo Institute of Emerging Technologies**
Project Address	**525, Andrews Drive Schererville**
Project Name	**Commercial Complex**
Project Number	**TIET/02/20**

3. In the **Project Information** dialog box, choose the **OK** button; the dialog box closes and the project parameters are saved in the project file.

    Next, you need to create an additional instance parameter for the project information.

4. Choose the **Project Parameters** tool from the **Settings** panel of the **Manage** tab; the **Project Parameters** dialog box is displayed.

5. Choose the **Add** button from the **Project Parameters** dialog box; the **Parameter Properties** dialog box is displayed.

6. In the **Parameter Properties** dialog box, scroll the list in the **Categories** area and then select the **Project Information** check box.

7. In the **Parameter Data** area, ensure that the **Instance** radio button is selected. Now, enter the name **Project Engineer** in the **Name** edit box in the **Parameter Data** area.

8. Next, select the **Common** option from the **Discipline** drop-down list, if it is not selected by default.

9. Select the **Text** and **Other** options from the **Type of Parameter** and **Group parameter under** drop-down lists, respectively.

10. Choose the **OK** button in the **Parameter Properties** dialog box; the **Project Parameters** dialog box is displayed, as shown in Figure 3-41.

*Figure 3-41 The **Project Parameters** dialog box*

11. Choose the **OK** button; the **Project Parameters** dialog box is closed.

12. Choose the **Project Information** tool from the **Settings** panel of the **Manage** tab; the **Project Information** dialog box is displayed.

13. In this dialog box, click in the **Value** field corresponding to the **Project Engineer** parameter and enter **Sham Tickoo**.

14. Next, choose the **OK** button; the **Project Information** dialog box closes and the value for the newly added parameter is saved in the project file.

Setting the Project Location
In this section, you will specify the geographical location of the project.

1. Choose the **Location** tool from the **Project Location** panel of the **Manage** tab; the **Location Weather and Site** dialog box is displayed.

2. In the **Location Weather and Site** dialog box, choose the **Site** tab and then the **Duplicate** button; the **Name** dialog box is displayed.

3. Enter **TIET-IN** in the **Name** edit box and then choose the **OK** button; the **Name** dialog box closes and the name entered is displayed and highlighted in the **Sites defined in this project** list box of the **Location Weather and Site** dialog box, refer to Figure 3-42.

Figure 3-42 TIET-IN selected in the Sites defined in this project list box of the Site tab

4. Next, choose the **Location** tab in the **Location Weather and Site** dialog box; the options in this tab are displayed.

5. Select the **Default City List** option from the **Define Location by** drop-down list.

6. Next, select the **Indianapolis, IN** option from the **City** drop-down list.

7. Next, select the **Use Daylight Saving time** check box and then choose the **OK** button; the dialog box closes and the settings for the project location are saved in the project file.

Setting the Browser Organization
In this section, you will specify the settings for customizing the **Project Browser** displayed in the drawing area of the project.

1. Choose the **Browser Organization** tool from **View > Windows > User Interface** drop-down; the **Browser Organization** dialog box is displayed.

2. Ensure that the **Views** tab is chosen, and then select the **Discipline** check box in this tab.

3. Next, choose the **Sheets** tab in the **Browser Organization** dialog box; the options in this tab are displayed.

4. In this dialog box, select the **Issue Date** check box.

5. Now to apply the modified settings, choose **Apply** and then **OK** from the **Browser Organization** dialog box; the modified settings are applied to the **Project Browser** and the **Browser Organization** dialog box is closed.

Modifying the Existing Levels

In this section, you will modify the existing levels in the project file. To do so, you need to select an elevation view from the **Project Browser** and then use the **Level** tool.

1. Before modifying the levels, move the cursor to the **Project Browser** and expand the Structural head and then the **Elevations (Building Elevation)** node. Now, double-click on the **North** node; the current view is changed to the North elevation view.

 Note
*In the north elevation view, make sure that the **Hidden Line** option is chosen for the **Visual Style** in the **View Control Bar**.*

2. Next, zoom in the drawing area to make the text on the level lines visible. Click on the **Level 1** level line and move the cursor over the text **Level 1**; the text is highlighted.

3. Click on the text; an edit box is displayed.

4. Enter **Below Grade** in the edit box and press ENTER; the **Confirm Level Rename** message box is displayed. This message box prompts you to confirm whether or not to rename the corresponding view of the selected level.

5. Choose the **Yes** button; the name of the level changes in the **Project Browser**. Also, notice that the name of the view corresponding to the changed level has been changed under the **Structural Plans** head in the **Project Browser**.

6. Next, move the cursor over the elevation value of the **Below Grade** level; the elevation value is highlighted.

7. Click on the highlighted elevation value; an edit box is displayed.

8. Enter value in the edit box as given below:
   For Imperial   **-4' 0"**
   For Metric   **-1220 mm**

   Press ENTER and then press ESC to exit from the modification controls.

9. Repeat the procedure followed in steps 2 through 7 to rename the **Level 2** level to **Entry** and modify its elevation as given below:
   For Imperial   **0'0"**.
   For Metric   **0** mm.

10. Next, right-click in the drawing area; a shortcut menu is displayed.

11. Choose the **Zoom To Fit** option from the shortcut menu; the extents of the level lines are displayed in the drawing area.

12. Next, select the **Below Grade** level line and then place the cursor over the grid length control displayed on the left.

13. Press the left mouse button and drag the mouse to the right; the level lines move along the cursor.

14. Click in the drawing area when the length of the level line reduces to half of their existing length.

15. Press ESC to exit from the edit controls.

16. Next, right-click in the drawing area and then choose **Zoom To Fit** from the shortcut menu; the current view fits the extent of the length of level lines.

Adding New Levels

In this section, you will add new levels to the project file using the **Level** tool.

1. Choose the **Level** tool from the **Datum** panel of the **Structure** tab; the **Modify | Place Level** contextual tab is displayed. Alternatively, you can press LL to activate the **Level** tool.

2. Choose the **Plan View Types** button from the **Options Bar**; the **Plan View Types** dialog box is displayed. In this dialog box, click and deselect **Floor Plan** and **Ceiling Plan**. Now, choose the **OK** button; the dialog box is closed.

3. Move the cursor near the left endpoint of the **Entry** level line, and when the alignment line appears, type value in the edit box displayed as given below:

    For Imperial   **12'6"**, refer to Figure 3-43.
    For Metric   **3810 mm**

    Press ENTER.

4. Next, move the cursor toward right until the alignment line appears above the **Entry** level bubble and then click to complete the level line, as shown in Figure 3-44. A new level line is created, displaying the level name as **Level 3** and the elevation as **12'6"** for imperial and for metric the elevation is **3810** .

Figure 3-43 *Specifying the distance of the new level line*

Figure 3-44 *Creating the new level line using the alignment line*

5. Without exiting the **Level** tool, repeat steps 2 and 3 to create a level line with the name **Level 4** at a distance from the **Level 3** level line as given below:

           For Imperial   **12'6"**
           For Metric   **3810**

    Note that the elevation of the **Level 4** level line is displayed as shown below:

           For Imperial   **25' 0"**
           For Metric   **7620**

6. Press ESC twice to exit from the **Level** tool.

7. Select the **Level 3** level line; the properties of the selected level line are displayed in the **Properties** palette.

8. In the **Properties** palette, click in the value field corresponding to the **Name** parameter and replace the existing name **Level 3** with **Second Floor**.

9. Choose the **Apply** button in this palette; the **Confirm Level Rename** message box is displayed.

10. In the **Confirm Level Rename** message box, choose the **Yes** button; the name of the level line **Level 3** changes to **Second Floor**. Also, notice that the name of the corresponding view in the **Project Browser** has changed to the new name.

11. Next, to rename the **Level 4** level view, select it from the drawing area; the properties of the selected level are displayed in the **Properties** palette.

12. Repeat steps 7 to 9 and rename **Level 4** to **Roof**.

13. Press ESC to exit from the tool.

14. Choose the **Level 1 - Analytical** option from the **Structural Plans** subhead in the **Project Browser**.

Note
*The **Structural Plans** head is a subhead in the **Structural** head of the **Views (Discipline)** hierarchy in the **Project Browser**.*

15. Right-click and then choose **Delete** from the displayed shortcut menu; the selected view name is deleted from the **Project Browser**.

16. Repeat steps 13 and 14 to delete the **Level 2- Analytical** option from the **Structural Plans** head.

Adding Grid Lines

In this section, you will add grids to the structural project. To add grids, you need to change the current view to the **Entry** level structural plan and then use the **Grid** tool.

1. Double-click on **Entry** from the **Structural Plans** head in the **Project Browser**; the **Entry** structural plan view will be displayed in the drawing area.

2. Invoke the **Grid** tool from the **Datum** panel of the **Structure** tab; the **Modify | Place Grid** contextual tab is displayed.

3. In this tab, ensure that the **Line** tool is invoked from the **Draw** panel. Next, move the cursor toward the lower left corner of the drawing area and then click to specify the start point of the first grid line; a grid line with temporary dimensions for angle emerges, refer to Figure 3-45 for location.

4. Move the cursor vertically up (at an angle of 90° from the horizontal plane) and click when it reaches near the **North** elevation arrow, refer to Figure 3-46 for location.

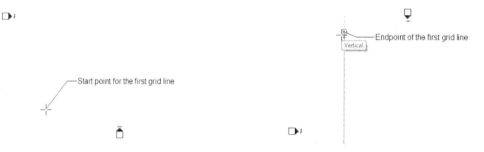

Figure 3-45 *Specifying the start point of the first grid line*

Figure 3-46 *Specifying the endpoint of the first grid line*

5. Now, move the cursor downward and position it near the right side of the endpoint of the grid line created previously, as shown in Figure 3-47.

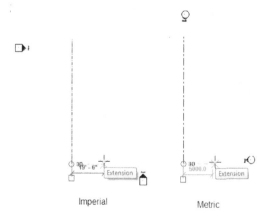

Imperial

Metric

Figure 3-47 *Specifying the start point of the second vertical grid line*

6. As you move the cursor toward right, a temporary dimension appears with an extension line and the **Extension** snap. Enter value as given below:

        For Imperial   **10'**
        For Metric   **3048**

Press ENTER; the second grid line starts at a distance of entered value from the start point of the first grid line.

7. Move the cursor vertically up and place it near the bubble of the first grid line and click when alignment line appears; second grid line is created.

8. Repeat steps 5 to 7 to create five more vertical grids with the distance specified in Figure 3-48.

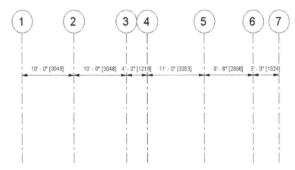

Figure 3-48 *Distance between the vertical grid lines*

9. After creating all the vertical grids, press ESC twice to exit the **Grid** tool.

10. Select the vertical grid line marked **4**. Now, place the cursor over the text in the grid bubble of the selected grid line and click; an edit box is displayed, as shown in Figure 3-49.

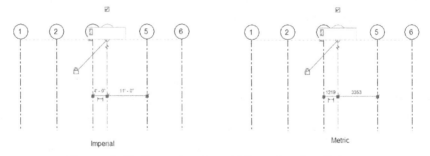

Figure 3-49 *Renaming the grid line using the edit box*

11. Enter **3.1** in the edit box and press ENTER; the selected grid line is renamed.

Note
*While renumbering the grid line, you can use the **Zoom in Region** and **Zoom Out(2x)** tools to view the grid numbers easily.*

12. Without exiting the editing mode, select the next grid marked **5** and then move the cursor over its grid bubble and click to display the edit box.

13. Enter **4** in the edit box and press ENTER to rename the selected line.

14. Repeat steps 10 and 11 to rename the grid lines marked **6** and **7** to **5** and **5.1**, respectively, as shown in Figure 3-50.

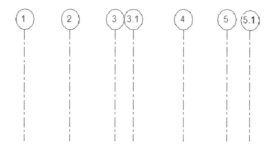

Figure 3-50 *The display of vertical grids after they are renumbered*

15. After renumbering all required vertical grids displayed in the drawing, press ESC to exit the editing mode.

Now you will add horizontal grids,

16. Invoke the **Grid** tool from the **Datum** panel of the **Structure** tab.

17. Next, move the cursor toward the top right of the vertical grid line marked **5.1** and click at the location shown in Figure 3-51.

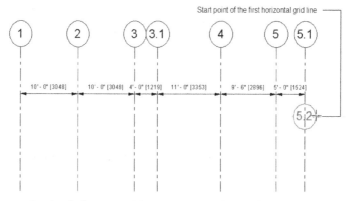

Figure 3-51 *The location of the start point of the first horizontal grid line*

18. Move the cursor horizontally toward the left until it has crossed the vertical grid line marked **1**. Click in the drawing area to create the first horizontal grid line, as shown in Figure 3-52.

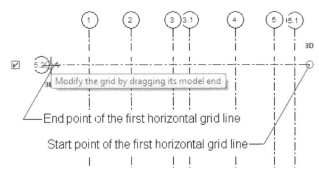

Figure 3-52 The location of the start point and endpoint of the first horizontal grid line

19. Move the cursor below the grid line alignment control of the start point of the first horizontal grid line (grid line created previously); an alignment line with a temporary dimension is displayed.

20. Type **8'** (or **2438 mm** for Metric); an edit box is displayed with the entered value. Press ENTER; the second horizontal grid line will start below the start point of the first horizontal grid line at a distance of **8'** (or **2438** mm in Metric) from it.

21. Move the cursor horizontally toward left and place it below the grid bubble (marked **5.2**) of the first horizontal grid line when the alignment line appears and then click to create the grid line.

22. Repeat steps 19 to 22 to create rest of the horizontal grid lines and rename them, refer to Figures 3-53 and 3-54.

Figure 3-53 *The horizontal grid lines to be created with the specified names and distances*

Figure 3-54 *The remaining horizontal grid lines in continuation of Figure 3-53*

Note
*To create the remaining horizontal grids from grid **B** to grid **I** refer to Figures 3-53 and 3-54. Note that both these figures are part of a single grid plan view. Figure 3-54 is in continuation with Figure 3-53 and is displayed separately to show the grid dimensions clearly. Further, the horizontal grids will be renamed using the same method used for vertical grids.*

Saving the Project
In this section, you will save the project file by using the **Save As** tool.

1. Choose the **Save As > Project** option from the **File** menu. On doing so, the **Save As** dialog box is displayed.

2. In this dialog box, browse to the C:*rst_2021* location and create a folder with name *c03_rst_2021_tut*. Now, open the *c03_rst_2021_tut* folder and enter **c03_Commercial-Complex_tut1** (for Imperial) **or M_c03_Commercial-Complex_tut1** (for Metric) in the **File name** edit box.

3. Choose the **Save** button; the **Save As** dialog box closes and the project file is saved.

Closing the Project
1. Choose the **Close** option from the **File** menu.

   The file is closed and this completes Tutorial 1 of Chapter 3.

Tutorial 2   Industrial Complex

In this tutorial, you will set various project settings such as project information, project location, and browser organization for the project created in the Tutorial 2 of Chapter 2. Further, you will add levels and grids to the project file. Use the following project specifications:

(Expected time: 1 hr 15 min)

1. Rename Level 1 and Level 2 as **Foundation Level** and **Entry**, respectively.

2. Specify the elevation of **Foundation Level** and **Entry** levels.
   - For Imperial   **-6' 0"** and **0' 0"**
   - For Metric   **-1829 mm** and **0 mm**

3. Levels to be added:
   - For Imperial   **Second Floor - Elevation 10' 0"**
                        Roof - Elevation 24' 0"
   - For Metric   **Second Floor - Elevation 10' 0"**
                        Roof - Elevation 7315 mm

4. File name to be assigned:
   - For Imperial   *c03_Industrial-Complex_tut2.rvt.*
   - For Metric   *M_c03_Industrial-Complex_tut2.rvt.*

The following steps are required to complete this tutorial:

a.   Open the Tutorial 2 of Chapter 2.
b.   Set project information and project location.
c.   Modify existing levels and add new levels.
d.   Add grid lines.
e.   Resizing and renaming the grid lines.
f.   Save the project using the **Save As** tool.
g.   Close the project by using the **Close** tool.

Opening the Existing Project

In this section, you will open the project file created in the Tutorial 2 of Chapter 2.

1.   Choose **Open > Project** from the **File** menu; the **Open** dialog box is displayed.

2.   In this dialog box, browse to *C:\rst_2021\c02_rst_2021_tut* folder and then choose the *c02_ Industrial-Complex_tut2.rvt* (for Imperial) *or M_c02_Industrial-Complex_tut2.rvt* (for Metric) project file. You can also download this file from *https://www.cadcim.com*. The path to download this file is as follows: *Textbooks > Civil/GIS > Revit Structure > Exploring Autodesk Revit 2021 for Structure*.

3.   Choose the **Open** button from the **Open** dialog box; the selected project file opens in the drawing window.

Setting the Project Information

In this section, you will add the project information to the industrial complex project file.

1.   Choose the **Project Information** tool from the **Settings** panel of the **Manage** tab; the **Project Information** dialog box is displayed.

2.   In the **Project Information** dialog box, specify the project parameters as follows:

Parameter	Value
Project Issue Date	**01/01/2020**
Project Status	**Started**
Client Name	**CADCIM Technologies**
Project Address	**525, Andrews Drive Schererville**
Project Name	**Industrial Complex**
Project Number	**CIT/02/20**

3.   Choose the **OK** button; the **Project Information** dialog box closes and the project parameters are saved in the project file.

Next, you will create an additional instance parameter for the project information.

4. Choose the **Project Parameters** tool from the **Settings** panel in the **Manage** tab; the **Project Parameters** dialog box is displayed.

5. Choose the **Add** button from the dialog box; the **Parameter Properties** dialog box is displayed.

6. In this dialog box, scroll the list in the **Categories** area and then select the **Project Information** check box.

7. In the **Parameter Data** area of the **Parameter Properties** dialog box, enter **Project Manager** in the **Name** edit box.

8. Next, in the same area, ensure that the **Instance** radio button is selected and then ensure that the **Common** option is selected in the **Discipline** drop-down list.

9. Select the **Text** and **Other** options from the **Type of Parameter** and **Group parameter under** drop-down lists, respectively.

10. Next, choose the **OK** button from the **Parameter Properties** dialog box; the **Project Parameters** dialog box is displayed.

11. Choose the **OK** button from the **Project Parameters** dialog box; the dialog box closes.

12. Choose the **Project Information** tool from the **Settings** panel of the **Manage** tab; the **Project Information** dialog box is displayed.

13. In this dialog box, click in the **Value** field corresponding to the **Project Manager** parameter and enter **Sham Tickoo**.

14. Now, choose the **OK** button; the **Project Information** dialog box closes and the value for the newly added parameter is saved in the project file.

Setting the Project Location
In this section, you will specify the geographical location of the project.

1. Choose the **Location** tool from the **Project Location** panel of the **Manage** tab; the **Location Weather and Site** dialog box is displayed.

2. Ensure that the **Location** tab is chosen in this dialog box. Then, select the **Internet Mapping Service** option from the **Define Location by** drop-down list.

Note
*While selecting the **Internet Mapping Service** option from the **Define Location by** drop-down list, ensure that the internet is connected to your system. If the internet is not connected, a message box will be displayed below the **Project Address** edit box, informing that the connection could not be established to the Internet Mapping Service.*

3. In the **Project Address** edit box, delete the default text and enter **Indianapolis IN**, and then choose the **Search** button; the desired location is displayed on the map in the area below the edit box. Note that the search uses the bing map service to display the location, refer to Figure 3-55.

Figure 3-55 The desired location displayed in the Location Weather and Site dialog box

4. Next, choose the **Site** tab from the **Location Weather and Site** dialog box and then choose the **Duplicate** button; the **Name** dialog box is displayed.

5. Enter **CADCIM-IN** in the **Name** edit box and then choose the **OK** button; the **Name** dialog box closes and the name entered is displayed and highlighted in the **Sites defined in this project** list box.

6. Now, choose the **Make Current** button and then choose the **OK** button; the **Location Weather and Site** dialog box closes and the settings for the project location are saved in the project file.

Modifying the Existing Levels

In this section, you will modify the existing levels in the project file. To do so, you need to select an elevation view from the **Project Browser** and then use the **Level** tool.

1. Before modifying levels, move the cursor to the **Project Browser** and then double-click on the **South** option displayed under the **Elevation (Building Elevation)** head; the current view is changed to the **South** elevation view.

Note

*In the **South** elevation view, make sure that the **Hidden Line** option is chosen for the visual style in the **View Control Bar**.*

2. Next, zoom in the drawing area to make the text on the level lines visible. Click on the **Level 1** level line and move the cursor over the text **Level 1**; the text is highlighted.

3. Again, click on the text; an edit box is displayed.

4. Enter **Foundation Level** in the edit box and press ENTER; the **Confirm Level Rename** message box is displayed, prompting you to confirm whether or not to rename the corresponding view of the selected level.

5. In the **Confirm Level Rename** message box, choose the **Yes** button; the name of the level is changed. Also, notice that the name of the view corresponding to the level changes in the **Structural Plans** head of the **Project Browser**.

6. Next, move the cursor over the elevation value of the **Foundation Level** level; the elevation value gets highlighted.

7. Click on the highlighted elevation value; an edit box is displayed.

8. Enter value in the edit box as given below:
     For Imperial   **-6' 0"**
     For Metric   **-1829 mm**
     Press ENTER and then press ESC to exit from the modification.

9. Repeat steps 2 to 8 to rename **Level 2** level to **Entry** and modify its elevation as given below:
     For Imperial   **0' 0"**
     For Metric   **0 mm**

10. Next, right-click in the drawing area; a shortcut menu is displayed.

11. Choose the **Zoom to Fit** option from the shortcut menu; the extent of the level lines are displayed in the drawing area.

12. Next, select the **Foundation Level** level line and place the cursor over the grid length control displayed on the left.

13. Press and hold the left mouse button and drag the mouse to the right; the level lines move along the cursor.

14. Click in the drawing area when the length of the level line reduces to almost half of its existing length.

15. Next, press ESC to exit from the edit controls.

16. Right-click in the drawing area and then choose **Zoom to Fit** from the shortcut menu displayed; the current view fits the extent of the length of the level lines.

Adding New Levels

In this section, you will add two levels to the project file using the **Level** tool.

1. Invoke the **Level** tool from the **Datum** panel of the **Structure** tab.

2. Clear the **Make Plan View** check box in the **Options Bar**.

3. Now, move the cursor near the left endpoint of the **Foundation Level** level line, and when the alignment line appears, enter the following values:

For Imperial	**6"**
For Metric	**152 mm**

    Press ENTER.

4. Move the cursor toward the right until the alignment line appears above and across the **Foundation Level** level bubble. Next, click to complete the level line. The new level line is created. It displays the level name as **Level 3** and the elevation as given below:

For Imperial	**-5' 6"**
For Metric	**-1680 mm**

5. Without exiting the **Level** tool, select the **Make Plan View** check box in the **Options Bar**.

6. Choose the **Plan View Types** button from the **Options Bar**; the **Plan View Types** dialog box is displayed. In this dialog box, click and deselect **Floor Plan** and **Ceiling Plan**. Now, choose the **OK** button; the dialog box is closed.

7. Move the cursor above the left endpoint of the **Entry** level line and when the alignment line appears, enter value as given below:

For Imperial	**10'**
For Metric	**3050 mm**

    Next, press ENTER.

8. Move the cursor toward the right till the alignment line appears above the **Entry** level bubble, and click to complete the level line. The new level line is created. It displays the level name as **Level 4** and the elevation.

For Imperial	**10' - 0"**
For Metric	**3050 mm**

9. Repeat steps 6 and 7 to create a level line with the default name **Level 5** at a distance of given distance from **Level 4**.

For Imperial	**14'**
For Metric	**4270 mm**

    Note that the elevation of the **Level 5** level line is displayed as:

For Imperial	**24' 0"**
For Metric	**7320 mm**

10. Next, press ESC twice to exit the **Level** tool.

11. Select the **Level 3** level line; the properties of the selected level line are displayed in the **Properties** palette.

12. In the **Properties** palette, click in the value field corresponding to the **Name** parameter and replace the existing name **Level 3** with **T.O.F**.

13. Choose the **Apply** button in the palette; the name of the level line changes in the project view.

14. Select **Level 4** from the drawing area; the properties of the selected level are displayed in the **Properties** palette.

15. In the **Properties** palette, click in the value field corresponding to the **Name** parameter and replace the existing name **Level 4** with **Second Floor**.

16. Choose the **Apply** button in the palette; the **Confirm Level Rename** message box is displayed.

17. Choose the **Yes** button from the message box; the **Confirm Level Rename** message box closes. Notice that the name of the selected level line as well as its corresponding view name have been changed.

18. Repeat steps 15 to 17 and rename the **Level 5** to **Roof**.

19. Press ESC to exit the **Level** tool.

20. Now, move the cursor to the **Project Browser** and choose the **Level 1 - Analytical** option from the **Structural Plans** head.

21. Right-click and then choose **Delete** from the shortcut menu; the name of the selected view is deleted from the **Project Browser**.

22. Repeat steps 19 and 20 to delete the **Level 2 - Analytical** option from the **Structural Plans** head.

Adding Grid Lines

In this section,you will add grids to the project using the Grid tool. For this, make **Entry** structural plan view as the current view.

1. Double-click on **Entry** from the **Structural Plans** head in the **Project Browser**; the **Entry** structural plan view is displayed in the drawing area.

2. Invoke the **Grid** tool from the **Datum** panel of the **Structure** tab; the **Modify| Place Grid** contextual tab is displayed.

3. Ensure that the **Line** tool is invoked from the list box in the **Draw** panel of this tab. Then, move the cursor toward the lower left corner of the drawing area (near the **South** elevation arrow) and click; a grid line emerges, as shown in Figure 3-56.

Figure 3-56 *The location for the start point of the first horizontal grid line*

4. Move the cursor horizontally to the right and click when it reaches a point below the **East** elevation arrow; refer to Figure 3-57 for location.

Figure 3-57 *The location for the endpoint of the first horizontal grid line*

5. Next, right-click in the drawing area; a shortcut menu is displayed. Choose **Snap Overrides > Endpoints** from the shortcut menu.

6. Move the cursor near the left endpoint of the first grid (grid created earlier) and place the cursor on it until it (the first grid line) is highlighted and the **Endpoint** snap appears.

7. Next, click as the **Endpoint** snap appears and the first grid line is highlighted; a grid line appears that displays the temporary dimension of its angle measured from the horizontal axis.

8. Next, move the cursor toward the right and above the grid bubble of the grid line created earlier.

9. Click when the temporary angular dimension displays **15.00°** and an alignment line appears from the endpoint of the previous grid line, refer to Figure 3-58.

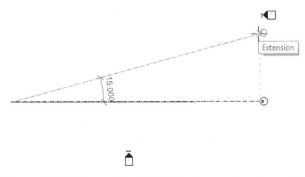

Figure 3-58 *The grid line displaying the angular dimension and an alignment line*

10. Repeat steps 5 to 9 to create the remaining five grid lines that emerge from the start point of the first grid line. The temporary dimensions that you will consider to create the five radial grids are : **30°**, **45°**, **60°**, **75°**, and **90°**, refer to Figure 3-59.

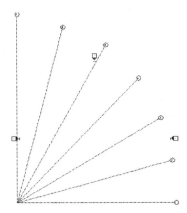

Figure 3-59 *The radial grid lines with varying angles*

Note
*Whenever a grid is created, you need to use the **Endpoints** snap override option to align the endpoint of each grid with the endpoint of the grid created earlier.*

11. Press ESC twice to exit the **Grid** tool.

12. Right-click in the drawing area and then choose **Zoom to Fit** from the shortcut menu.

13. Now, invoke the **Grid** tool from the **Datum** panel of the **Structure** tab.

14. Choose the **Center-ends Arc** tool from the list box in the **Draw** panel of the **Modify | Place Grid** contextual tab.

15. Now move the cursor toward the start point of the first grid line and click when the **Endpoint** snap appears; a circle appears with temporary dimensions denoting its radius and the start angle of the arc with the first grid line.

16. Move the cursor vertically upward along the last grid line created (the vertical grid line).

17. Enter **30'** (or **9144 mm** in Metric) and press **ENTER** when linear temporary dimension displays **36'** (or **10973 mm** in Metric) and angular temporary dimension displays **90°**; a curved arc emerges and starts from a distance of **30'** (or **9144 mm** in Metric) from the start point of the first grid line.

18. Move the cursor clockwise until it is placed below the first grid line and click when the first alignment line with the **Extension** snap emerges from the start point of the first grid line.

19. Now, repeat steps 15 to 18 to create a curved grid line with a radial distance of **50'** (or **15240 mm** in Metric) from the start point of the first grid, refer to Figure 3-60.

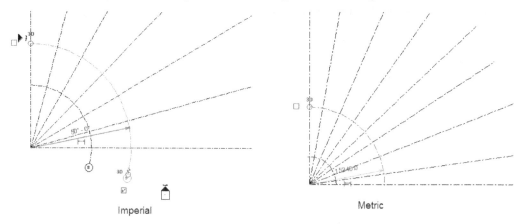

Imperial   Metric

Figure 3-60 *The curved grid lines created*

20. Next, press ESC to exit the **Grid** tool.

21. Invoke the **Grid** tool and use the **Line** tool from the list box in the **Draw** panel of the **Modify | Place Grid** contextual tab, to create the remaining grids with the specified distance, as shown in Figure 3-61.

Figure 3-61 *The dimensions of the remaining grid lines*

Resizing the Grid Lines

In this section, you will resize the grids using the drag controls.

1. Select the first grid line of the project and then move the cursor toward its endpoint near the grid bubble, as shown in Figure 3-62.

2. Now, press and drag the cursor toward the left and release the mouse when the cursor along with the grid endpoint reaches to the location, shown in Figure 3-63.

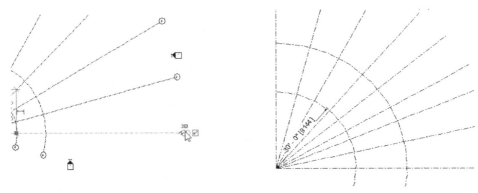

Figure 3-62 *Moving the cursor toward the   **Figure 3-63** *Dragging the grid endpoint to resize*
endpoint*

3. Press ESC to exit from the editing mode.

4. Select the other grids individually and repeat steps 1 to 4 to resize all the grids in the project view.

Note
While resizing the grids, you can align them in reference to their previous grids with the help of the alignment control.

Renaming Grids

In this section, you will rename all grids created in the previous section.

1. Select the curved grid, as shown in Figure 3-64.

2. Move the cursor over the grid bubble of the selected grid and click; an edit box is displayed. Enter **A'** in the displayed edit box and press ENTER. The selected curved grid is renamed.

3. Press ESC to exit the editing mode.

4. Select them individually and repeat steps 2 and 3. Refer to Figure 3-65 for new names of the grids.

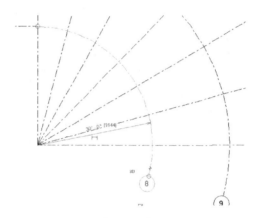

Figure 3-64 Selecting the curved line to rename

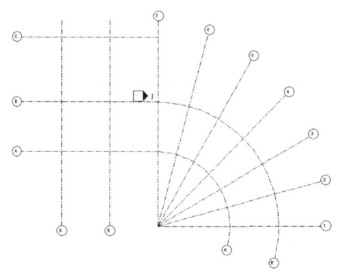

Figure 3-65 The grid lines with new names

Saving the Project

In this section, you will save the project file using the **Save As** tool.

1. Choose **Save As > Project** option from the **File** menu; the **Save As** dialog box is displayed.

2. In this dialog box, browse to the *C:\rst_2017\c03_rst_2021_tut* location and enter **c03_Industrial-Complex_tut2** (for Imperial) or **M_c03_Industrial-Complex_tut2** (for Metric) in the **File name** edit box.

3. Now, choose the **Save** button; the **Save As** dialog box closes and the project file is saved.

Closing the Project

1. Choose the **Close** option from the **File** menu.

    The file is closed and this completes Tutorial 2 of Chapter 3.

Self-Evaluation Test

Answer the following questions and then compare them to those given at the end of this chapter:

1. _____ is the default template file in Autodesk Revit 2021.

2. To define the geographical location of a project, you need to invoke the _____ tool from the **Manage** tab.

3. To transfer project standards from source file to the target file, you need to invoke the _____ tool from the **Manage** tab.

4. You can use the _____ tool to manage the **Project Browser**.

5. In a grid line, you can create a gap between two end segments by setting the _____ parameter in the **Type Properties** dialog box to **None**.

6. You can use the _____ option in the **Options Bar** to create a grid line that starts at a specified offset distance from a point defined in the drawing area.

7. _____ can be used as datum planes to act as guideline for creating elements.

8. The visibility of a work plane grid can be controlled by using the _____ tool from the **Work Plane** panel of the **Structure** tab.

9. To add name of the author in a project, you need to invoke the _____ tool from the **Manage** tab.

10. In Revit, you can include project information to the schedules of linked models. (T/F)

11. The visibility of level bubble on either sides of a level line cannot be controlled. (T/F)

Review Questions

Answer the following questions:

1. The visibility of datum elements can be controlled by using the_____ tool.

2. The **Project Browser** displays the _____ folder which contains the element families loaded into the project file.

3. To create browser organization for sheets, choose the _____ tab from the **Browser Organization** dialog box.

4. To add levels to a project view, you need to invoke the **Level** tool from the _____ panel.

5. You can use the_____tool to create curved grids.

6. To make a hidden level line visible, choose _____from the **View Control Bar**.

7. A _____level does not hold any plan view but acts as a host for placing objects and information.

8. You can clear the _____check box in the **Options Bar** of the **Modify | Place Level** tab to create a nonstory level.

9. You cannot copy project standards from a project to the current project. (T/F)

10. A work plane can be horizontal, vertical, or inclined at any specified angle. (T/F)

EXERCISES

Exercise 1   Academic Institution

In this exercise, you will create project information for the project created in the Exercise 1 of Chapter 2. Further, you will add levels and grids to the project file. Refer to Figure 3-66 for grid dimensions and names. Use the following project specifications:

(Expected time: 1 hr 15 min)

1. Project file to be used:
   - For Imperial   *c02_Academic-Institution_exer1.rvt.*
   - For Metric   *M_ c02_Academic-Institution_exer1.rvt.*

2. Rename Level 1 and Level 2 as **Foundation Level** and **Entry**, respectively.

3. Specify the elevation of **Foundation Level** and **Entry** levels as:
   - For Imperial   **-5'6" 0"** and **0' 0"**.
   - For Metric   **-1676 mm** and **0 mm**, respectively.

4. Story levels to be added:
    For Imperial   **Second Floor - Elevation 12' 6"**
                    Roof - Elevation 25' 0"
    For Metric   **Second Floor - Elevation 3810 mm**
                    Roof - Elevation 7620 mm

5. Nonstory level to be added:
    For Imperial   **T.O.F- Elevation -5'**
    For Metric   **T.O.F- Elevation -1524 mm**

6. Project information to be added:
    Project Issue Date   **01/01/2019**
    Project Status   **Started**
    Client Name   **CADCIM Technologies**
    Project Address   **525, Andrews Drive Schererville**
    Project Name   **Academic Institution**
    Project Number   **AI/03/13**

7. Grids to be added to the **Entry** project view using the dimensions and names as shown in
    Figure 3-66.

Figure 3-66 *The grid lines with new names for the Academic
Institution structure*

8. File name to be assigned:
    For Imperial   *c03_Academic-Institution_exer1.rvt.*
    For Metric   *M_c03_Academic-Institution_exer1.rvt.*

Exercise 2   Factory Shed

In this exercise, you will add levels and grids to the project file created in Exercise 2 of Chapter 2. Refer to Figure 3-67 for grid dimensions and names. Use the following project specifications:

(Expected time: 1 hr 15 min)

1. Project file to be used:
   For Imperial   *c02_Factory-Shed_exer2.rvt.*
   For Metric   *M_c02_Factory-Shed_exer2.rvt.*

2. Rename Level 1 and Level 2 as **Below Ground** and **Plinth**, respectively.

3. Specify the elevation of **Below Ground** and **Plinth** levels.
   For Imperial   **-2'0"** and **1'0"**, respectively
   For Metric   **-610 mm** and **305 mm**

4. Story levels to be added:
   For Imperial   **Second Floor - Elevation 14'**
                    Roof - Elevation 24' 0"
   For Metric   **Second Floor - Elevation 4200 mm**
                    Roof - Elevation 7315 mm

5. Grids to be added in the **Plinth** project view using dimensions and names, as shown in Figure 3-67.

Figure 3-67 *The grid lines with new names for the Factory Shed structure*

6. File name to be assigned: *c03_Factory-Shed_exer2.rvt.*

Exercise 3   Residential Building

Download the *c03_Residential_Build_exer3* file from *https://www.cadcim.com*. The path of the file is as follows: *Textbooks > Civil/GIS > Revit Structure > Exploring Autodesk Revit 2021 for Structure*. In this exercise open the *c03_Residential_Build_exer3* file (for Imperial) and *M_c03_Residential_Build_exer3* file (for Metric) and add levels and grids to it. Refer to Figures 3-68, 3-69, and 3-70. Further, you will add project information to the project. Use the following specifications to complete the exercise: **(Expected time: 45 min)**

1. Rename Level 1 and Level 2 as **Subgrade** and **GL**, respectively.

2. Specify the elevation of **Subgrade** and **GL** levels.
    For Imperial   **-4'6" 0"** and **0' 0"**.
    For Metric   **-1372 mm** and **0 mm**

3. Story levels to be added:
    For Imperial   **FL- Elevation 11'0"**
                        TL- Elevation 19'-6"
    For Metric   **FL- Elevation 3353 mm**
                        TL- Elevation 5944 mm

4. Nonstory level to be added:
    For Imperial   **T.O.F- Elevation -4'**
    For Metric   **T.O.F- Elevation -1219 mm**

5. Project information to be added:
    Project Issue Date   **01/01/2019**
    Project Status   **Started**
    Client Name   **CADCIM Technologies**
    Structural Consultant   **CADCIM-Structural Engineers**
    Mechanical Consultant   **Sham Tickoo**
    Quantity Surveyors   **CADCIM-Quantity Surveyors**
    Project Name   **Residential Building**
    Documented Contract
    Commencement Date   **20/02/2019**
    Documented Contract Completion Date   **31/07/2019**
    Provisional Period Allowed in Contract   **30 Days**
    Gross Area of the Project   For Imperial   **1200 sq. ft.**
                                 For Metric   **112 sq. meter**

6. File name to be assigned:
    For Imperial   *c03_Residential_Build_exer3_final*.
    For Metric   *M_c03_Residential_Build_exer3_final*.

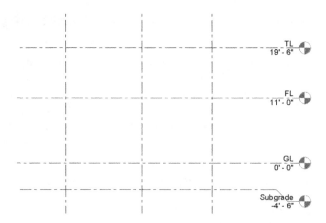

Figure 3-68 *Elevation of the project displaying the name of the levels and their respective elevations*

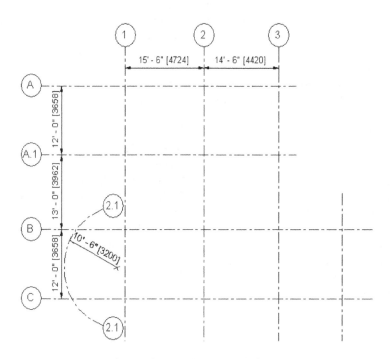

Figure 3-69 *The grid lines with the specified names and distances*

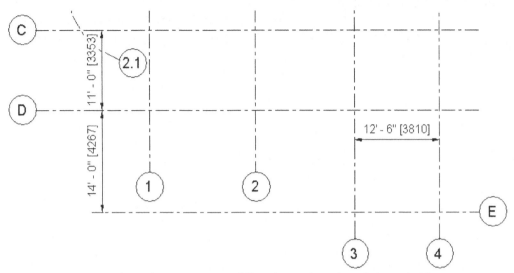

Figure 3-70 *The remaining grid lines in continuation of Figure 3-69*

Answers to Self-Evaluation Test

1. Structural Analysis-Default, 2. Location, 3. Transfer Project Standards, 4. Browser Organization, 5. Center Segment, 6. Offset, 7. Reference Planes, 8. Show, 9. Project Parameters, 10. T, 11. F

Chapter 4

Structural Columns and Walls

Learning Objectives

After completing this chapter, you will be able to:
- *Create Structural Columns*
- *Modify Structural Columns*
- *Create Structural Walls*
- *Modify Structural Walls*

In the previous chapter, you learned to add datums such as structural levels and grids to a project and also learned to add project information to a project. In this chapter, you will learn to add structural elements such as columns and walls. Also, you will learn to work with structural columns and walls in a project in detail.

STRUCTURAL COLUMNS

Structural column is an integral part of the primary structural framing of a building system. The basic function of structural columns is to carry vertical load from the roof system, floor slab, and beam to the foundation. Functionally, columns are subjected to axial loads which form the basis of its design.

In Revit, you need to add columns to a plan view. But before adding columns, it is recommended that you create a grid system. The grid lines and grid intersections of the grid system help you place columns at appropriate locations. When you add columns at grid intersections, they are anchored to it. As a result, whenever there is a change in the grid spacing, the columns move with grid intersections. Before you add structural columns to a project, you need to learn about different types of structural columns. In the following sections, you will learn about different types of structural columns, loading structural columns, adding structural columns and much more.

Types of Structural Column

In Revit, there are three types of structural columns that can be added to a building. These columns are made of three types of material: steel, concrete, and wood. Out of these, steel and concrete columns are commonly used in the construction of a building. While working in Revit, you will get to know that some of the families of these column types are pre-loaded in the project template. You can load other families from the Imperial or Metric structural column libraries that become available on installing Autodesk Revit.

In a project, you can add two types of predefined steel columns depending on your requirement. These columns are rolled steel columns and light gauge steel columns. For rolled steel columns, there are thirteen predefined families which are available in the **English-Imperial > Structural Columns > Steel** folder location. These families are **Double C-Channel-Column**, **HSS-Hollow Structural Section-Column**, **L-Angle-Column**, **Pipe-Column**, **WWF-Welded Wide Flange-Column**, and more. Similarly, there are other predefined families available in the **English-Metric > Structural Columns > Steel** folder location. These families are **CHS-Circular Hollow Section-Column**, **M_L-Angle-Column**, **M_M-Miscellaneous Wide Flange-Column**, **M_W-Wide Flange Column**, **PFC-Parallel Flange Channel-Column**, and **SHS- Square Hollow Section-Column**. For light gauge steel columns, there are seven predefined families which are available at the **English-Imperial > Structural Columns > Light Gauge Steel** folder location. The predefined light gauge steel families for columns are **Light Gauge-Channel Studs-Column**, **Light Gauge-Furring Channels-Column**, and **Light Gauge-Studs-Column** and so on. The predefined light gauge steel families for columns available at the **English-Metric > Structural Columns > Light Gauge Steel** folder location are **M_Light Gauge-Zeds-Column**.

Note

Apart from using the predefined sections available in Autodesk Revit, you can also customize a section with different physical properties for your project. To use customized sections, first you need to create families and then load them into your project.

There are two types of concrete columns in both English-Imperial and English-Metric that can be added to a project: casted (in-situ) concrete columns and pre-cast concrete columns. For casted concrete columns in English-Imperial, there are several pre-defined families that can be used such as **Concrete-Rectangular-Column with Drop Caps**, **Concrete-Round-Column**, and more. For casted concrete columns in **English-Metric**, several pre-defined families available are **M_Concrete-Rectangular-Column with Drop Caps**, **M_Concrete-Rectangular-Column**, and more. For pre-cast concrete columns in **English-Imperial**, you can use any of the given predefined families such as **Precast-Rectangular Column with Bearing**, **Precast-Rectangular Column with Multi Layer Corbels**, **Precast-Rectangular Column with Rectangular Fork bearing**, and **Precast-Square Column**. For pre-cast concrete columns in **English-Metric**, you can use any of the given predefined families such as **M_Precast-Rectangular Column with Bearing**, **M_Precast-Rectangular Column Cone-Shaped Fork bearing**, and **M_Precast-Square Column**.

To add wood (timber) columns for Imperial project, you can use any of the following families such as **Glulam-Southern Pine-Column**, **Timber-Column**, and more. To add wood (timber) columns in a Metric project, you can use any of the following families: **M_Dimension Lumber-Column**, **M_PSL-Parallel Strand Lumber-Column**, **M_Timber-Column**, and more.

Loading Structural Column Families

As discussed in the previous section, Autodesk Revit comes with some predefined families. When you start a new project with the default template, you can access the **W Shapes-Column** family in the Imperial template and **UC-Universal Columns-Column** in the Metric template. Note that before adding structural columns to a project, you need to access more families that are present in the software. To do so, choose the **Load Family** tool from the **Load from Library** panel of the **Insert** tab, as shown in Figure 4-1; the **Load Family** dialog box will be displayed.

Figure 4-1 *Choosing the* **Load Family** *tool*

In this dialog box, for Imperial unit system browse to **English-Imperial > Structural Columns** folder location and for Metric unit system browse to **English-Metric > Structural Columns** folder location and then select any of the desired sub-folders such as **Concrete**, **Light Guage steel**, **Precast Concrete**, **Steel**, and **Wood** from the list. On choosing a sub-folder, the list of available family files (*.rfa*) will be displayed. Click on the desired file or press SHIFT and then click on multiple files in the folder for multiple selection. Then, choose the **Open** button; the selected family (ies) will be loaded in the project.

Note
In case the files that you are trying to load using the **Load Family** *dialog box are already present in the project file, the* **Family Already Exists** *window will be displayed. You can choose* **Overwrite the existing version** *or* **Overwrite the existing version and its parameter values** *from the window based on your project requirement.*

Adding Structural Columns to a Project

After loading families for columns, you can add them to a project based on the design requirement. Before adding columns, the grid patterns and levels should be created. This will help you in placing the column on grids or grid intersections. For adding columns, it is recommended that they should be modeled and placed on your project as they are constructed at site. The advantage of following this practice is that the column placed this way will give you a more accurate BIM model and you will spend less time in creating sections, schedules, quantity take-offs, and estimation of materials. You can place structural columns in your project, both vertically and inclined. You can add them individually (without grids) on grids, or on existing architectural columns. The methods of placing vertical and slanted structural columns are discussed next.

Placing Vertical Columns

Ribbon: Structure > Column

To place vertical columns, select an appropriate structural plan view and then choose the **Column** tool from the **Structure** panel of the Structure tab; the **Modify | Place Structural Column** contextual tab will be displayed, as shown in Figure 4-2. This tab contains twelve panels and the **Options Bar**. By default, the **Vertical Column** tool is invoked from the **Placement** panel. In the **Modify | Place Structural Column** contextual tab, you can select the desired column type from the **Type Selector** drop-down list in the **Properties** palette. Also, you can change the instance and type properties of the selected element by using various parameters displayed in the **Properties** palette. The parameters in this palette differ depending on the type of column selected from the **Type Selector** drop-down list. For example, if you select **Concrete-Rectangular-Column** from the **Type Selector** drop-down list, the **Properties** palette will display those parameters that are required for designing concrete column. In the **Properties** palette, the properties of the concrete columns are classified under seven heads: **Constraints**, **Materials and Finishes**, **Structural**, **Dimensions**, **Identity Data**, **Analytical Properties**, **Analytical Alignment**, **Releases/Member Forces**, and **Analytical Model**. The parameters under these heads are discussed later in this chapter.

Figure 4-2 The Modify / Place Structural Column contextual tab

Note
The Analytical Model, Analytical Properties, Analytical Alignment, and Releases/Member Forces parameters will be displayed only for Analytical Columns in the Properties palette.

To change the type properties of a selected column type, choose the **Edit Type** button from the **Properties** palette; the **Type Properties** dialog box will be displayed. This dialog box displays different parameters for different column types. You can select column types from the **Type Selector** drop-down list. This dialog box displays parameters under three heads: **Structural**, **Dimensions**, and **Identity Data**. Various parameters under these heads are discussed later in this chapter.

Note
The Structural head and its parameters will not be displayed in the Type Properties dialog box for concrete columns.

After setting the instance and type properties for a selected column type, you need to specify whether to place columns at the desired location without grids, at grids, or at existing architectural columns. To place structural columns anywhere in the drawing area (without grids), click the left mouse button in the drawing area; a column of the selected type will appear at the location where you have clicked.

If you want to place a column at the intersection of grids, then choose the **At Grids** tool from the **Multiple** panel in the **Modify | Place Structural Column** contextual tab; the **Modify | Place Structural Column > At Grid Intersection** contextual tab will be displayed, and in the **Status Bar**, you will be prompted to select grid lines to place the structural column at the intersection of grids. Select the first grid line and then the other grid line that intersects the first grid line; a column will be inserted at the intersection of the two selected grid lines. You can add more columns in a drawing. To do so, press the CTRL key; a "+" symbol will appear with the cursor. Select the other grid lines that intersect with grid line (highlighted) selected last; multiple columns will be inserted at grid intersections. Next, choose the **Finish** button from the **Multiple** panel in the **Modify | Place Structural Column > At Grid Intersection** contextual tab; the columns will be inserted at the specified grid intersections. Figures 4-3 and 4-4 show the examples of **Concrete-Rectangular-Column** column type placed at the intersection of two grid lines and at multiple grid line intersections.

Figure 4-3 Concrete column placed at grid intersection

Figure 4-4 Concrete columns placed at multiple grid intersections

Note

*You can tag a structural column while placing it in structural model. To do so, choose the **Tag on Placement** tool from the **Tag** panel of the **Modify | Place Structural Column** contextual tab; a tag will appear with the column while adding to the drawing. Refer to Figure 4-5 for an example of a tag added to a concrete column.*

Figure 4-5 Concrete rectangular column with a tag

Using the Options in Options Bar

When you invoke the **Column** tool from the **Structure** panel of the **Structure** tab, the **Modify | Place Structural Column** contextual tab is displayed. At the same time, various options related to the alignment and annotation of column are also displayed in the **Options Bar** below it, as shown in Figure 4-6.

*Figure 4-6 The **Options Bar** displaying various options for columns*

In the **Options Bar**, the **Rotate after placement** check box is clear by default. As a result, the column will be placed in the model in the same alignment as it was created in the family. To rotate the column before it has been inserted in the model, select the **Rotate after placement** check box and click on the screen; the column will be inserted and displayed in blue color along with the rotation line. Next, move the cursor; you will notice that a temporary angular dimension is displayed, as shown in Figure 4-7. Click on the screen to achieve the desired alignment or enter the required angle. On doing so, the column will be placed at the desired alignment. Note that you can also enter the value for the rotation angle in the **Angle** edit box that will be displayed in the **Options Bar** while defining the rotation angle.

Figure 4-7 Temporary angular dimension displayed

In the **Options Bar**, there are two drop-down lists and one edit box displayed next to the **Rotate after placement** check box, refer to Figure 4-8. The options in the two drop-down lists are used to align the column vertically along levels or at a particular height. For example, if your current view is the structural plan for level 1 and you need to place a column whose base is at level 1 and its top is constrained to another level, say level 2, which is at a distance of 9' in Imperial system and in Metric system level is at a distance of 2743 mm above level 1, then select the **Height** and **Level 2** options from drop-down lists marked as **1** and **2** respectively in the **Options Bar**, refer to Figure 4-8.

*Figure 4-8 The **Height** and **Level 2** options displayed in the drop-down lists marked 1 and 2*

Note

*If you select the **Unconnected** option for height from the drop-down list marked as **2**, the edit box marked as **3** will be activated. In the edit box, you can enter value to assign the unconnected height of the column from the current level.*

Similarly, if you need to place another column with its base below the current level at a certain depth, select the **Depth** option from the drop-down list marked as **1**, refer to Figure 4-8. Next, select an option to assign a level below the current level from the drop-down list marked as **2**. Alternatively, you can select the **Unconnected** option from the drop-down list marked **2** and enter a value in the edit box located next to it to assign an unconnected depth to column.

Figure 4-9 displays two columns in the North elevation view. The columns are placed in the plan view with different level constraints for their top and base. The column marked as **1** has been placed in the structural plan view of level 1 with the **Height** option assigned to **Level 2** from the **Options Bar**. The column marked **2** has also been placed in level 1 but with the **Depth** option assigned to an unconnected depth of **4'6"**(Imperial) and **1372 mm** (Metric) from the **Options Bar**.

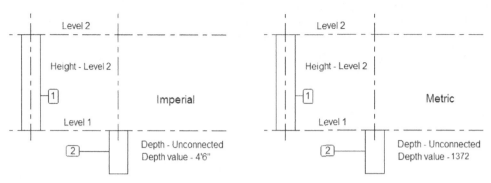

Figure 4-9 Two columns with different level constraints displayed in the North Elevation view

Placing Slanted Structural Columns

Slanted columns are commonly used in a structural design. In Revit, you can add these columns to a structural model. Unlike vertical columns, you can add these columns in a 3D view, an elevation view, or in section view. To add a slanted column, you first need to change the view of the structural model to an elevation, section, or 3D view. To place a slanted column in a 3D view, invoke the **Column** tool and then select the desired column type from the **Type Selector** drop-down list in the **Properties** palette. Next, choose the **Slanted Column** tool from the **Placement** panel in the **Modify | Place Structural Column** contextual tab; the options to place the slanted column will be displayed in the **Options Bar**, refer to Figure 4-10.

*Figure 4-10 The **Options Bar** displaying options for placing slanted structural column*

Tip
*After placing the column, you can further rotate it. To do so, choose the **Rotate** tool from the **Modify** panel in **Modify / Place Structural Column** contextual tab and rotate the column at the desired angle.*

In the **Options Bar**, select the level options from the **1st Click** and **2nd Click** drop-down lists to define the associated levels and offset the endpoints of a slanted column. In the **1st Click** drop-down list, you can select a level for the endpoint of the column that you will define first. Similarly, you can select a level for the other end point of the column by selecting a level option from the **2nd Click** drop-down list. You can also use the edit boxes next to the **1st Click** and **2nd Click** drop-down lists to define offset values, if required, for the levels that you will define for the elevations of the column ends. After selecting the levels for the column end elevations, you can select the **3D Snapping** check box in the **Options Bar** to snap the points of the existing structural elements.

After setting the options in the **Options Bar**, move the cursor to a location in the structural model to define the first endpoint of the slanted column. Click on the desired location in the structural model in reference to the level option selected from the **1st Click** drop-down list in the **Options Bar**. Next, move the cursor to another location and click to specify the other endpoint of the slanted column based on the selection made in the **2nd Click** drop-down list in **Options Bar**. Figures 4-11 to 4-13 illustrate the insertion of a slanted column in a structural model.

Figure 4-11 *Specifying the first endpoint of the slanted structural column*

Figure 4-12 *Specifying another endpoint of the slanted structural column*

Figure 4-13 *The slanted column after insertion*

Creating Openings in Structural Columns

Ribbon: Structure > Opening > By Face

While working with columns in a structural project, you may need to cut openings through it to allow other structural elements such as beams and girders to pass through. To create an opening in a column, first align the view preferably to 3D view and zoom in the column in which you want to create the opening. Next, choose the **By Face** tool from the **Opening** panel of the **Structure** tab, refer to Figure 4-14; the cursor will change into a selection cursor. Move the selection cursor toward the face of the column where you want to cut the opening; a plane will be displayed on that face, as shown in Figure 4-15. Click on the plane; the **Modify | Create Opening Boundary** contextual tab will be displayed.

Figure 4-14 *Choosing the **By Face** tool to cut an opening in the column*

Figure 4-15 *A plane displayed on the face of the column*

In the **Draw** panel of this tab, you will notice that the sketching tools to sketch the opening profile are displayed in a list box. You can choose any of these tools to create the opening in columns. After choosing a tool, align the view using the **ViewCube** or can be sketched in the required elevation view. Next, sketch the desired profile, using the tool invoked from the **Draw** panel. After sketching the desired profile, choose the **Finish Edit Mode** button from the **Mode** panel; an opening of the desired profile will be created on the selected face. Figure 4-16 shows a column with the sketch of the opening profile and Figure 4-17 shows an opening cut through the face of the column.

Figure 4-16 *The opening profile created on the face of the column*

Figure 4-17 *An opening cut through the face of the column*

 Note
While selecting the face for sketching the opening profile, Revit allows you to select any of the perpendicular planes that align with the major or minor axis of the column section.

You can modify the opening on the face of the column by using the options in the **Modify | Structural opening cut** contextual tab. Note that the **Modify|Structural opening cut** contextual tab is displayed on creating the opening in the column. In the **Modify| Structural opening cut** contextual tab, you can use various tools to edit the sketch. In this tab, you can use various modification tools such as **Move, Rotate, Array**, and **Mirror** and more to modify the profile. In this tab, you can also use other tools related to clipboard operations and visibility graphics. To edit the sketched profile of the opening, choose the **Edit Sketch** tool from the **Mode** panel; the **Modify | Structural opening cut > Edit Boundary** contextual tab will be displayed and the profile will be highlighted in the sketch mode. You can modify the profile by using different tools from various panels in this tab. After editing the sketch of the opening profile, choose the **Finish Edit Mode** button from the **Mode** panel, the opening cut will be modified as per the revised sketch. After exiting the **Modify | Structural opening cut** contextual tab, if you want to display it again, select the created opening.

Modifying the Element Properties of Structural Columns

Element properties for a structural column include its instance and type properties. The instance properties of a column refer to the individual instances of the column placed in a project. For example, if you select a column and modify its instance properties, the change in the properties will be reflected only on the selected column.

The type properties of a column may vary from one column to another. If there is a change in the type property of a column, it may affect other columns of the same type. The type properties for steel columns are different from the concrete columns. The type properties of these columns will be discussed individually in detail in the later sections of this chapter.

To modify the instance properties of a column, select it from the project. For example, you can select a concrete column type from the project. On doing so, the **Properties** palette will display the instance properties of the selected column, as shown in Figure 4-18.

You can modify various properties of a column of a particular instance, such as its location in the elevation, its height or height constraint, material assigned, room bounding properties, and so on. You can also modify the structural properties such as cover distances for rebars at the top, bottom, and other faces. To modify the type properties of a selected column, select the column from the project and then choose **Edit Type** from the **Properties** palette; the **Type Properties** dialog box will be displayed. In this dialog box, you can modify the type properties of a column such as its cross-sectional dimensions and schedule data. Note that the parameters in the **Type Properties** dialog box for a column differ depending upon the type of column selected from the project. For instance, the parameters in the **Type Properties** dialog box for a steel column may differ from that of a concrete column. Some of the instance and type properties of different columns are discussed in the next sections.

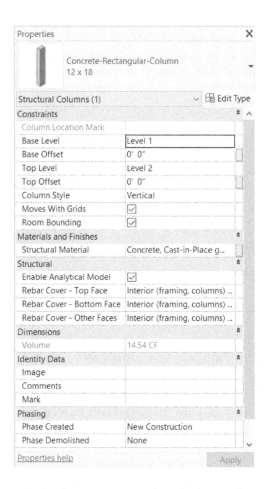

Figure 4-18 The **Properties** palette displaying the instance properties in a column

The Instance Properties of the Steel and Concrete Columns

The instance properties of a column may vary depending upon the column families specified during the installation of Revit software. The instance properties can be specified from the properties displayed in the **Properties** palette, when you select the column. For example, in the **Properties** palette, you can specify the top and base constraints of a column by specifying a level. Figure 4-19 shows some of the references of the instance properties of a column in a project view. You can also modify various analytical parameters of the column.

Figure 4-19 *References of the instance properties of a column in a project view*

Brief description of some of the instance parameters in the **Properties** palette is given in the table next:

Parameter	Description
Column Location Mark	Specifies the coordinate location of a vertical column on the project grid.
Base Level	Sets a level to constrain the column base. For example, refer to Figure 4-19, **01-Entry Level** is the base level for a particular column.
Base Offset	Specifies the offset distance of the base of the column from the base level assigned. The value specified for this parameter is negative. For example, in Imperial unit system the base of the column is 5' and in Metric unit system, the base of the column is 1500mm down from the **01-Entry Level** level (base level). Refer to Figure 4-19.
Top Level	Sets a level to constrain the top of a column. For example, in Figure 4-19, **02-First Floor** is the top level for a particular column.
Top Offset	Specifies the offset distance of the top of a column from the top level assigned to it. The value specified for this parameter is positive. For example, in Figure 4-19, in Imperial system, the top of the column is 2'-6" and in Metric system, the top of the column is 760mm up from the **02-First Floor** level (top level).

Moves With Grids	Specifies whether a column associated with a particular grid intersection will move when the grid intersection moves. If the check box corresponding to this parameter is selected, the column will move when the associated grid intersection moves. This parameter will be available only for vertical columns.
Enable Analytical Model	Specifies whether the given element is to be included for structural analysis.
Column Style	Specifies the style of a column. Select any of the options such as **Vertical**, **Slanted - End Point Driven**, or **Slanted - Angle Driven** from the drop-down list corresponding to this parameter.
Top Connection	Turns on the visibility of a moment or shear connection symbol of a steel column. This parameter is applicable only for steel columns. Select any of the options from the drop-down list corresponding to this parameter. The options available in the drop-down list are **None**, **Shear Column Connection**, and **Moment Column Connection**. Note that the top connection symbol is visible only in the elevation views and sectional views that are cut parallel to the main axis of the column.
Base Connection	Turns on the visibility of base plate symbols. Select the check box corresponding to this parameter to display the base plate symbols. The symbols are visible only in the elevations that are cut parallel to the main axis of the column.
Structural Material	Specifies the material to be assigned for a column. To specify a material for a column, invoke the **Material Browser** dialog box by choosing the **Browse** button displayed in the value field of this parameter.
Rebar Cover - Top Face	Sets the rebar cover distance of a concrete column from the top face of its section. This parameter is applicable for concrete columns only.
Rebar Cover - Bottom Face	Sets the rebar cover distance from the bottom face of the column. This parameter is applicable to the concrete columns only.
Rebar Cover - Other Faces	Sets the cover distance of rebars in the column to the faces of other elements.
Volume	Specifies the volume of a selected column. The value displayed for this parameter is non-editable or read-only.

Image	Specifies the image of the column. Select the Browse button to add the image of column.
Comments	Specifies a comment that a user can assign to a column.
Top Release	Specifies the top release condition for a column. Select any of the options such as **Fixed**, **Pinned**, **Bending Moment**, or **User-Defined** from the drop-down list corresponding to this parameter.
Top Fx	Specifies the translational release at the top end of a column along the X-axis. The option to set this parameter will be available only if the **Top Release** parameter is set to **User-Defined**.
Top Fy	Specifies the translational release at the top end of the column along the Y-axis. The option to set this parameter will be available only if the **Top Release** parameter is set to **User-Defined**.
Top Fz	Specifies the translational release at the top end of a column along the Z-axis. The option to set this parameter will be available only if the **Top Release** parameter is set to **User-Defined**.
Top Mx	Specifies the rotational release at the top end of a column along the X-axis. The option to set this parameter will be available only if the **Top Release** parameter is set to **User-Defined**.
Top My	Specifies the rotational release at the top end of the column along the Y-axis. The option to set this parameter will be available only if the **Top Release** parameter is set to **User-Defined**.
Top Mz	Specifies the rotational release at the top end of a column along the Z-axis. The option to set this parameter will be available only if the **Top Release** parameter is set to **User-Defined**.
Base Release	Specifies the bottom release condition for a column. Select any of the options such as **Fixed, Pinned, Bending Moment**, and **User-Defined** from the drop-down list corresponding to this parameter.
Base Fx	Specifies the translational release at the bottom end of a column along the X-axis. Select the check box corresponding to this parameter to enable this parameter. Note that this parameter will be available only when the **Bottom Release** parameter is set to **User-Defined**.

Base Fy	Specifies the translational release at the bottom end of a column along the Y-axis.
Base Fz	Specifies the translational release at the bottom end of a column along the Z-axis.
Base Mx	Specifies the rotational release at the bottom end of a column along the X-axis.
Base My	Specifies the rotational release at the bottom end of a column along the Y-axis.
Base Mz	Specifies the rotational release at the bottom end of a column along the Z-axis.
Analyze As	Specifies whether a column will be analyzed as Hanger, Gravity, Lateral, or Not for analysis. This parameter is used by external analysis applications to determine whether the column contributes to lateral analysis.
Analytical Links	Specifies whether to keep a analytical link between the analytical model of a beam and the analytical model of a column. Select the check box corresponding to this parameter to enable the rigidity in the linkage between a beam and a column. When the analytical link is enabled, an analytical segment is added in the model between the ends of the analytical models of a beam and a column.
Base Alignment Method	Specifies a method of justifying the horizontal and vertical reference of a column base. Click on the value field corresponding to this parameter and select the **Auto-detect** or **Projection** option from the drop-down list displayed.
Base x-Projection	It is enabled on assigning the **Projection** option to the **Base Extension Method** parameter. The **Base x-Direction** specifies the horizontal limits of the analytical model at the base of the column.
Base y-Projection	It is enabled on assigning the **Projection** option to the **Base Alignment Method** parameter. The **Base y-Direction** specifies the vertical limits of the analytical model at the base of the column.
Base z-Projection	It is enabled on assigning the **Projection** option to the **Base Alignment Method** parameter. The **Base z-Direction** specifies the vertical extension location of the analytical model at the base of the column.
Base Extension Method	Specifies the method for justification of the vertical extension of the column base.

Top Alignment Method	Specifies a method of justifying the horizontal and vertical reference of a column top. Click on the value field corresponding to this parameter and select the **Auto-detect** or **Projection** option from the drop-down list displayed.
Top x-Projection	It is enabled on assigning the **Projection** option to the **Top Extension Method** parameter. The **Top x-Direction** specifies the horizontal limits of the analytical model at the top of the column.
Top y-Projection	It is enabled on assigning the **Projection** option to the **Top Alignment Method** parameter. The **Top y-Direction** specifies the vertical limits of the analytical model at the top of the column.
Top z-Projection	It is enabled on assigning the **Projection** option to the **Top Alignment Method** parameter. The **Top z-Direction** specifies the vertical extension location of the analytical model at the top of the column.
Top Extension Method	Specifies the method for justification of the vertical extension of the column top.

The Type Properties of Steel Columns

The type properties of steel columns include its area, weight flange width, actual depth of section, name of the manufacturer, and so on. Some of the relevant type properties, which can be assigned to a steel column, in the **Type Properties** dialog box are described in the table given next.

Parameter	Description
A	Specifies the section area of the steel section.
W	Specifies the nominal weight of the steel column.
bf	Specifies the flange width of a section.
d	Specifies the actual depth of a section.
tf	Specifies the thickness of a flange.
tw	Specifies the web thickness of the steel column.

Note
After assigning type parameters in the Type Properties dialog box, you can preview the changes made to a model. To do so, choose the Preview button in the Type Properties dialog box; the preview of the selected type will be described in the expanded area of this dialog box.

The Type Properties of Concrete Columns

The type properties of a concrete column include its depth, width, and so on. Some of the type properties of a concrete column are described in the following table:

Parameter	Description
b	Specifies the width of a column.
h	Specifies the depth of a column.
Keynote	Specifies the keynote associated to a column. To assign a keynote, click in the **Value** field of this parameter and then choose the Browse button; the **Keynotes** dialog box will be displayed. In this dialog box, you can assign a keynote to the desired column.
Cost	Specifies the cost of a column.
Description	Specifies the description of a column.

ARCHITECTURAL COLUMNS

Ribbon: Architecture > Build > Column drop-down > Column: Architectural

Architectural columns are non load bearing members that are placed in a structural project to add ambience to the structure. Generally, very few architectural columns are placed in a structural model. The placing of architectural columns in a model depends upon the design requirement, both architectural and structural.

You can add architectural columns only in plan view. To add an architectural column, activate the desired plan view and then invoke the **Column: Architectural** tool from the **Build** panel; the **Modify | Place Column** contextual tab will be displayed, as shown in Figure 4-20.

Figure 4-20 The *Modify / Place Column* contextual tab

Note
*On invoking the **Column: Architectural** tool, the **Revit** message box may appear informing that no column family is loaded in the project. The message box will prompt you to load a column family in the project. To load a column family, choose the **Yes** button; the **Open** dialog box will be displayed. Browse to the **Column** sub-folder in the **English-Imperial** folder for Imperial (for Metric browse to **Column** sub-folder in the **English-Metric**) in this dialog box to load the desired column family in your project.*

The tools in the **Modify | Place Column** contextual tab are the same as those discussed in the **Modify | Place Structural Column** contextual tab. After using the tools from the **Modify| Place Column** contextual tab, you can use options in the **Options Bar** to set the alignment and location of the column that you need to place. After setting the options in the **Options Bar**, click on the desired location in the structural plan view; the architectural column will be placed at the point you click. The placed column can now be used for aesthetic purpose as well as to add structural column to it. Figure 4-21 shows a three-dimensional view of an architectural column placed in a structural model. The method of adding structural column to a architectural column is discussed next.

Figure 4-21 *Three-dimensional view of a structural model displaying architectural columns*

Adding Structural Column to an Architectural Column

After adding an architectural column to a project, you can add a structural column to it so that it can become a part of the analytical model. To do so, choose the **Structural Column** tool from **Architecture > Build > Column** drop-down list; the **Modify |Place Structural Column** contextual tab will be displayed. In this tab, choose the **At Columns** tool from the **Multiple** panel; the **Modify | Place Structural Column > At Architectural Columns** contextual tab will be displayed. In the **Type Selector** drop-down list in the **Properties** palette, you can select the desired type of column and then click on any existing architectural column from the structural model in the drawing area; the selected structural column type will be placed at the center of the selected architectural column. You can add more structural columns to other architectural columns that are present in the project. To do so, select the architectural columns, press and hold the CTRL key and then click on the architectural columns one by one; the structural columns will be placed at the center of each selected architectural columns. While adding architectural columns to the selection, you can also remove the elements from the selection. To do so, press and hold the SHIFT key and click on the selected column that you need to remove; the selected structural column will be removed from the selected columns.

After placing the structural column(s) in the architectural column(s), choose the **Finish** button from the **Multiple** panel; the structural column(s) will be placed at the desired architectural columns.

DIFFERENCE BETWEEN A STRUCTURAL COLUMN AND AN ARCHITECTURAL COLUMN

In Autodesk Revit, you can add two types of columns that are classified based on their functionality. These are: Architectural and Structural Columns. The major differences between Structural columns and Architectural columns are given next.

Structural columns are load-bearing members and are part of the analytical model for structural analysis of Revit. Architectural columns are non-load bearing members and appear in a project for aesthetic and overall ambience of model.

*   Structural columns attach themselves to other structural members such as beams, columns, and slabs, whereas Architectural columns functionally cannot attach themselves to any of the structural elements.

*   Structural columns are displayed in Graphical Column Schedule, whereas Architectural columns are not.

Despite differences in the functional behavior, Architectural columns and Structural columns may appear same in a structural model.

STRUCTURAL WALLS

Structural walls are those walls in a building that carry and transfer the weight of the building from the roof to the foundation thus, carrying load of the building and hence, they are also called load-bearing walls. These walls support structural members such as beams, slabs and walls of above floors. The materials of structural walls include bricks, concrete blocks, stones and reinforced cement concrete. Structural walls include walls such as masonary walls, retaining walls, precast concrete walls, stone walls and so on.

Adding Structural Walls

You can add a structural wall either in a structural plan view or in a 3D view, based on your project requirement. To add a structural wall, choose the **Wall: Structural** tool from **Structure > Structure > Wall** drop-down; the **Modify| Place Structural Wall** contextual tab along with other options in the **Options Bar** will be displayed. In this tab, you can use various options to sketch the wall and assign different instances and type properties to the structural wall, as shown in Figure 4-22.

*Figure 4-22 Various options and tools in the **Modify / Place Structural Wall** contextual tab*

On invoking the **Wall: Structural** tool, the **Properties** palette displays various instance properties and wall types. To select a type of structural wall, select a wall type from the **Type Selector** drop-down list. The wall types that you can select from the drop-down list are **Basic Wall**, **Curtain Wall**, and **Stacked Wall**. These wall types have various sub-types. In Imperial system, by default the **Generic-8"** wall sub-type is selected and in Metric system, by default the **Generic-200mm** is selected in this drop-down list.

Note
At the initial phase of a structural design, you can add generic structural walls to the structural model. These walls act as placeholders for the height, width, and wall type of actual walls.

After selecting a type from the **Type Selector** drop-down list, you can assign instance and type properties to the selected type. You can also change the instance properties of the selected wall type such as its top and base constraints, and rebar cover by using the parameters displayed in the **Properties** palette, as shown in Figure 4-23. Different instance parameters in the Properties palette for a structural wall are discussed in the next section.

Instance Parameters of Structural Wall

After invoking the **Wall: Structural** tool, you can set the instance parameters of a structural wall in the **Properties** palette. The **Location Line** parameter in the palette is used to specify the location line of the structural wall to be placed in a model. The location line represents the vertical plane in the structural wall that does not change on changing the wall type. You can select any of the options such as **Wall Centerline**, **Core Centerline**, **Finish Face: Exterior**, **Finish Face: Interior**, **Core Face: Exterior**, and **Core Face: Interior** from the drop-down list in the value field corresponding to the **Location Line** parameter. The **Base Constraint** parameter is used to specify the level to constrain the base of the wall. From the drop-down list in the value field of this parameter, you can select a level to constraint the base of the structural wall. After setting the **Base Constraint** parameter of the structural wall, you can set the offset distance that can be used to extend or offset the base of the wall from the base level. To do so, click in the value field of the **Base Offset** parameter and specify a numeric (positive or negative) value for the offset distance of the base of the wall. Similar to constraining the base of the wall, you can also constrain the top of the wall. To do so, you can use the **Top Constraint** and the **Top Offset** parameters from the **Properties** palette. To set the value for the **Top Constraint** parameter, click on

*Figure 4-23 The instance properties of a structural wall displayed in the **Properties** palette*

its value field and select an option from the drop-down list displayed. The option thus selected will represent a level in the structural model. After setting the top constraint for the wall, click on the value field corresponding to the **Top Offset** parameter and specify the offset value. You can use this value to extend or offset the top of the wall from the level set in the **Top Constraint** parameter in the **Properties** palette. Note that if you select the **Unconnected** option from the drop-down list in the value field of the **Top Constraint** parameter, the **Unconnected Height** parameter will be enabled. The default unconnected height in Revit in the **Unconnected Height** parameter is **20'0"** in Imperial and **4000** mm in Metric. In the value field of this parameter, you can enter a numeric value to specify the unconnected height of the wall measured from its base.

In the **Properties** palette of the structural wall, the structural and dimensional parameters are specified respectively under the **Structural** and **Dimensions** heads, refer to Figure 4-23. Under the **Structural** head, the following structural parameters of the wall are available: **Structural**, **Enable Analytical Model**, **Rebar Cover - Exterior Face**, **Rebar Cover - Interior Face**, **Rebar Cover - Other Faces**, and **Structural Usage**. Note that the value corresponding to the **Structural Usage** parameter is set to **Bearing** and is read-only. The other parameters are used to specify the rebar cover distance from the exterior or interior face of the wall, or from the face of the adjacent element.

Note
*The value of the **Structural Usage** parameter can be changed from **Bearing** to other values such as **Non-Bearing**, **Shear**, and **Structural combined** only when you modify the instance property of the wall.*

Under the **Dimensions** head, the following instance parameters are available: **Area** and **Volume**. These parameters are read-only and display the volume and area of walls when they are selected. Note that when you select a structural wall and use the **Properties** palette, an additional parameter, **Length**, is displayed under the **Dimensions** head. This parameter displays the length of the wall selected.

The parameters displayed under the **Identity Data** head in the **Properties** palette are **Image**, **Comments** and **Mark**. These parameters are used to specify image, comments and marks that can be assigned to a wall. The value assigned in the value field of the **Mark** parameter should be unique for each wall in the project as it serves as a label for the wall.

The **Phasing** head in the **Properties** palette of the structural wall displays two parameters: **Phase Created** and **Phase Demolished**. In these parameters, you can specify the information related to the phasing of the wall created and the wall demolished. This means that in the **Phase Created** parameter, you can specify the information regarding the phase in which the wall was created. Similarly, you will specify relevant information in the value field of the **Phase Demolished** parameter for the phase of the wall in which it was demolished.

Note
*The **Phasing head** parameter is displayed in the **Properties** palette only when the created wall is selected from the drawing.*

In the **Properties** palette for the structural wall, select the check box corresponding to the **Structural** parameter to enable the visibility of the analytical model of a wall. In the project view, you can view and edit the instance properties of the analytical model of the wall. Note that the instance properties of the analytical model of a wall are different from the instance properties of the physical model of the wall. To enable the display of the analytical model of the wall, choose the **Show Analytical Model** button from the **View Control Bar.** Using this button, you can toggle between the two options: **Show Analytical Model** and **Hide Analytical Model**. By default, the **Show Analytical Model** is selected in the options. As a result, the analytical model will be displayed along with the physical model. To highlight the analytical model in the project view, select the structural wall from the project view and then choose the **Highlight Analytical** option from the **Analytical** panel in the **Modify|Walls** tab.

Alternatively, you can choose the **Hide Analytical Model** option from the **View Control Bar**. As a result, only the analytical model will be displayed in the project view. You can select the analytical model of the structural wall to modify its instance properties. The instance properties for the analytical model of a structural wall are different from its associated physical model. As you select the analytical model of the structural wall, its instance properties are displayed in the **Properties** palette. The instance properties for the analytical model are: **Alignment Method**, **Top Extension Method**, **Base Extension Method** and **Analyze As**. After setting various instance parameters for the structural wall in the **Properties** palette, you can set the type parameters. To do so, choose the **Edit Type** button from the palette; the **Type Properties** dialog box will be displayed, as shown in Figure 4-24. In this dialog box, you can set various type parameters related to the structural wall. The type parameters for structural walls are discussed next.

Figure 4-24 The **Type Properties** dialog box for structural walls

Type Properties of Structural Walls

The type properties of a structural wall refer to the properties assigned to a particular type of wall. To define the type properties of a wall, invoke the **Type Properties** dialog box and specify the parameters in their specific fields. Some of the type properties that can be specified in the **Type Properties** dialog box are described in the table given next.

Parameter	Description
Structure	Specifies the layers that exist in a structural wall. To edit wall layers, choose the **Edit** button from the **Value** field of the **Structures** parameter; the **Edit Assembly** dialog box will be displayed. You can use this dialog box to specify different layers for a structural wall.
Wrapping at Inserts	Specifies the layer wrapping of walls at the insertion of doors, windows, and openings. To specify an option for this parameter, click on its **Value** field and select any of these options, namely **Do not Wrap**, **Exterior**, **Interior**, and **Both** displayed in the drop-down down list.
Wrapping at Ends	Specifies layer wrapping of wall end caps. To specify an option for this parameter, click on its **Value** field and select any of the options from **None**, **Exterior**, and **Interior** options displayed in the drop-down list.
Width	Specifies the width of a wall. This is a read only parameter.
Function	Specifies the function of a wall that provides a way to schedule walls in a structural model. To specify an option for this parameter, click on the **Value** field corresponding to this parameter and select any of these options, namely **Interior**, **Exterior**, **Foundation**, **Retaining**, **Soffit**, and **Core-Shaft**.
Coarse Scale Fill Pattern	Specifies the hatch pattern for the wall in a coarse view. To assign a pattern, click in the **Value** field corresponding to this parameter and choose the Browse button to invoke the **Fill Patterns** dialog box. In this dialog box, you can select a specific hatch pattern to assign it to a wall that can be viewed in the coarse view.

Coarse Scale Fill Color	Specifies the color assigned to the hatch pattern applied to a wall. To assign a different color, choose the button displayed in the **Value** field corresponding to this parameter; the **Color** dialog box will be invoked. In this dialog box, you can select a color and assign it to the hatch fill pattern applied to the structural wall.
Structural Material	Specifies the material composition of wall.
Fire Rating	Specifies the fire rating of a wall in compliance with the building codes. The fire rating determines the duration which a fire resistant wall can withstand in case of fire.
Cost	Specifies the cost of a wall.

After you have specified the instance and type properties of a structural wall, you can select a sketching tool from the list box in the **Draw** panel to sketch the wall. The tools available in the list box to sketch the wall are discussed in the next section.

Sketching Structural Walls

You can sketch a structural wall by using the tools available in the list box in the **Draw** panel of the **Modify | Place Structural Wall** contextual tab, refer to Figure 4-25. To sketch the wall, you can also use the options available in the **Options Bar** along with the tools from the **Draw** panel. The sketching tools available in the **Draw** panel of the **Modify | Place Structural Wall** contextual tab and their applications are discussed next.

*Figure 4-25 Various sketching tools in the **Draw** panel*

Sketching Structural Walls Using the Line Tool

You can use the **Line** tool to sketch straight walls in a drawing. You can invoke this tool from the **Draw** panel of the **Modify | Place Structural Wall** contextual tab. After invoking this sketching tool, specify the location of the start point and endpoint of the wall segment. To specify the location of the start point, click in the drawing area. Next, move the cursor in the drawing area. On doing so, you will notice that a wall segment has started from the specified point and displays a dimension on it. This dimension is called a temporary dimension or listening dimension, and it shows the length and angle of the wall segment in Imperial unit system at the cursor location, as shown in Figure 4-26. Also, you will notice that the length of the wall segment is displayed in Metric system, refer to Figure 4-26. Note that the cursor is moving in fixed increments. This increment is determined by the value set in the **Dimension Snaps** option of the **Snaps** dialog box. The options in this dialog box have already been discussed in Chapter 2.

Figure 4-26 *Structural wall with its temporary dimensions*

The angle subtended by the wall on the horizontal axis is also displayed and it keeps on changing dynamically as you move the cursor to modify the inclination of the wall. On moving the cursor near the horizontal or the vertical axis, a dashed line will appear on the wall segment. This line is called alignment line and helps you sketch components with respect to the existing components. You will also notice that a tooltip is displayed at the endpoint of the wall, indicating that the wall segment being sketched is horizontal, as shown in Figure 4-27.

Figure 4-27 *Sketching a horizontal wall*

Autodesk Revit provides you with the option to specify the length of walls in different ways. The first option is to specify the start point of the wall and then moving the cursor in the desired direction and then click when the angle and the temporary dimension attain the required values. The second option is to sketch the wall and then modify its length and angle to the exact value. For example, to sketch a 18'0" (or 5400 mm) long horizontal wall after specifying the starting point, you need to move the cursor to the right until you see a dashed horizontal line parallel to the sketched wall. Click when the temporary dimension shows approximately 20'0" (or 6000 mm). Note that the length of the wall may not be exactly 18'0"(or 5400 mm). You can now use the wall controls to modify the dimensions of the wall to its exact value. To modify a wall, select the wall segment and view its control and properties. When you select the wall segment, it gets highlighted in blue and three symbols appear above the wall segment in blue. These highlighted symbols are called wall controls, as shown in Figure 4-28.

Figure 4-28 Wall controls displayed on wall segment

The exact dimension of the sketched wall is visible in the dimension text of the temporary dimension. The conversion control symbol, which appears below the dimension value, is used to convert a temporary dimension into a permanent dimension. The two blue arrows, which also appear on the upper face of the wall, indicate the flip control symbols for the sketched walls. They appear on the side interpreted as the exterior face of the wall. By default, the walls drawn from the left to right have the external face on the upper side and the walls drawn from the top to bottom have external face on the right side. You can flip the orientation of the wall by clicking on the arrow symbol. Alternatively, you can place the cursor on the flip control symbol and notice the change in its color. After the color of the flip control is changed, press SPACEBAR to flip the wall. The two blue dots that appear at the two ends of the wall segments are the drag control symbols. You can use them to stretch and resize the walls. To set the wall to the exact length, click on the temporary dimension; an edit box will be displayed, showing the current dimension of the wall segment. You can replace this value by specifying the exact length, for example **14' 8"** (or 4470), in the edit box, as shown in Figure 4-29. The length of the wall will be modified to **14' 8"** (or 4470). Alternatively, you can create a straight wall by typing the dimension of the length before choosing its endpoint. As soon as you enter the value of the length, an edit box appears above the dimension line. Enter the value of the length and press ENTER to create a wall segment of the specified length. To sketch a wall at a given angle, sketch it at any angle and then click on the angular dimension symbol; an edit box will be displayed. In the edit box, you can enter the exact angular dimension.

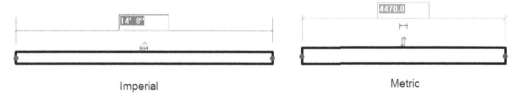

Figure 4-29 Specifying the exact length of the wall

Note
*The **Project Browser** shows **Level 1** in bold letters. This indicates that the wall has been sketched in that level.*

Sketching a Structural Wall Using the Circle Tool

The **Circle** tool is used to sketch a circular wall profile. To sketch one such profile, invoke this tool from the **Draw** panel of the **Modify|Place Structural Wall** contextual tab. Next, click in the drawing area to specify the center point of the circular wall. As you move the cursor away from this point, you will notice that a circular wall profile has been created. This circle extends dynamically, taking the specified points as the center and the cursor location as the other end. The temporary radial dimension will also be displayed, as shown in Figure 4-30. Click when the desired value for the radius is displayed. Alternatively, before clicking on the second point, type the value for the radius of the circular profile. On doing so, an edit box with the type value will be displayed as the temporary dimension. Press ENTER to complete the profile. Note that the dimension that you entered is the distance of the center point to the location line of the profile.

Figure 4-30 *Temporary dimensions displayed on the circular wall*

Sketching a Wall Using the Start-End-Radius Arc Tool

The **Start-End-Radius Arc** sketching tool enables you to sketch an arc wall by specifying the start point, the endpoint, and the intermediate point that determines the radius of the arc. To create an arc wall, invoke the **Start-End-Radius Arc** tool from the **Draw** panel of the **Modify | Place Structural Wall** contextual tab; you will be prompted to specify the start point of the proposed arc wall. Specify the start point by clicking in the drawing area; you will be prompted to specify the endpoint of the curved wall. Specify the endpoint of the curved wall; a curved wall with a variable radius will stretch dynamically between the two specified points. Specify the location of the third point between the two specified points to specify the subtended angle or the radius of the arc. As you specify the third point, the temporary angular and radial dimensions are displayed along with the curve on the screen. Next, click in the drawing area to specify the third point; the curved wall will be sketched. You can also modify the parameters of the sketched walls such as their curvature, radius, angle subtended, orientation, and so on. To modify the curvature, select the sketched wall, click on the parameter such as radial dimension, and enter a new value in the edit box, as shown in Figure 4-31. You can also use the drag controls to increase or decrease the extents of the wall. The central blue dot can be used to stretch the wall, keeping the subtended angle

Imperial   Metric

Figure 4-31 *Editing the dimension of the arc wall*

Sketching a Wall Using the Tangent End Arc Tool
To sketch a curved wall profile that starts tangentially from an existing wall, invoke the **Tangent End Arc** tool from the **Draw** panel in the **Modify | Place Structural Wall** contextual tab; the start point of the wall will be specified as the endpoint of the existing wall. After specifying the start point, move the cursor to the desired distance and click to define the curved wall profile.

Sketching a Wall Using the Fillet Arc Tool
To create a curved fillet wall between two existing walls, choose the **Fillet Arc** tool from the **Modify | Place Structural Wall** contextual tab. Next, click on the walls one by one to create a fillet wall. On doing so, a fillet wall will appear showing its possible locations, as shown in Figure 4-32. Click to specify the location of the fillet. Once the fillet wall has been sketched, you can modify its radius by clicking on it and typing its value. Notice that the walls are automatically trimmed after placing the fillet arc.

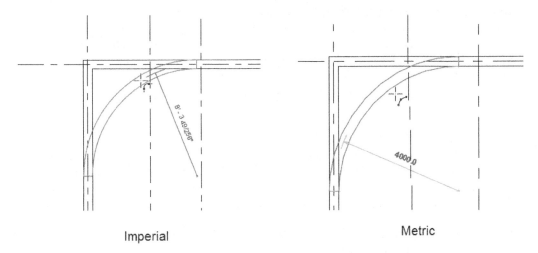

Imperial   Metric

Figure 4-32 *Fillet wall created between two structural walls*

Creating a Wall Using Elliptical Tool

To sketch an elliptical wall, choose the **Ellipse** tool from the **Modify | Place Wall** tab. Now click in the drawing area to specify the center of the ellipse and move the cursor away from the center in any direction. After specifying the direction, you can drag and click the cursor when the required value of the radius is displayed or you can enter the required value in the temporary dimensions box. Next, move the cursor in the direction perpendicular to the direction specified previously and click; the elliptical wall will displayed, as shown in Figure 4-33

Figure 4-33 *Sketching and modifying an elliptical wall profile*

Creating a Wall Using the Pick Lines Tool

The **Pick Lines** tool can be used to create a wall from the existing model lines, edge, or grid lines. Invoke this tool from the **Draw** panel of the **Modify | Place Structural Wall** contextual tab; you will be prompted to select an edge or a line. Move the cursor over the desired line or edge; the desired edge or line will be highlighted. Next, click on the highlighted edge or line, a wall will be created. You can keep on selecting multiple lines and edges to add more walls.

Creating a Wall Using the Pick Faces Tool

The **Pick Faces** tool can be used to create a wall from an existing face of a massing object. Invoke this tool from the **Draw** panel in the **Modify | Place Structural Wall** contextual tab; you will be prompted to select a face from a massing object. Move the cursor over the desired face of the massing object and click over it, a wall will be created on the desired face.

Using the Options from the Options Bar

You can also use the options from the **Options Bar** to sketch a wall. The options in the **Options Bar**, as shown in Figure 4-34, can be used to set the height of a wall, alignment of the location line, offset value of the location line of the wall, and the radius of the circular or arc wall, if required.

Figure 4-34 *Various options in the* ***Options Bar***

The first drop-down list in the **Options Bar** is used to set the reference to which the height of the wall is to be measured. The drop-down list contains two options: **Height** and **Depth**. On selecting the **Height** option from the drop-down list, you can assign a constraint for the top of the wall from the drop-down list available next to the first drop-down list. In this drop-down list, you can select a level that is at a higher elevation from the current level or select the **Unconnected** option to assign an unconnected height which is not constrained to any level. On selecting the **Unconnected** option from the drop-down list, an edit box next to it will be activated. In this edit box, you can enter the unconnected height of the wall. Similarly, while adding a wall, if it is required to constrain the base of the structural wall, then select the **Depth** option from the first drop-down list of the **Options Bar**. After selecting the **Depth** option from the drop-down list, select any option from the drop-down list next to it to specify a level to constrain the base. You can select the **Unconnected** option from this drop-down list to specify the unconnected depth. To specify the unconnected depth, enter a value in the edit box displayed next to the drop-down list.

After setting the constraint for the top or base of the wall, you can select an option from the **Location Line** drop-down list to set the justification of the wall. In this drop-down list, you can select any of these options: **Wall Centerline**, **Core Centerline**, **Finish Face: Exterior**, **Finish Face: Interior**, **Core Face: Exterior**, and **Core Face: Interior**. Note that when you select an option from the **Location Line** drop-down list, the spacing between other structural element and the structural wall is also affected. So, you need to carefully select an option from the **Location Line** drop-down list, based on the project requirement. If you select the

Wall Centerline option from the drop-down list, the structural wall will be justified to the center of the wall section that is calculated on the basis of its two outermost faces. You should select this option while adding a structural wall for single element wall type such as concrete foundation wall or concrete masonry unit. Figure 4-35 shows the example of a structural wall where the **Wall Centerline** option is selected from the **Location Line** drop-down list while adding a **Foundation - 12" Concrete** (for Imperial) and **Foundation - 300mm Concrete** (for Metric) type of wall in a project. Similarly, you can select the **Finish Face: Exterior** option or **Finish Face: Interior** option from the **Location Line** drop-down list to justify the location line of the structural wall either to the exterior finished face or to the interior finished face of the wall.

Figure 4-35 Structural wall justified to the center of the wall

Refer to the example in Figure 4-36 which shows the location of the location line for justification to the exterior and interior finished faces of the **Brick on CMU** type of wall. It is recommended to select the **Core Face: Exterior** or **Core Face: Interior** option from the **Location Line** drop-down list whenever a compound structural wall type is to be placed in a project. Refer to the example in Figure 4-37 which shows the placement of the location line at the exterior and interior faces of the core layers of the walls.

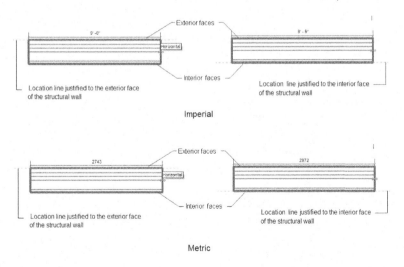

Figure 4-36 Structural walls justified to the exterior and interior finished faces

Figure 4-37 Structural walls justified to the exterior and interior finished faces of the core layers

In the **Options Bar**, you can select the **Chain** check box to create a continuous wall with wall segments connected end-to-end. The endpoint of the previous wall becomes the start point of the next wall. In the **Options Bar**, you can also enter a value in the **Offset** edit box to create a structural wall that starts at a specified offset distance from a point defined in an existing element. You can enter the offset distance value in the edit box provided in the **Options Bar**. After entering the offset value in the **Offset** edit box, click near the element to define the offset distance. When you move the cursor, the wall will start at the specified distance from the selected point. For example, this option can be used for creating boundary walls that are placed at a specific distance from the building profile. In **Options Bar**, the **Radius** check box can be selected to sketch walls with circular or arc profile. On selecting the **Radius** check box, an edit box next to will be enabled. You can enter a value in this edit box to specify a fixed radius for the circular wall to be added.

Sketching Slanted Walls

In Revit 2021, you can create slanted walls. To create slanted walls, sketch the desired wall profile and choose the **Slanted** option from the drop-down corresponding to the **Cross-Section** option of the **Properties** palette. Enter the desired value of angle of inclination of the wall from the vertical in the **Angle From Vertical** option to make the wall inclined.

Modifying Structural Walls

You can modify profile, element properties (type and instance), and attachments at the top or base of a structural wall. To do so, select the wall that you want to modify; the **Modify | Walls** contextual tab will be displayed. In this tab, you can use the options in the **Mode**, **Modify Wall**, and **Reinforcement** panels to edit the profile of the wall, modify the attachments of the top and base of a wall, and add reinforcement to the wall. To modify the instance property of a selected structural wall, you can use various parameters displayed in the **Properties** palette. You can modify the type properties of a structural wall by invoking the **Type Properties** dialog box. To invoke this dialog box, choose the **Edit Type** button from the **Properties** palette. Apart from modifying the element properties of the selected structural wall, you can also edit its elevation profile. To edit the elevation profile, select a wall in a structural floor plan view and choose the **Edit Profile** tool from the **Mode** panel in the **Modify | Walls** contextual tab; the **Go To View** dialog box will be displayed. Select an option from this dialog box to specify a suitable view. Now, choose the **Open View** button from the **Go To View** dialog box; the specified view with the wall profile of the selected wall will be displayed in an editable mode, as shown in Figure 4-38. Next, you can use various sketching and editing tools from the **Modify| Walls > Edit Profile** contextual tab. On selecting the **Edit Profile** tool from the **Mode** panel. After editing the profile, choose the **Finish Edit Mode** button from the **Mode** panel in the **Modify | Walls > Edit Profile** contextual tab to complete the editing process. Figure 4-39 shows a structural wall before and after editing its profile.

Figure 4-38 Structural wall in editing mode as a wall profile

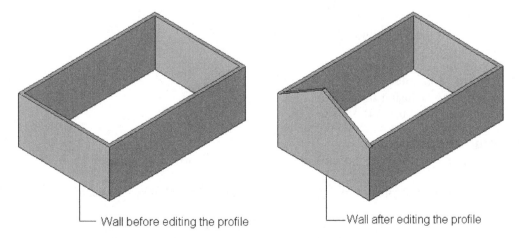

Figure 4-39 Structural wall before and after editing its profile

TUTORIALS

Tutorial 1   Commercial Complex

In this tutorial, you will add structural columns and structural walls to the *Commercial Complex* project created in Tutorial 1 of Chapter 3. Use the following project parameters and specifications for completing the project.   **(Expected time: 1 hr)**

1. Structural column:
    > For Imperial   Type: **Concrete-Rectangular-Column**
    >   Dimension: 12" x 24"
    > For Metric   Type: **M_Concrete-Rectangular-Column**
    >   Dimension: 300 x 600mm

2. Structural concrete walls:
    > For Imperial   Width - **12"**
    >   Function - **Core-shaft**
    > For Metric   Width - **300mm**
    >   Function - **Core-shaft**

3. File name to be assigned:
    > For Imperial   *c04_Commercial-Complex_tut1.rvt.*
    > For Metric   *M_c04_Commercial-Complex_tut1.rvt.*

The following steps are required to complete this tutorial:

a. Start a Revit session and open the project file.
    > For Imperial   *c03_Commercial-Complex_tut1.rvt*
    > For Metric   *M_c03_Commercial-Complex_tut1.rvt*

b. Create a structural column type.
c. Add columns.
d. Modify the height of columns.
e. Add structural walls.
f. Save the project using the **Save As** tool.
g. Close the project using the **Close** tool.

Opening the Project
In this section, you will open the project file created in Tutorial 1 of Chapter 3.

1. Choose **Open > Project** from the **File** menu; the **Open** dialog box is displayed.

2. In this dialog box, browse to the *C:\rst_2021\c03_rst_2021_tut* location and then choose the *c03_Commercial-Complex_tut1.rvt* (for Imperial) *or M_c03_Commercial-Complex_ tut1.rvt* (for Metric) project file. You can also download this file from *https://www.cadcim.com*. The path of the file is as follows: *Textbooks > Civil/GIS > Revit Structure > Exploring Autodesk Revit 2021 for Structure*.

3. Choose the **Open** button from the **Open** dialog box; the selected project file opens in the drawing window in the **Entry** structural plan view.

Creating a Structural Column Type

In this section, you will create a concrete rectangular column type to add to the project view.

1. Choose the **Column** tool from the **Structure** panel of the **Structure** tab; the **Modify | Place Structural Column** contextual tab is displayed.

2. In the **Properties** palette, select the specified option from the **Type Selector** drop-down list.

    For Imperial   **Concrete-Rectangular-Column: 12 x 18**
    For Metric   **M_Concrete-Rectangular-Column: 300 x 450mm**

3. Choose the **Edit Type** button; the **Type Properties** dialog box is displayed.

4. In this dialog box, choose the **Duplicate** button; the **Name** dialog box is displayed.

5. In the **Name** dialog box, enter **12 x 24** (in Imperial unit system) and **300 x 600mm** (in Metric unit system) in the **Name** edit box and choose **OK**; the **Name** dialog box is closed.

6. In the **Type Properties** dialog box, click in the **Value** field corresponding to the **h** parameter; the existing value, **1' 6"** (for Imperial) and **450.0** (for Metric), is highlighted.

7. Replace the existing value with **2' 0"** (for Imperial) and **600.0** (for Metric), and then choose the **OK** button; the **Type Properties** dialog box closes and preview of the new column type attached with the cursor is displayed in the drawing area.

Adding Structural Columns

In this section, you will add structural columns to the model.

1. In the drawing area, right-click and then choose the **Zoom In Region** option from the shortcut menu; the cursor the cursor gets modified into zoom icon.

2. Move the cursor and place it between the grid lines marked **1** and **A**. Click at an appropriate location, as shown in Figure 4-40; a rectangular selection window appears.

Figure 4-40 *Placing the cursor to mark the first corner of the zoom window*

3. Move the cursor downward toward right. Click between the grid lines marked 5.1 and C.2, refer to Figure 4-41. On doing so, the project view zooms in so that the columns can easily be added at the desired location.

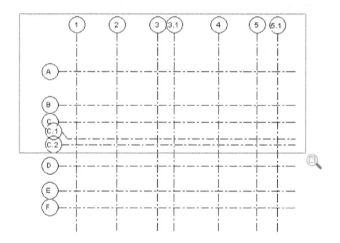

Figure 4-41 *Placing the cursor to mark the other corner of the zoom window*

4. In the **Options Bar**, select the **Rotate after placement** check box and then select the **Height** option from the first drop-down list next to it.

5. Ensure that the **Room Bounding** check box is selected in the **Options Bar**. Place the cursor at the intersection of grid 1 and grid A; the grid 1 and grid A are highlighted.

6. Click when both grids are still highlighted; a preview of the column with its center aligned to the intersection of grid 1 and grid A is displayed.

7. Move the cursor up toward the right; a rotation alignment line appears with temporary angular dimension.

8. Type **90**; an edit box with typed value is displayed near the temporary dimension.

9. Press ENTER; a column is inserted at the intersection of grid 1 and grid A, as shown in Figure 4-42.

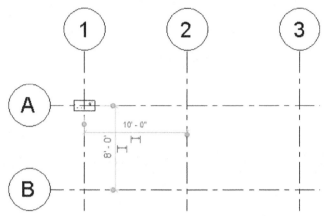

Figure 4-42 *A column added at the intersection of grid 1 and grid A*

10. Repeat steps 5 to 9 to insert other columns of the same type and alignment at different grid intersections, refer to Figure 4-43. Do not exit the **Column** tool even though you have inserted all columns at different grid intersections.

Note
While inserting columns at different grid intersections, you can zoom out the current view and then zoom into the area where you need to insert columns.

11. After inserting all the columns, choose the **At Grids** tool from the **Multiple** panel of the **Modify | Place Structural Column** contextual tab; the **Modify | Place Structural Column > At Grid Intersection** contextual tab is displayed.

12. Place the cursor on grid B. Click when the grid is highlighted; the grid B is selected.

13. Press and hold the CTRL key and click on grid 4, grid 5, and grid G.1 to select them; columns are inserted at the grid intersections of the selected grids, as shown in Figure 4-44.

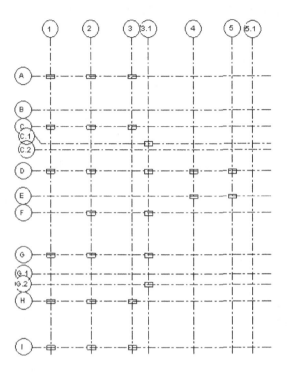

Figure 4-43 *Alignment and columns of same type inserted in the grid*

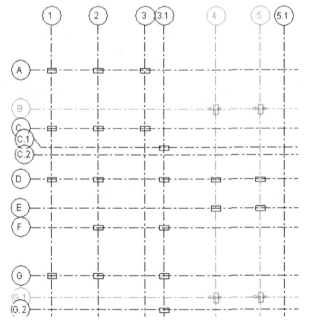

Figure 4-44 *Columns added at the intersections of the highlighted grids*

14. Now, choose the **Finish** button from the **Multiple** panel in the **Modify | Place Structural Column > At Grid Intersection** contextual tab; the **Modify | Place Structural Column** contextual tab is displayed.

15. Choose the **Modify** button from the **Select** panel in the **Modify | Place Structural Column** contextual tab.

Modifying the Height of Columns

In this section, to adjust the thickness of the slab (floor) in the structural model, you will modify the height of the inserted columns (except for stairs and lifts) by adjusting their top offset distances.

1. Place the cursor between grid A and grid 1, refer to Figure 4-45.

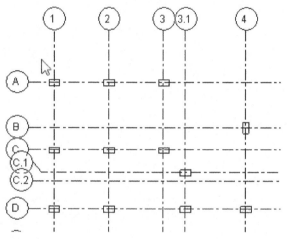

Figure 4-45 *Specifying the first point of the selection window*

2. Next, press and hold the left mouse button and then drag the cursor downward toward right along the selection window until it is placed at the location shown in Figure 4-46.

3. Release the mouse button and click; all the columns inside the selection window are selected and the **Modify | Structural Columns** contextual tab is displayed.

4. In the **Properties** palette of the selected columns, click in the value field corresponding to the **Top Offset** instance parameter. Clear the existing value and then enter **-1'** (in Imperial) and **-304.8mm** (in Metric).

5. Next, choose the **Apply** button in the **Properties** palette and then the **Modify** button in the **Select** panel of the **Modify | Structural Columns** contextual tab.

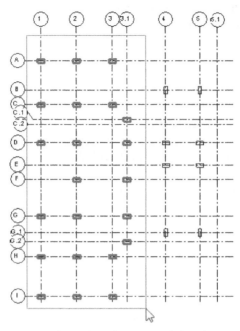

Figure 4-46 *Specifying the other point of the selection window*

6. Now, select all the columns using the selection window, as done earlier.

7. In the **Properties** palette of the selected columns, select the **Entry** option for the **Base Level** parameter and the **Second Floor** option for the **Top Level** parameter if not selected.

8. Choose the **Apply** button; the height of the columns is set between the **Entry** and **Second** floor levels.

Adding Structural Walls

In this section, you will create a structural wall type and add it to the project view.

1. Choose the **Wall: Structural** tool from **Structure > Structure > Wall** drop-down; the **Modify | Place Structural Wall** contextual tab is displayed.

2. In the **Properties** palette, select the desired option from the **Type Selector** drop-down list.
    For Imperial   **Exterior - 10" Concrete**
    For Metric   **Exterior - 225mm Concrete**
    Now, choose the **Edit Type** button; the **Type Properties** dialog box is displayed

3. Choose the **Duplicate** button in this dialog box; the **Name** dialog box is displayed.

4. Type the specified values in the **Name** edit box of the **Name** dialog box.
    For Imperial   **Core-Shaft - 12" Concrete**
    For Metric   **Core-Shaft - 300mm Concrete**
    Next, choose **OK**; the **Name** dialog box is closed.

5. In the **Type Properties** dialog box, choose the **Edit** button displayed in the **Value** column of the **Structure** parameter; the **Edit Assembly** dialog box is displayed.

6. In the **Layers** area of the **Edit Assembly** dialog box, click in the edit box in the **Thickness** column corresponding to the **Structure [1]** function and enter **12"**(for Imperial) and **300mm** (for Metric). Next, press ENTER to replace the existing value.

7. Choose the **OK** button; the **Edit Assembly** dialog box closes and the **Type Properties** dialog box is displayed.

8. In the **Type Properties** dialog box, select the **Core-shaft** option from the drop-down list corresponding to the **Function** parameter from the **Construction** area and then choose the **OK** button; the **Type Properties** dialog box is closed.

9. In the **Options Bar**, select the **Height** option from the first drop-down list; a warning message box appears at the bottom of the screen. Close the message box.

10. Select the **Second Floor** option from the second drop-down list in the **Options Bar** and then clear the **Chain** check box.

11. Zoom in the drawing and move the cursor toward the column at the intersection of grid 4 and grid B. Place the cursor on the right face of the column. Click when the right face is highlighted and the **Midpoint** snap is displayed, as shown in Figure 4-47.

Figure 4-47 Specifying the start point at the intersection of grid 4 and grid B

12. Now, move the cursor horizontally toward the right and place it at the midpoint of the left face of the column located at the intersection of grid 5 and grid B, as shown in Figure 4-48. Click when the **Midpoint and Horizontal** snap appears.

Figure 4-48 *Specifying the endpoint at the intersection of grid 5 and grid B*

13. Move the cursor and place it at the lower face of the column, located at the intersection of grid 5 and grid B. Click when the **Midpoint** snap appears, as shown in Figure 4-49.

Figure 4-49 *Specifying the start point of the other wall at the midpoint of the lower face of the column at the intersection of grid 5 and grid B*

14. Move the cursor vertically down and place it at the upper face of the column at the intersection of grid 5 and grid D. Click when the **Endpoint and Vertical** snap appears.

15. Next, place the cursor at the lower face of the column, at the intersection of grid 5 and grid D. Click when the lower face is highlighted and the **Midpoint** snap appears.

16. Move the cursor vertically downward and place it at the upper face of the column located at the intersection of grid 5 and grid E. Click when the **Endpoint and Vertical** snap appears at the intersection point.

17. Repeat the method of adding structural walls discussed in Steps 13 to 16 to add the remaining structural walls to the project, as shown in Figure 4-50.

Figure 4-50 The structural walls added

18. Choose the **Modify** button from the **Select** panel to exit the **Wall: Structural** tool.

19. Select the wall placed on grid Band then right-click; a shortcut menu is displayed. Choose the **Select All Instances > Visible in View** from the shortcut menu; all walls in the project view will be highlighted.

20. In the Properties palette, enter **-2'** in the **Top Offset** edit box.

Saving the Project
In this section of the tutorial, you will save the project file using the **Save As** tool.

1. Choose **Save As > Project** from the **File** menu. On doing so, the **Save As** dialog box is displayed.

2. In this dialog box, browse to the *C:\rst_2021* location and create a folder with the name *c04_rst_2021_tut*. Next, open the *c04_rst_2021_tut* folder and enter **c04_Commercial-Complex_tut1** (for Imperial) and **M_c04_Commercial-Complex_tut1** (for Metric) in the **File name** edit box.

3. Choose the **Save** button; the **Save As** dialog box closes and the project file is saved.

Closing the Project
1. Choose the **Close** option from the **File** menu.

The file is closed and this completes Tutorial 1 of Chapter 4

Tutorial 2   Industrial Complex

In this tutorial, you will add structural columns to the *Industrial-Complex* project created in Tutorial 2 of Chapter 3. Use the project parameters and specifications that are given next:

(Expected time: 30 min)

1. Structural column:

   For Imperial Type: **Concrete-Square-Column**
           Dimension: **24" x 24"**
           Type: **W-Wide Flange-Column**
           Dimension: **W10x33**
   For Metric   Type: **M_Conrete-Square-Column**
           Dimension: **600 x 600mm**
           Type: **M_W-Wide Flange-Column**
           Dimension: **W840x251**

2. File name to be assigned:

   For Imperial *c04_Industrial-Complex_tut2.rvt.*
   For Metric   *M_c04_Industrial-Complex_tut2.rvt.*

The following steps are required to complete this tutorial:

a. Start a Revit session and open Tutorial 2 of Chapter 3.
b. Create a structural column type.
c. Add columns, refer to Figures 4-51 to 4-52.
d. Modify the height of structural columns by using the **Base Level** parameter.
e. Save the project using the **Save As** tool.
f. Close the project using the **Close** tool.

Opening the Project
In this section, you will open the project file created in Tutorial 2 of Chapter 3.

1. Choose **Open > Project** from the **File** menu; the **Open** dialog box is displayed.

2. In this dialog box, browse to the *C:\rst_2021\c03_rst_2021_tut* location and then choose the *c03_Industrial-Complex_tut2.rvt* (for Imperial) and *M_c03_Industrial-Complex_tut2.rvt* (for Metric) project file. You can also download this file from *https://www.cadcim.com*. The path of the file is as follows: *Textbooks > Civil/GIS > Revit Structure > Exploring Autodesk Revit 2021 for Structure*.

3. Next, choose the **Open** button from the **Open** dialog box; the selected project file opens in the drawing window in the **Entry** structural plan view.

Creating a Structural Column Type

In this section, you will create a concrete rectangular column type and add it to the structural model.

1. Ensure that the **Entry** structural plan view is opened as the current view and then choose the **Column** tool from the **Structure** panel of the **Structure** tab; the **Modify | Place Structural Column** contextual tab is displayed.

2. Choose the **Load Family** tool from the **Mode** panel of the **Modify | Place Structural Column** tab; the **Load Family** dialog box is displayed.

3. In this dialog box, click on the **Up one level** button placed next to the **Look in** drop-down list; the **English-Metric** and **English-Imperial** folders are displayed.

4. Browse to **English-Imperial > Structural Columns > Concrete folder** and then select the **Concrete-Square-Column** option for Imperial and for the **M_Concrete-Square-Column** option browse the **English-Metric** folder.

5. In the **Properties** palette, select the specified option from the **Type Selector** drop-down list.

    For Imperial   **Concrete-Square-Column: 24 x 24**
    For Metric   **M_Concrete-Square-Column: 600 x 600mm**

Note
*In case you do not find the above mentioned column in the **Type Selector** drop-down list, you can load the families from the **Load Family** dialog box.*

Adding Structural Columns

In this section, you will add new and existing structural column types to the project.

1. In the **Options Bar**, select the **Height** option from the first drop-down list on left and ensure that the **Second Floor** option is selected in the other drop-down list.

2. Choose the **At Grids** tool from the **Multiple** panel of the **Modify | Place Structural Column** contextual tab; the **Modify | Place Structural Column > At Grid Intersection** contextual tab is displayed.

3. Place the cursor over grid C and click when it is highlighted; grid C is selected.

4. Next, press and hold the CTRL key and click over grid A, grid B, grid 7, grid 8, and grid 9 to select them; columns are inserted at the intersections of the selected grids, as shown in Figure 4-51.

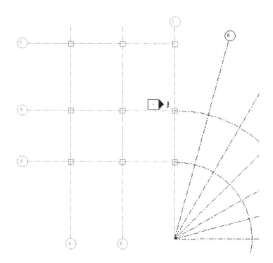

Figure 4-51 *Columns added at the intersection of the selected grids*

5. Choose the **Finish** button from the **Multiple** panel; the **Modify | Place Structural Column** contextual tab is displayed.

6. In the **Properties** palette, select the specified option from the **Type Selector** drop-down list.

> For Imperial   **W Shapes-Column W10x33**
> For Metric   **M_W Shape-Column W840x251**

Note
In case you do not find the above mentioned column family in the **Type Selector** *drop-down list, you can load the family from the* **Load Family** *dialog box.*

7. Choose the **At Grids** tool from the **Multiple** panel in the **Modify | Place Structural Column** contextual tab; the **Modify | Place Structural Column > At Grid Intersection** contextual tab is displayed.

8   Move the cursor and place it on circular grid A' and click when it is highlighted; grid A' is selected.

9. Press and hold the CTRL key and click over the circular grid B', grid 1, grid 2, grid 3, grid 4, grid 5, and grid 6 to select them; columns are inserted at the intersections of the selected grids, as shown in Figure 4-51.

10. Choose the **Finish** button from the **Multiple** panel; the **Modify | Place Structural Column** tab is displayed.

11. Choose the **Modify** button from the **Select** panel.

Notice that a column is added at the intersection of all grid lines.

12. Select the column refer to figure 4-52 and press **DELETE** to remove it from the model..

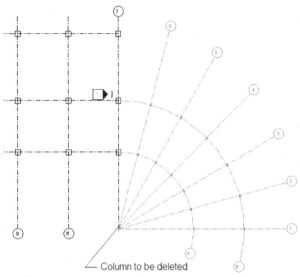

Figure 4-52 The **W-Shape-Column W10x33** *type added to the selected grids*

Note
*Some of the structural columns added may not be aligned as required in the project. These columns can be aligned by using the **Rotate** tool which will be discussed later in Tutorial 2 of Chapter 6.*

Modifying the Height of Columns

In this section, you will modify the height of the inserted rectangular concrete columns by adjusting their **Base Level** parameter.

1. Select all the **Concrete-Square-Column: 24x24** type (of Imperial) and **M_Concrete-Square-Column: 600x600mm** type (of Metric) concrete columns from the drawing. To select the desired columns, click on an individual **Concrete-Square-Column: 24x24** (of Imperial) and **Concrete-Square-Column: 600x600mm** (of Metric) column type. Then, press and hold the CTRL key and click on other columns for multiple selection.

2. On selecting all the square concrete columns, the **Modify | Structural Columns** contextual tab is displayed. In the **Properties** palette of the selected columns, click in the value field corresponding to the **Base Level** instance parameter and then select the **T.O.F.** level from the drop-down list displayed.

3. Choose the **Apply** button in the **Properties** palette and then choose the **Modify** button from the **Select** panel in the **Modify | Structural Columns** contextual tab.

Saving the Project

In this section of the tutorial, you will save the project file using the **Save As** tool.

1. Choose **Save As > Project** from the **File** menu; the **Save As** dialog box is displayed.

2. In this dialog box, browse to the *C:\rst_2021\c04_rst_2021_tut* location and enter **c04_Industrial-Complex_tut2** (for Imperial) and **M_c04_Industrial-Complex_tut2** (for Metric) in the **File name** edit box.

3. Now, choose the **Save** button; the **Save As** dialog box closes and the project file is saved.

Closing the Project

1. Choose the **Close** option from the **File** menu.

    The file is closed and this completes Tutorial 2 of Chapter 4.

___

Self-Evaluation Test

Answer the following questions and then compare them to those given at the end of this chapter:

1. In Revit, you can add three types of columns based on material: Concrete, Steel, and _____.

2. When you start a new project, by default you can use two families for inserting columns: **W Shapes-Column** and _____.

3. The _____ walls play an active role in transferring load from one structural element to the other.

4. In the **Properties** palette for a structural wall, the _____ parameter specifies the level that constrains the base of a wall.

5. The _____ parameter is used to specify the location line of a structural wall that is placed in the model.

6. The _____ instance parameter for a column specifies the plane of the column used for analysis and design.

7   Invoke the _____ sketching tool to sketch straight walls in the drawing.

8. The _____ columns are load-bearing members that are placed in a structural project to add ambience to the structure.

9. In Revit, you cannot create openings in structural columns. (T/F)

10. You can add slanted structural columns to a structural model. (T/F)

Review Questions

Answer the following questions:

1. You can use the _____ tool to create openings in structural columns.

2. The _____ parameter can be used to specify whether to keep rigid link between the analytical model of a beam and column.

3. The _____ parameter specifies the information regarding the phase in which a wall is created.

4. To constrain the **Top** of the wall, you can use the **Top Constraint** and _____ parameters from the **Properties** palette.

5. The _____ tool can be used to create a wall from existing model lines, edge, or grid lines.

6. The _____ tool from the **Modify | Place Structural Column** tab is used to display tags with columns in a drawing.

7. The _____ tool located in the **Draw** panel of the **Modify | Place Structural Wall** tab is used to sketch a circular wall profile in a drawing.

8. The _____ parameter can be used to apply a material to a column.

9. In Revit, the faces of a massing object can be used to create walls. (T/F)

10. In Revit, you can add a structural column to an architectural column. (T/F)

EXERCISES

Exercise 1   Academic Institution

In this exercise, you will add structural columns with tags and structural walls to the exercise file created in Exercise 1 of Chapter 3, refer to Figure 4-53. Use the following project parameters and specifications: **(Expected time: 1 hr 15 min)**

1. Structural column:

For Imperial	Type: **Concrete-Rectangular-Column**	
	Dimension: **18" x 24"**	
For Metric	Type: **M_Concrete-Rectangular-Column**	
	Dimension: **450 x 600mm**	

2. Structural wall:

For Imperial	Type: **Exterior-10" Concrete**.
For Metric	Type: **Exterior-250mm Concrete**.

3. Project file to be used:
            For Imperial   *c03_Academic-Institution_exer1.rvt.*
            For Metric   *M_c03_Academic-Institution_exer1.rvt*

4. Base and Top constraints for walls and columns are **Entry** and **Second Floor** levels.

5. Columns and walls are to be added in the **Entry** structural plan view.

6. File name to be assigned:
            For Imperial   *c04_Academic-Institution_exer1.rvt.*
            For Metric   *M_c04_Academic-Institution_exer1.rvt*

7. For locations and placement of columns and walls, refer to Figure 4-53.

Figure 4-53   *The walls and columns added to the Academic-Institution project*

Exercise 2   Factory Shed

In this exercise, you will add structural columns and walls to the project file created in Exercise 2 of Chapter 3. Refer to Figure 4-53 for grid dimensions and names. Use the following project parameters and specifications: **(Expected time: 45 min)**

1. Project file to be used:
            For Imperial   *c03_Factory-Shed_exer2.rvt.*
            For Metric   *M_c03_Factory-Shed_exer2.rvt.*

2. Structural column:
            For Imperial   Type: **Concrete-Rectangular-Concrete**
                                   Dimension: **18" x 24"**
            For Metric   Type: **M_Concrete-Rectangular-Concrete**
                                   Dimension: **450 x 600mm**

3. Structural wall:
            For Imperial   Type: **Exterior-18" Concrete** (Create a new type)
            For Metric   Type: **Exterior-450mm Concrete** (Create a new type)

4. Project file to be used:

        For Imperial   *c03_Factory-Shed_exer2.rvt*
        For Metric   *M_c03_Factory-Shed_exer2.rvt*

5. Columns and walls need to be added in the **Plinth** structural plan view.

6. File name to be assigned:

        For Imperial   *c04_Factory-Shed_exer2.rvt*
        For Metric   *M_c04_Factory-Shed_exer2.rvt*

7. Base and Top constraints for walls and columns are the **Plinth** and **Second Floor** levels.

8. For the location and placement of columns and walls, refer to Figure 4-54.

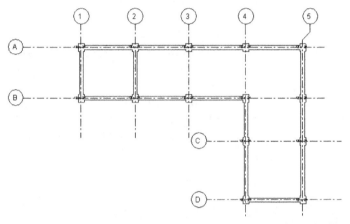

Figure 4-54 The walls and columns added to the Factory-Shed project

Exercise 3   Residential Building

Download the *c04_residential_bldg_exer3* (for Imperial) and *M_c04_residential_bldg_exer3* (for Metric) file from *https://www.cadcim.com*. The path of the file is as follows: *Textbooks > Civil/GIS > Revit Structure > Exploring Autodesk Revit 2021 for Structure*. In this exercise, you will add structural columns and walls to the *Residential_Building* project. Refer to Figure 4-54 for grid dimensions, column locations, and placement of the structural walls. Use the following project parameters and specifications: **(Expected time: 45 min)**

1. Structural column:
    - For Imperial   Type: **Concrete-Rectangular-Column**
                          Dimension: **18" x 24"**
                          Type: **Concrete-Rectangular-Column**
                          Dimension: **24" x 24"**
    - For Metric   Type: **M_Concrete-Rectangular-Column**
                          Dimension: **450 x 600mm**
                          Type: **M_Concrete-Rectangular-Column**
                          Dimension: **600 x 600mm**

2. Structural wall:
    - For Imperial   Type: **Retaining -18" Concrete** (Create a new type)
    - For Metric   Type: **Retaining -450mm Concrete** (Create a new type)

3. Project file to be used:
    - For Imperial   *c04_residential_bldg_exer3.rvt*.
    - For Metric   *M_c04_residential_bldg_exer3.rvt*.

4. Top and Base constraints for columns at intersections (B,1.1), (C,1.1), (3,3.1) and (4,3.1) are the **FL** and **Subgrade** levels.

5. Top and Base constraints for other columns are TL and Subgrade.

6. Top offset for columns at intersections (B,1.1), (C,1.1), (3,3.1) and (4,3.1) are:
    - For Imperial   -2'6".
    - For Metric   -762mm.

7. Top offset for columns is 2'6" (for Imperial) and 762mm (for Metric).

8. File name to be assigned:
    - For Imperial   *c04_residential_bldg_exer3a.rvt*.
    - For Metric   *M_c04_residential_bldg_exer3a.rvt*.

9. For the location and placement of columns and walls, refer to Figure 4-55.

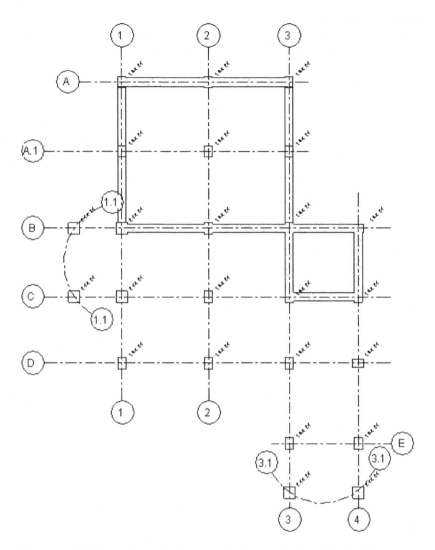

Figure 4-55 *The walls and columns added to the Residential_Building project*

Answers to Self-Evaluation Test

1. Wood, **2. Concrete-Rectangular-Column**, **3.** Load-Bearing, **4. Base Constraint**, **5. Location Line**, **6. Top Vertical Project**, **7. Line**, **8.** Architectural, **9.** F, **10.** T

Chapter 5

Foundations, Beams, Floors, and Open Web Joists

Learning Objectives

After completing this chapter, you will be able to:
- *Create foundations*
- *Add structural floors*
- *Modify structural floors*
- *Add beams*
- *Modify beams*
- *Understand open web joists*

In the previous chapter, you learned to add different structural components such as walls, columns, and so on. In this chapter, you will learn about different types of foundations. You will also understand how to add and modify beams and structural floor and later on add them in your project. Moreover, you will learn to add slab edge to floor and also about the open web steel joists.

FOUNDATIONS

Foundation is one of the important components in a structural model. The function of foundation in any of the construction project is to provide support to the entire building. Foundation acts as an interface between building structure and earth strata for transferring load. For a structural model, you can either have a shallow or deep foundation depending on the bearing capacity of the soil on which the building structure is to be erected. Shallow foundation can be further subcategorized as strip footing and raft footing while deep foundation as pile foundation. Depending on soil bearing capacity (SBC) and structure we can provide either of them.

In Autodesk Revit, you can add foundations of different types such as Isolated, Pile, Wall, and Slab. These types represent different physical foundations that are applicable to sites such as isolated footing (for columns), retaining wall, stepped footing, bearing footings and raft foundation. In this chapter, you will learn how to add both the shallow and deep foundations.

Foundation Wall

After adding structural walls, you can add a foundation wall to the existing structural model. This wall serves as a basement wall or a retaining wall that goes down below the ground level to a level from where the top of the foundation starts. To add a foundation wall, first you need to create the required levels to constrain the ends of the wall. For example, if you want to create a basement wall for an existing structural model, you need to have two levels, one level to constrain the top of the basement wall and the other level to constrain the bottom of the basement wall. The top of the basement wall may be at a level above or at ground level whereas the bottom of this wall will be at a level that coincides with the top of the footing. Figure 5-1(a) and Figure 5-1(b) display a basement wall with its top constrained to the **Entry Level** level and its bottom constrained to the **T.O. Footing** level in the imperial and metric forms respectively.

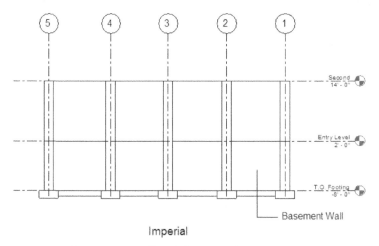

Figure 5-1(a) *The basement wall with the top and bottom constraints (Imperial)*

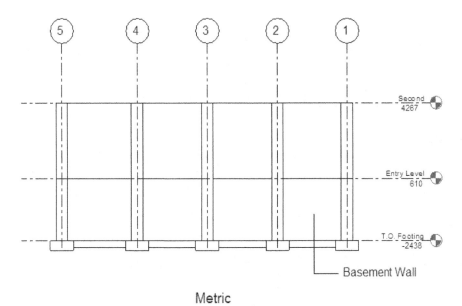

Metric

Figure 5-1(b) *The basement wall with the top and bottom constraints (Metric)*

To add a foundation wall to a structural model, change the display of the current view to a level such that it displays the top of the wall. For example in Figure 5-1, the level that represents the top of the wall is **Entry Level**. Now, after displaying the current view, invoke the **Wall: Structural** tool from **Structure > Structure > Wall** drop-down; the **Modify | Place Structural Wall** contextual tab will be displayed. In the **Type Selector** drop-down list, select the **Foundation - 12" Concrete** option for Imperial unit system or select the **Foundation-300mmConcrete** for Metric unit system, refer to Figure 5-2. After selecting the desired type for the foundation wall, notice that in the **Options Bar**, the **Depth** option is selected by default from the first drop-down list from the left. To assign a level that will constrain the depth to the foundation wall, you can select a level from the drop-down list displayed next to it, refer to Figure 5-3. The selected level (for example the **T.O. Footing** level) will have

Figure 5-2 *Selecting the* ***Foundation - 12" Concrete*** *option from the* ***Type Selector*** *drop-down list*

a lower elevation value as compared to the current level. Alternatively, you can assign an unconnected depth to the foundation wall by selecting the **Unconnected** option in the second drop-down list from the left in the **Options Bar** and then specifying a value in the edit box displayed next to it. The unconnected depth will be measured in reference to the elevation of the current view.

Figure 5-3 *Selecting the **T.O. Footing** option from the drop-down list in the **Options Bar***

Note
You cannot enter negative values or 0 in the edit box to specify the unconnected depth of the foundation wall. If you do so, a warning message box will appear asking you to enter a positive value less than 30000' in Imperial system and for Metric system enter a positive value less than 9144000 mm.

Now, after setting the constraint for the base of the foundation wall, you can click in the drawing area and start creating the foundation wall. Figure 5-4 displays a foundation wall added to a structural model.

Figure 5-4 *The foundation wall added to a structural model*

Shallow Foundations

Shallow foundations are used to transfer load from a building to the Earth strata near the ground surface. Shallow foundations include strip footing foundations, spread footing foundations, mat-slab, and slab-on-grade foundations. In Revit, you can add a shallow foundation as a wall foundation (strip footing foundation), isolated foundation (spread footing foundation) for columns, or foundation slabs. To add these foundations, you need to invoke various tools such as **Isolated**, **Wall**, and **Foundation Slab** from the **Foundation** panel in the **Structure** tab. Figure 5-5 shows various tools that can be invoked to add different types of foundations to a structural model. In the **Foundation** panel, you can invoke the **Wall** tool to add a wall foundation in the existing structural model. You can use this tool to add two types of wall foundations: Bearing footing foundation and Retaining footing foundation. Each of these foundations has separate element properties

Figure 5-5 *Various tools to add foundation*

and placement methods. These properties and methods will be discussed later in this chapter. You can use the **Isolated** tool to add the spread or isolated foundations to the columns of the structural model. The element properties and the placement method for this type of foundation will also be discussed later. Note that the wall and the isolated footings are dependent on the host element to which they are attached. Figure 5-6 shows the associativity of a structural wall with a wall foundation.

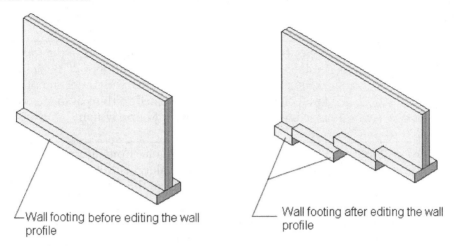

Wall footing before editing the wall profile

Wall footing after editing the wall profile

Figure 5-6 *The wall foundation before and after editing the wall profile*

The **Slab** tool in the **Foundation** panel can be used to add a foundation slab to the structural model. Unlike the isolated and wall foundations, the slab foundations are not attached to any host element. Slab foundations are created independent of other structural elements present in a structural model. The placement and the properties of this type of foundation will be discussed later in this chapter.

Wall Footing Foundation

A wall foundation is a footing that is attached to a wall. In actual practice, strip footing is a good example of this kind of foundation. The advantage of using Revit over other similar software to place wall footing is that they are associated with the host wall. It means the foundation wall will remain attached to its host wall even if the host wall is moved, or its shape or type is changed. In Revit , you can add two types of wall foundations: bearing foundation and retaining foundation. These foundations differ from each other in terms of their functions and geometries. The method of adding and placing these foundations is discussed in the next sections.

Tip
The footings are attached to columns or walls. This means that a relationship is established between the footing and its host element (wall or column). As a result, whenever there is a change in the shape or position of the wall or the column, the footing also changes accordingly.

Adding Bearing Foundations

In a structural model, you can add a bearing shallow foundation to an existing structural wall by invoking the **Wall** tool from the **Foundation** panel of the **Structure** tab. On invoking this tool, the **Modify | Place Wall Foundation** contextual tab will be displayed. Next, select the **Bearing Footing - 36" x 12"** option (for Imperial) or **Bearing Footing - 900 x 300** (for Metric) from the **Type Selector** drop-down list in the **Properties** palette. Now, you can change the instance parameters such as the eccentricity, cover lengths of the rebar (at top, bottom, or from other faces of the foundation), and analytical settings of the selected bearing footing type.

To change the instance parameter, you can use various options in the **Properties** palette. The different instance parameters available in this palette are discussed next.

Parameter	Description
Eccentricity	Specifies the distance at which the center of the foundation will be offset from the center of the host wall. By default, the center of the foundation is aligned with the center of the host wall. The default value assigned to this parameter is "**0' 0"** for Imperial system or **0** for Metric system.
Rebar Cover - Top Face	Specifies the rebar cover distance from the top face of the wall foundation. Click on the value field of this parameter and select the desired option from the drop-down list displayed.
Rebar Cover - Bottom Face	Specifies the rebar cover distance from the bottom face of the wall foundation. Click on the value field of this parameter and select the desired option from the drop-down list displayed.
Rebar Cover - Other Face	Specifies the rebar cover distance from the other face of the wall foundation. Click on the value field of this parameter and select the desired option from the drop-down list displayed.
Enable Analytical Model	Specifies whether to enable analytical model of the wall foundation. Select the check box in its value field to enable the analytical model.

After assigning the instance parameters to the bearing foundation from the **Properties** palette, you can assign its type parameters in the **Type Properties** dialog box. To invoke this dialog box, choose the **Edit Type** button from the **Properties** palette or choose the **Type Properties** tool from the **Properties** panel of the **Modify | Place Wall Foundation** contextual tab. Using this dialog box, you can access the type properties of the wall foundation and change them based on your project requirement. Various type properties in the **Type Properties** dialog box are discussed next.

Parameter	Description
Structural Material	Specifies the material assigned to the concrete wall foundation. To change the material of the current foundation type, choose the Browse button displayed in the **Value** field of this parameter; the **Material Browser** dialog box will be displayed. In this dialog box, you can specify settings to change the appearance and physical properties of the material to be assigned.
Structural Usage	Specifies the type of wall usage for the foundation wall. For a bearing foundation wall, the value assigned to this parameter is **Bearing**.
Default End Extension Length	Specifies the distance of the wall foundation that will extend beyond the end of the wall.
Width	Specifies the width of the bearing wall foundation.
Foundation Thickness	Specifies the thickness of the bearing wall foundation.
Do Not Break At Inserts	Specifies whether the wall foundation will remain continuous beneath the opening of the structural wall when doors and windows are added. Select the check box displayed in the **Value** field of this parameter to enable the wall foundation to continue beneath the opening of the structural wall, refer to Figure 5-7.

In a structural project, you may need to add different types of bearing wall foundations based on your requirement. To add a different type of bearing wall foundation, first you need to create it. To create a new type, invoke the **Type Properties** dialog box from the **Properties** palette of the bearing foundation wall. In the **Type Properties** dialog box, choose the **Duplicate** button; the **Name** dialog box will be displayed. Replace the existing name in this dialog box with a suitable name for the new foundation type and then choose **OK**; the **Name** dialog box will close. In the **Type Properties** dialog box, you will notice that the name of the bearing foundation type in the **Type** drop-down list has been changed to the new name that you have entered in the **Name** dialog box. Next, change the desired type parameter from its corresponding **Value** fields and choose the **Apply** button; the modified parameters will be applied to the new type. To close the **Type Properties** dialog box, choose the **OK** button.

Note
*You can assign a new bearing foundation type to an existing bearing foundation. To do so, select the desired wall foundation from the structural model; the **Modify / Structural Foundations** contextual tab will be displayed. In the **Properties** palette, select the newly created type from the **Type Selector** drop-down list. On doing so, the selected wall foundation will inherit the properties of the newly created type and change according to the parameters assigned to the new property.*

After specifying the instance and type parameters, you can add the selected bearing foundation type to a structural wall. To do so, click on an existing structural wall in the model; the bearing foundation will be added to the entire length of the selected wall, refer to Figure 5-7. Note that you can also select multiple walls while adding wall foundations. To do so, choose the **Select Multiple** button from the **Multiple** panel of the **Modify | Place Wall Foundation** contextual tab and then make a window selection or press the CTRL key for selecting multiple structural walls to host wall foundations. You will notice that on choosing the **Select Multiple** button; the other two buttons in this panel, **Finish** and **Cancel**, will be activated. Choose the **Finish** button to finish the multiple selection process or choose the **Cancel** button to terminate the multiple selection process.

Discontinuous wall foundation

Continuous wall foundation beneath the opening

Figure 5-7 *Foundations with the **Do not Break At Inserts** parameter enabled and disabled*

Tip
*The added foundation will be visible only in the plan view that has view depth to display the bottom of the wall. To display the added foundation in any other plan view, make the plan view active and then choose the **Edit** button in the value field of the **View Range** parameter in the **Properties** palette. On doing so, the **View Range** dialog box will be displayed. In this dialog box, select the **Unlimited** option from the **Level** drop-down list in the **View Depth** area and then choose **OK** to close the dialog box. On doing so, you will notice that the added foundation is displayed along its host wall.*

Adding Retaining Wall Foundations

You can add the retaining footing foundation to a structural model in a similar way as you did in the Bearing footing foundation. To add a retaining wall foundation to a structural wall, invoke the **Wall** tool from the **Foundation** panel of the **Structure** tab and then select the retaining wall type from the **Type Selector** drop-down list in the **Properties** palette. After selecting the desired option from the drop-down list, you can add the foundation to an existing structural wall.

Isolated Footing Foundation

An isolated footing foundation is a concrete slab that is placed under a column subjected to the application of load. The isolated foundation is a part of the foundation family in Revit. Unlike the wall footing foundation, these foundations may not be hosted. Also, these foundation types can be inserted into a model independently. To add an isolated footing to the model, you need to invoke the **Isolated** tool from the **Foundations** panel of the **Structure** tab. On doing so, the **Modify | Place Isolated Foundation** contextual tab will be displayed. The options in this tab, as shown in Figure 5-8, can be used to specify the element properties (instance and type), alignment, locations, as well as to create in-place model of different geometries or load existing family for the isolated foundation to be placed. In the **Properties** palette, you can select an existing isolated footing type from the **Type Selector** drop-down list. By default, the **Footing-Rectangular 72" x 48" x 18"** option (in Imperial) or **M_Footing-Rectangular 1800 x 1200 x 450 mm** (in Metric) is selected in this drop-down list.

Figure 5-8 Various options displayed in the Modify / Place Isolated Foundation tab

You can also add other footing type to the **Type Selector** drop-down list. To do so, you need to load families from the existing foundation library. To load a family, choose the **Load Family** tool from the **Mode** panel of the **Modify | Place Isolated Foundation** contextual tab; the **Load Family** dialog box will be displayed. In this dialog box, browse to **English Imperial** or **English Metric** and then choose the **Structural Foundations** folder; the files of foundation families will be displayed, as shown in Figure 5-9.

Figure 5-9 Various families in the Load Family dialog box

You can select any of the families from this list. To add multiple families, select multiple families from the dialog box and then choose the **Open** button; the **Load Family** dialog box will close and the selected families will be loaded into the current drawing file. You can select the desired foundation family type from the **Type Selector** drop-down list.

After selecting the desired type from this list, you can modify the existing element properties (instance and type) using various options in the **Properties** palette, as shown in Figure 5-10.

Figure 5-10 *The **Properties** palette displaying the instance properties for the isolated footing*

In the **Properties** palette, the **Structural Material** parameter can be used to specify the constructional material associated with the isolated footing foundation to be added in the project. To specify a different constructional material, click on the value field corresponding to the **Structural Material** parameter and then choose the Browse button that will be displayed in it; the **Material Browser** dialog box will be displayed. You can use this dialog box to specify different materials for the graphic, render, and physical appearances of the foundation. After specifying the desired materials, choose the **OK** button to close the **Material Browser** dialog box.

In the **Properties** palette of the isolated footing foundation, the parameters listed under the **Structural** head are used to set the rebar cover distance of the footing foundation. The parameters listed under the **Structural** head of this palette are **Enable Analytical Model, Rebar Cover - Top Face, Rebar Cover - Bottom Face,** and **Rebar Cover - Other Faces**. These parameters can be modified by clicking on their respective value fields and selecting the desired options from the drop-down lists displayed. To change the analytical properties, select **New Analytical**

Isolated Foundation option from the drop-down list located on the left of the **Edit Type** button in the **Properties** palette. Various parameters related to analytical properties of foundation are displayed under **Identity Data**, **Analytical Model** and **Analytical Properties** heads. The **Analyze As** parameter can be used to specify whether the concerned isolated footing foundation should be analyzed as a Foundation or not. By default, the **Foundation** option is specified in the value field of this parameter. To change the value in the value field, click on it and then select the **Not for analysis** option from the drop-down list displayed.

Slab Foundation

Ribbon: Structure > Foundation > Slab drop-down > Structural Foundation: Slab

Slab foundations are used to transmit the load of the superstructure elements (wall, columns, and other structural elements) to the earth. Slab foundations can be constructed near the ground surface or at the bottom of the basements of a structure as in high-rise buildings. These foundations can be several meters thick with extensive reinforcement to ensure that the load is uniformly transferred to the earth strata.

To add a slab foundation to a structural model, choose the **Structural Foundation: Slab** tool from **Structure > Foundation > Slab** drop-down; the **Modify | Create Floor Boundary** contextual tab will be displayed. You can use this tab to invoke the sketching tools to draw the boundary of the foundation slab as well as edit the sketched boundary. You can also use the **Modify | Create Floor Boundary** contextual tab to modify the instance and type properties of the foundation slab to be created.

The **Draw** panel of the **Modify | Create Floor Boundary** contextual tab contains the tools that can be used to sketch the boundary and the slope arrows for the foundation slab. The slope arrows define the sloping direction of the foundation slab. Before you sketch the boundary line of the slab foundation, you need to specify the instance and type parameters required for it. Various options required for specifying the instance and type properties of the foundation slab are discussed next.

Defining Instance Properties

To specify the instance properties for the foundation slab, you can use various options in its **Properties** palette, as shown in Figure 5-11. The instance parameters in the **Properties** palette are categorized under seven heads: **Constraints**, **Structural**, **Dimensions**, **Identity Data**, **Phasing**, **Analytical Properties**, **Analytical Alignment** and **Analytical Model**, refer to Figure 5-11. The heads and the options in them are discussed next.

Figure 5-11 *The **Properties** palette displaying the instance properties for the slab foundation*

Constraints: The **Constraints** head contains three parameters: **Level, Height Offset From Level**, and **Related to Mass**. To specify a desired level to constrain the foundation slab, click on the value field corresponding to the **Level** parameter; a drop-down list will be displayed. Select the desired option from the drop-down list to constrain the foundation slab. After specifying the desired level for the foundation slab, you can specify the offset distance of the foundation slab from the constraint level. The offset distance will be measured from the top surface of the slab to the constraint level. To assign an offset distance to the foundation slab, click on the value field corresponding to the **Height Offset From Level** parameter and enter the desired distance value in this field. The **Related to Mass** parameter is a read-only parameter and shows whether or not a foundation slab has been created from a mass object.

Structural: In the **Properties** palette for a foundation slab instance, you can specify the structural parameters under the **Structural** head. This head contains five parameters: **Structural, Rebar Cover - Top Face, Rebar Cover - Bottom Face, Rebar Cover - Other Faces**, and **Enable Analytical Model**. The **Structural** parameter is used to specify whether or not the foundation slab will have an analytical model that can be exported to another analytical software for structural analysis. To specify the **Structural** parameter, you can use the check box displayed in the value field corresponding to it. By default, this check box is selected, which indicates that the foundation slab will have an analytical model and can be exported to an analytical software for analysis. You can clear this check box if you do not want it to be used for analysis.

The **Rebar Cover - Top Face** and **Rebar Cover - Bottom Face** parameters are used to specify the rebar cover distances from the top and bottom faces of the foundation slab, respectively. To specify appropriate values for these parameters, click on their respective value fields and select the desired option from the drop-down lists displayed. Apart from specifying the rebar cover distance from the top and bottom faces of the foundation slab, you can also specify the rebar cover distance in the foundation slab in reference to the face of the adjacent foundation slab. To do so, click on the value field corresponding to the **Rebar Cover - Other Faces** parameter and select the desired option from the drop-down list displayed.

Analytical Model: The **Analytical Model** head will be displayed in the **Properties** palette for the analytical model of the foundation slab. This head contains the **Analyze As** parameter. By default, the **Foundation** option is specified in this parameter. To modify the default value, click on the value field corresponding to this parameter; a drop-down list will be displayed. You can select the **Slab on Grade** option from this list. Note that if you specify the **Foundation** option for the **Analyze As** parameter, the foundation slab will bear the load of other elements connected to it. If you specify the **Slab On Grade** option, the foundation slab will only bear its own weight.

Analytical Alignment: This head will be displayed in the **Properties** palette for the analytical model of the foundation slab. This head contain two parameters: **Alignment Method** and the **z Projection**. In the value field of the **Alignment Method** parameter, the **Auto - Detect** option is selected by default. As a result, Revit will automatically detect the projection plane of the foundation slab. Also, in the **Properties** palette, you will notice that **z Projection** parameter is disabled. To enable the **z Projection** parameter, select the **Projection** option from the drop-down list corresponding to the **Alignment Method** parameter. To assign a value to the **z Projection** parameter, click on its value field, a drop-down list will be displayed. From the drop-down list, you can select any of the options to define the projection plane of the slab.

Analytical Properties: This head will be displayed in the **Properties** palette for the analytical model of the foundation slab. This head contains four parameters: **Family Type**, **Physical Properties Asset**, **Area**, and **Perimeter**. These parameters are read-only parameters. In the value field of the **Area** and **Perimeter** parameters, you can view the area and perimeter of the slab. The **Family Type** parameter in the **Properties** palette displays the family of slab.

Dimensions: The parameters under the **Dimensions** head display the values associated with the slope, perimeter, area, volume, width, length, elevation at bottom, and thickness of an existing selected slab. All parameters displayed under this head are read-only parameters.

Identity Data: The **Identity Data** head in the **Properties** palette contains three parameters: **Image**, **Comments**, and **Mark**. In the **Image** parameter, you can place the image by choosing the **Browse** button from the corresponding value field. You can use the other two parameters to write a general comment and to specify the mark for the foundation slab, respectively. Note that the value specified for the **Mark** parameter should be unique for each foundation slab element.

Phasing: The parameters under the **Phasing** head for the foundation slab are used to specify the creation and demolition phases of the foundation slab.

Defining Type Properties

After specifying the desired instance parameters of the foundation slab from the **Properties** palette, choose the **Edit Type** button to invoke the **Type Properties** dialog box, as shown in Figure 5-12. In addition, you can use the options in this dialog box to modify the type properties of the foundation slab to be created. You can use this dialog box to add a new family type of a foundation slab and change its parameters as per your requirement. To do so, choose the **Duplicate** button; the **Name** dialog box will be displayed. In this dialog box, enter a name of the new type in the **Name** edit box and then choose the **OK** button; the **Name** dialog box will be closed and new type will be added. You can now use the various options in the **Type Properties** dialog box to assign different properties to the new foundation slab type. Apart from the new family type that has been added, you can select any of the options from the **Type** drop-down list to specify the foundation type to be assigned to the foundation slab. The options that you can select from the drop-down list for Imperial unit system are **6" Foundation Slab, 8" Foundation Slab, 10" Foundation Slab**, and **12" Foundation Slab** and the options for the Metric unit system are **150mm Foundation Slab, 200mm Foundation Slab, 250mm Foundation Slab, and 300mm Foundation Slab**. After selecting the desired type, you can edit its type properties such as its thickness, structural details. Now, choose the **OK** button to return to the **Type Properties** dialog box. Notice that the option selected in the **Type** drop-down list in the **Type Properties** dialog box displays the new name that you have entered in the **Name** dialog box. Also, the type parameters are displayed with their values in a tabular format in the **Type Properties** dialog box. The type parameters are displayed under five heads: **Construction, Graphics, Material and Finishes, Identity Data**, and **Analytical Properties**. These heads are discussed next.

Note
The new family type created will be project specific.

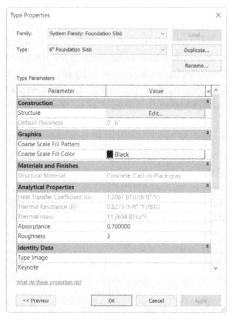

Figure 5-12 *The **Type Properties** dialog box of the foundation slab*

Construction: The **Construction** head contains two parameters: **Structure** and **Default Thickness**. The **Default Thickness** parameter remains inactive. This parameter displays the thickness of the foundation slab that can be defined in the **Edit Assembly** dialog box and is discussed next.

Note
*The value displayed for the **Default Thickness** parameter indicates the thickness of a foundation slab type which is determined by the cumulative thickness of its layers.*

To change the value of the **Structure** parameter, choose the **Edit** button displayed in the **Value** column corresponding to it; the **Edit Assembly** dialog box will be displayed, as shown in Figure 5-13.

*Figure 5-13   The **Edit Assembly** dialog box for the slab foundation*

In this dialog box, the **Layers** area displays the layers that constitute the structural detail of the foundation slab. The structural detail of the foundation slab is displayed in tabular format. The table contains five columns: **Function**, **Material**, **Thickness**, **Wraps**, and **Structural Material**. Each row of the table represents the layer in the cross-section of the foundation slab. Note that the top and bottom rows in the table denote the outermost layers between which the other layers are wrapped. Also, these layers are used as references while adding a new layer or deleting an existing layer. To add a layer to the existing cross-section of the foundation slab, choose the **Insert** button from the **Layers** area of the **Edit Assembly** dialog box; a new row denoting a new layer (**Structure [1]**, default name) will be added in the table.

The **Function** field is used to specify the exact function of a layer added. To specify the function of a layer, click on the **Function** field of the new layer; a drop-down list will be displayed. You can select an option from the drop-down list to specify the exact function of the layer added. For example, if you have added a layer in the foundation slab for a vapor retarder, you can select the **Thermal/Air Layer [3]** option from the drop-down list displayed. To assign a material to the layer, click on the **Material** field of the desired layer; a browse button will be displayed. Choose that browse button; the **Material Browser** dialog box and the **Material Editor** pane will be displayed. You can use this dialog box to specify the shading, rendering, identity, and physical parameters of the material to be assigned to the desired layer. For example, if you assign the vapor retarding function for a new layer, the material to be applied to the layer should correspond to it. To specify a material for the vapor retarder, select the **Vapor Retarder** material from the **Project Materials: All** area in the **Material Browser** dialog box and then choose the **OK** button; the selected material will be assigned to a new layer. Next, to specify the thickness for the layer added, click on the **Value** field corresponding to the added layer and enter a value in the **Thickness** column. For example, you can specify the value **1/8"** for Imperial or **3 mm** for Metric in the **Thickness** field to denote the thickness of the membrane of the vapor retarder. After specifying the desired parameters of the added layer you can re-order the location of the added layer in the cross-section of the foundation slab. To do so, choose the **Up** and **Down** buttons displayed in the **Layers** area of the **Edit Assembly** dialog box. To move a layer up in the order, select the row corresponding to it and choose the **Up** button; the selected layer will move one step up. To see the change in the cross-section due to re-ordering, choose the **Preview** button; the **Edit Assembly** dialog box will expand and the preview of the section will be displayed in a preview box on the left of the dialog box. You can choose the **Down** button to move a layer down. In the **Edit Assembly** dialog box, a layer can be deleted if it is not required for the cross-section detail. To do so, select the desired layer and choose the **Delete** button located in the **Layers** area; the selected layer will be deleted from the list in the table. After assigning all the parameters to the layers and reordering them as per the requirement, choose the **OK** button to return to the **Type Properties** dialog box.

Graphics: In the **Type Properties** dialog box, the **Graphics** head contains two parameters: **Coarse Scale Fill Pattern** and **Coarse Scale Fill Color**. These parameters are used to control the graphical display (color and pattern of the fill) of the slab foundation cross-section in a coarse-scale view. To specify a value for the **Coarse Scale Fill Pattern** parameter, click on the **Value** field corresponding to it; a button will be displayed in this field. Choose the button; the **Fill Patterns** dialog box will be displayed. In this dialog box, you can select different patterns for the slab foundation cross-section, create a new pattern, or edit an existing pattern. The list box in the left of this dialog box displays the list of available patterns that can be applied for the display of the foundation slab cross-section in a coarse-scale view.

To select a different pattern, click on any of the available patterns; the selected pattern will get highlighted. Alternatively, you can create a new pattern as per your requirement. To do so, choose the **New** button from the **Fill Patterns** dialog box; the **New Pattern** dialog box will be displayed. In this dialog box, you can define a simple pattern by using lines, or import a customized pattern file (*.pat* format) and apply it to the slab foundation cross-section. After specifying the options in the **New Pattern** dialog box, choose the **OK** button from it; a new pattern will be displayed with its name and preview in the list box.

You can also edit the patterns displayed in the list box of the **Fill Patterns** dialog box. To do so, select any of the patterns from the list box and choose the **Edit** button; the **Edit Pattern Properties - Drafting** dialog box will be displayed. You can modify the properties of the selected pattern using the options in this dialog box. After editing the selected pattern, choose the **OK** button to apply the modification and return to the **Fill Patterns** dialog box. In this dialog box, choose the **Delete** button to delete the unwanted fill patterns from the list. Next, in the **Fill Patterns** dialog box, you can either choose the **No Pattern** option, if the cross-section of the slab foundation does not need a fill pattern in its display, or choose the **OK** button to apply the selected pattern. When you choose either of the options, the **Fill Pattern** dialog box will close and you will return to the **Type Properties** dialog box.

After a filled pattern has been assigned to the cross-section of the foundation, you can assign a different color to it. By default, the pattern is displayed in black. To assign a different color to the fill pattern, choose the **Black** button displayed in the **Value** field corresponding to the **Coarse Scale Fill Color** parameter; the **Color** dialog box will be displayed. In this dialog box, you can select a color from the color swatch and then choose the **OK** button. On doing so, the **Color** dialog box will close and the selected color will be assigned to the **Coarse Scale Fill Color** parameter.

Identity Data: The **Identity Data** head of the **Type Properties** dialog box contains the following parameters: **Type Image, Keynote, Model, Manufacturer, Type Comments, URL, Description, Assembly Description, Assembly Code, Type Mark,** and **Cost.** The **Keynote** parameter indicates the keynote assigned to the slab foundation. To add or edit the value of this parameter, click on the **Value** field corresponding to this parameter; a browse button will be displayed. Choose the browse button; the **Keynotes** dialog box will be displayed. In this dialog box, select the desired keynote and then choose the **OK** button; the selected keynote will be assigned to the **Keynote** parameter.

The **Model** parameter is used to assign an internal code or number that the manufacturer of the foundation slab will use. The **Manufacturer** parameter is used to specify the name of the manufacturer of the foundation slab. The **Type Comments** parameter is used to specify a general comment about the type of the foundation slab. The value assigned to this parameter can be used in the schedule for the foundation slab.

The **URL** parameter can be used to specify a link to a web page that contains information about the foundation slab type. Using the **Type Properties** dialog box, you can specify the desired information regarding the foundation slab type. To do so, you can use the **Description** parameter. The **Assembly Code** parameter is used to specify a uniformat assembly code for the foundation slab. The value in this parameter can be used to mark or refer the foundation slab in the construction phase of the building structure associated with it. To specify a value for the **Assembly Code** parameter, click on the **Value** field corresponding to this parameter; a button will be displayed. Choose this button; the **Choose Assembly Code** dialog box will be displayed. In this dialog box, ensure that the **Structural Foundations** option is selected in the **Show classifications for** drop-down list. This dialog box displays two columns: **Uniformat Classification** and **Revit Category.** The **Uniformat Classification** column contains the list of classifications for the desired foundation type and the **Revit Category** column shows the category to which the classification belongs. Select the desired assembly code from the list and then choose the **OK** button; the **Choose Assembly Code** dialog box will close and the selected code will be assigned to the **Assembly Code** parameter in the **Type Properties** dialog box. The **Assembly Description** parameter in the **Type Properties** dialog box is a non-editable parameter, which takes value from the **Assembly Code** parameter assigned to the desired foundation type.

The **Type Mark** parameter is used to specify a unique value for a specific slab. The value used in this parameter is used to demarcate slab foundations. The **Cost** parameter is used to specify the cost of manufacturing the desired foundation slab. After assigning the type properties from the **Type Properties** dialog box, choose the **OK** button; the **Type Properties** dialog box will close and the **Properties** palette for the foundation slab instance will be displayed.

After specifying the instance and type properties for the foundation slab, you will use the tools in the **Draw** panel of the **Modify | Create Floor Boundary** contextual tab to sketch the boundary and define the slope arrow of the foundation slab. Various options and tools to draw the boundary line and to define the slope arrow for the foundation slab are discussed next.

Sketching the Boundary Line

To sketch the boundary line and the slope arrow for the foundation slab, you can use different tools from the **Draw** panel of the **Modify | Create Floor Boundary** contextual tab. In this tab, you can use the **Boundary Line** and **Slope Arrow** tools to draw the boundary line and the slope arrow for the foundation slab. It is recommended that you draw the boundary of the foundation slab before drawing the slope arrow for it.

To draw the boundary of the foundation slab, invoke the **Boundary Line** tool from the **Draw** panel; various tools to sketch the boundary line of the foundation slab will be displayed in a list box next to it, refer to Figure 5-14. In the list box, the **Pick Walls** tool is invoked, by default.

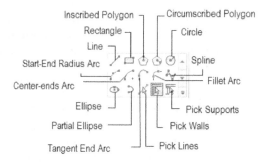

Figure 5-14 *Various sketching tools for sketching the boundary line of the foundation slab*

The **Pick Walls** tool is used to define the boundary of the foundation slab along the perimeter of the existing structural walls. On invoking this tool, the **Options Bar** will display the **Offset** edit box and the **Extend into wall (to core)** check box. In the **Offset** edit box, you can enter a value to offset the boundary line from a selected wall. The **Extend into wall (to core)** check box is selected by default. As a result, the offset distance entered in the **Offset** edit box will be measured from the core boundary of the wall. If you clear the check box, the offset distance will be measured from the outermost face of the wall. After specifying the options in the **Options Bar**, click on the wall in the drawing to make the reference for the boundary line. On clicking the wall, a pink line with flip arrow will be displayed along the perimeter of the wall, refer to Figure 5-15. You can click on the flip arrow to flip the boundary line to either side of the selected wall. You can select the other walls to finish the definition of the boundary of the foundation slab. Note that the boundary that you define should form a closed loop. After defining the boundary, choose the **Finish Edit Mode** button from the **Mode** panel of the **Modify | Create Floor Boundary** contextual tab; the **Revit** message box will be displayed. Choose the **Yes** button from this message box; the foundation slab will be created at the perimeter of the picked walls and the walls will be attached to the foundation slab. If you choose the **No** button from the **Revit** message box, the foundation slab will be created but it will not be attached to the walls that are picked to define its boundary.

Figure 5-15 *The boundary line displayed along the wall perimeter*

Similar to the **Pick Walls** tool, you can use the **Pick Supports** tool from the list box in the **Draw** panel to sketch the boundary of the foundation slab. The **Pick Supports** tool can be used when you require to create a foundation slab above an existing structural wall or beam. The structural wall or the beam will be the supporting element for the foundation slab. After invoking the **Pick Supports** tool from the list box in the **Draw** panel, pick the existing structural walls or beams from the drawing to define the boundary of the foundation slab. Note that the boundary that you define by picking the support should be a closed loop. On invoking the **Pick Supports** tool, various options related to the position of the boundary line will be displayed in **Options Bar**. The options in the **Options Bar** are the same as those discussed for the **Pick Walls** tool.

The **Pick Lines** tool is used to sketch the boundary of the foundation slab by picking the edges of beams or structural walls or model lines present in a structural model. On invoking this tool, the **Options Bar** will display various options to position the boundary lines. In the **Options Bar**, you can enter a suitable value in the **Offset** edit box to specify the offset distance of the boundary lines from the picked edges. The **Lock** check box is cleared by default. You can select this check box to lock the position of the boundary lines defined for the foundation slab. After selecting the desired options from **Options Bar**, click on the desired wall edges, beam edges, or lines to define the boundary of the foundation slab.

From the list box in the **Draw** panel of the **Modify | Create Floor Boundary** contextual tab, you can use other tools such as **Line**, **Rectangle**, **Circle**, and so on to sketch the boundary of the foundation.

Note
*The options in the **Options Bar** will differ depending on the sketching tool invoked.*

After sketching the boundary of the foundation slab, you can use the **Slope Arrow** and **Span Direction** tools to specify the slope of the foundation slab and the direction of the metal decks in the foundation slab, respectively. To finish the creation of the foundation slab, choose the **Finish Edit Mode** button from the **Mode** panel of the **Modify | Create Floor Boundary** contextual tab.

STRUCTURAL FLOORS

The structural floor in a structural model represents a floor deck or a floor slab. In Autodesk Revit, you can specify various structural parameters such as thickness, structural composition, rebar sizes, and more to the added structural floor. You can also add slope and create opening in the added structural floor. Figure 5-16 shows a structural floor in a model. In the next sections, you will learn how to add structural floors.

Structural Floor

Figure 5-16 Structural model displaying a structural floor deck

Adding Structural Floors

| **Ribbon:** | Structure > Floor drop-down > Floor: Structural |

To add a structural floor to a structural floor plan, choose the **Floor: Structural** tool from **Structure > Floor** drop-down; the **Modify | Create Floor Boundary** contextual tab will be displayed, as shown in Figure 5-17.

*Figure 5-17 Various options in the **Modify / Create Floor Boundary** contextual tab*

You can use the options in this tab to draw, modify, and assign various properties to the structural floor. In the **Draw** panel of this tab, there are three tools: **Boundary Line**, **Slope Arrow**, and **Span Direction**. The **Boundary Line** tool is chosen by default. You can use this tool to create the floor boundary or the periphery of the structural floor of your project. To draw the floor boundary, you can choose a sketching tool from the list box located next to the **Boundary Line** option. In the list box, the **Pick Walls** tool is chosen by default. As a result, you can pick structural walls from your structural model to define the floor boundary of the structural floor. You can use the other sketching tools such as **Pick Supports**, **Pick Lines**, **Rectangle**, **Circle**, and so on from the list box to create the floor boundary. While sketching the floor boundary, you can use various options displayed in the **Options Bar** to set the floor boundary based on the project requirement. The options in the **Options Bar** change according to the sketching tool selected from the list box next to the **Boundary Line** option. In the **Offset** edit box of the **Options Bar**, you can enter a value to specify the offset distance of the edges of the floor boundary from the sketched location. This option is useful for creating cantilever slabs. In the **Options Bar**, select the **Radius** check box; the edit box located on its right will become active. Enter a value in the edit box to specify the radius of the curved boundary that you will sketch using any of the curve sketching tools such as **Circle**, **Center-ends Arc**, and so on. Notice that when you use tools such as the **Line** tools and the arc tools, the **Chain** check box is selected in the **Options Bar**. As a result, you can create the floor boundary continuously.

After creating the floor boundary, you can choose the **Slope Arrow** tool in the **Draw** panel to assign slope to the structural floor in the project. On choosing the **Slope Arrow** tool, the list box on its right will display two sketching tools: **Line** and **Pick Lines**. You can use these tools to sketch the slope arrow and define its direction for the structural floor. In the list box, the **Line** tool is chosen by default. As a result, you can sketch the slope arrow as a line. To sketch the slope arrow, you need to specify the start point and the end point of the arrow, refer to Figure 5-18. To specify the start point of the slope arrow, move the cursor and place it inside the floor boundary by clicking at a point inside the floor boundary. On doing so, a blue dashed line with an arrow head will be displayed. Next, move the cursor toward the direction of the slope of the floor and then click at an appropriate location to define the endpoint of the slope arrow. As you click, the **Properties** palette will display various properties of the slope arrow. In the **Properties** palette, click on the value field corresponding to the **Specify** parameter to specify the method for defining the slope of the structural floor. On doing so, a drop-down list will be displayed with two options: **Height at Tail** and **Slope**. In this drop-down list, the **Height at Tail** option is selected by default. As a result, you can define the levels and the offset distances of the endpoints of the slope arrow. To specify the level of the start point of the slope arrow, click on the value field corresponding to the **Level at Tail** parameter in the **Properties** palette, and then select an option from the drop-down list displayed. To specify the offset distance of the start point from the specified level, click on the value field corresponding to the **Height Offset at Tail** parameter in the **Properties** palette and enter a value in the value field. Similarly, you can use the **Level at Head** and **Height Offset at Head** parameters to specify the desired values in their corresponding fields to assign a level and offset distance of the endpoint of the slope arrow.

Figure 5-18 Specifying the start and end points of slope arrow

Alternatively, if you select the **Slope** option from the **Specify** drop-down list in the **Properties** palette, you can define the slope of the slope arrow by using the **Level at Tail** and **Height Offset at Tail** parameters.

Note
In a structural floor, the start and end points of the slope arrow define the start and end, respectively, of a slope.

After specifying the slope arrow of the structural floor, you can specify the boundary line of the structural floor corresponding to which the metal decks in the floor structure will run parallel. In the structural floor boundary, you will notice two parallel lines at one of its edge. When you sketch the floor boundary, by default these lines are displayed on the first edge you sketch. These lines represent the direction of the run of metal decks in the structural floor. To change the direction of these parallel lines, you can choose the **Span Direction** tool from the **Draw** panel in the **Modify | Create Floor Boundary** contextual tab. When you choose the **Span Direction** tool, the list box next to it displays the **Line** and **Pick Lines** tools. You can use any of these tools to define the boundary line of the structural floor to which metal decks in the floor structure will run parallel.

After defining the boundary line, slope arrow, and span direction of the structural floor, you can specify its instance and type properties by using the options in the **Properties** palette. The instance and type properties for the structural floor are discussed in the following sections:

Specifying the Instance and Type Properties of a Structural Floor
You can change the instance and type properties of a structural floor while or after adding them to a structural model. To change the instance properties, use the various parameters displayed in the **Properties** palette, as shown in Figure 5-19. Some of the instance parameters in the **Properties** palette are discussed in the following table:

Parameter	Description
Level	Specifies a level to which a structural floor is constrained. Click in its value field to select an option from the drop-down list displayed.
Height Offset From Level	Specifies the distance of the top surface of the structural floor relative to the level selected from the **Level** parameter.
Structural	The check box in its value field is selected by default.

Figure 5-19 The *Properties* palette
displaying the instance properties of
a structural floor

In the **Properties** palette, choose the **Edit Type** button to invoke the **Type Properties** dialog box. In this dialog box, you can select an option in the **Type** drop-down list and change the type parameters of the concerned structural floor from the **Type Parameters** area. By default, the **3" LW Concrete on 2" Metal Deck** option in Imperial unit or **Floor: Generic 300mm** in Metric unit is selected in this list. In the **Type Properties** dialog box, you can choose the **Duplicate** button to create a new type by modifying various parameters. On choosing the **Duplicate** button, the **Name** dialog box will be displayed. In the **Name** edit box of this dialog box, enter a name for the new type of structural floor and then choose the **OK** button; the **Name** dialog box will be closed. Note that the **Type** drop-down list displays the name of the type created. In the **Type Parameters** area, you can change the type parameters displayed under various heads. Some of the type parameters in the **Type Properties** dialog box are described in the table given next.

Parameter	Description
Structure	Specifies the structural composition of the structural floor. Choose the **Edit** button in the **Value** field to display the **Edit Assembly** dialog box. You can use this dialog box to specify the composition of a compound floor.
Default Thickness	Is a read-only parameter. The **Value** field of the parameter displays the value of the thickness of a floor type, which is determined by adding the thickness of its layers.
Function	Specifies whether a floor is interior or exterior. Click in its **Value** field and select any of the two options: **Interior** and **Exterior**.
Coarse Scale Fill Pattern	Specifies the pattern assigned to the structural floor. To change pattern of the current floor type, choose the Browse button displayed in the value field of this parameter; the **Fill Patterns** dialog box will be displayed. In this dialog box, you can select different patterns for the floor cross-section.
Coarse Scale Fill Color	Specifies the color assigned to the structural floor. To change color of the current floor type, choose the button displayed in the value field of this parameter; the **Color** dialog box will be displayed. In this dialog box, you can select any color for the floor cross-section.
Structural Material	Specifies the material assigned to the structural floor. To change the material of the current floor type, choose the Browse button displayed in the value field of this parameter; the **Material Browser** dialog box will be displayed. In this dialog box, you can specify settings to change the appearance and physical properties of the material to be assigned.

After specifying various options in the **Type Properties** dialog box, choose the **OK** button to close this dialog box. Next, to exit the **Structural Floor** tool, choose the **Finish Edit Mode** button from the **Mode** panel of the **Modify | Create Floor Boundary** contextual tab; the **Modify | Floors** contextual tab will be displayed. You can use various options in this tab to change the shape properties and type of the created structural floor. Some of the options in this tab are discussed in the next section.

Modifying Structural Floors

To modify a structural floor in a structural model, select it; the **Modify | Floors** contextual tab will be displayed. You can use various options in this tab to edit the shape and boundary of a floor, edit the boundary of the floor, add reinforcement to the floor, and modify geometry.

To edit the shape of a floor, you can use the options displayed in the **Shape Editing** panel of the **Modify | Floors** contextual tab. The tools in this panel are: **Modify Sub Elements**, **Add Point**, **Add Split Line**, and **Pick Supports**. After changing the shape of the selected structural floor, choose the **Reset Shape** button to restore the changed shape of the floor to its original shape. You can edit the sketch of the floor boundary by choosing the **Edit Boundary** tool from the **Mode** panel of the **Modify| Floors** contextual tab. On choosing the **Edit Boundary** tool; the **Modify | Floors > Edit Boundary** contextual tab will be displayed and the selected structural floor will change to edit mode and its boundaries will be highlighted in pink. Now, you can use various editing tools from this tab to change the geometry of the floor boundary. Next, choose the **Finish Edit Mode** button from the **Mode** panel to exit the editing mode and return to the options displayed in the **Modify | Floors** contextual tab.

To modify the floor type and change the instance and type properties of the selected structural floor, use the **Type Selector** drop-down list and various options displayed in the **Properties** palette.

Adding Openings to a Structural Floor

You can create an opening in a structural floor to create stairs, ramps, and shafts for allowing access between levels. In Autodesk Revit , you can create openings in the structural floors by using the options displayed in the **Opening** panel of the **Structure** tab of the ribbon. In the **Opening** panel, you can use the **Shaft**, **By Face**, and **Vertical** tools to create the openings in the structural floors. In the next section, you will learn how to create openings by using the **By Face** tool.

Creating Openings Using the By Face Tool

To create an opening on a face of a structural floor, choose the **By Face** tool from the **Opening** panel of the **Structure** tab; the cursor will change to a cross mark and you will be prompted at the **Status Bar** to select a planar face of the floor surface. Move the cross mark toward the edge (any) of the floor surface and click when the floor surface corresponding to this edge gets highlighted. On clicking, the **Modify | Create Opening Boundary** contextual tab will be displayed. Use the sketching tools in the **Draw** panel of this tab and then choose the **Finish Edit Mod**e button from the **Mode** panel; the **Modify | Floor opening cut** contextual tab will be displayed. You can choose the **Edit Boundary** tool from the **Mode** panel of this tab to edit the boundary of the opening created. Figure 5-20 shows an opening created in a structural floor.

Figure 5-20 *Opening created in a structural floor*

ADDING A SLAB EDGE TO A STRUCTURAL FLOOR

You can also add a slab edge to your structural floor. To do so, choose the **Floor: Slab Edge** tool from the **Structure** panel of the **Structure** tab; the **Modify | Place Slab Edge** contextual tab will be displayed and you will be prompted at the **Status Bar** to click on the floor edge to add the slab edge. Move the cursor at the desired edge of the floor; the edge will get highlighted. Click at the highlighted edge; slab edge under the floor will be created. After clicking on the edge, two flip arrows will be displayed at the selected edge. You can flip the direction of the slab edge using these arrows. In the **Properties** palette you can modify the type and instance properties of the created slab. To modify the type properties, choose the **Edit Type** button from the **Properties** palette; the **Type Properties** dialog box will be displayed. In this dialog box, you can specify the desired values in the **Value** fields of the parameters either by entering a new value or by selecting an option from the drop-down list in the **Type Properties** dialog box. Similarly, you can modify the instance properties of a slab by entering a new value or by selecting an option from the drop-down list displayed in the value field of the corresponding parameter.

 Note
If you place a slab segment at the adjacent side of the existing slab edge, both the existing and the new segments will mitter and form a single continuous slab.

BEAMS

Beams are structural elements that can be used to resist load. Beams generally carry vertical forces. They can also carry horizontal forces as that of wind and earthquake. Figure 5-21 shows steel beams between vertical steel columns.

Figure 5-21 *Steel beams between vertical steel columns*

In Autodesk Revit , you can add different families of beams to your structural model. You can assign different properties to a beam by assigning various instance and type parameters to it. In the following sections, you will learn how to add and modify beams.

Adding Beams

Ribbon: Structure > Structure > Beam

In Autodesk Revit, you can add beams to a structural plan view. To add beams to a project, choose the **Beam** tool from the **Structure** panel of the **Structure** tab; the **Modify |Place Beam** contextual tab will be displayed. In this tab, you can choose the **Tag on Placement** tool in the **Tag** panel to make the beam tags visible while adding the beams to the project. In the **Multiple** panel of the **Modify |Place Beam** contextual tab, you can choose the **On Grids** tool to place the beam between the intersection points of grid lines in the project view.

Note
*The **Tag on Placement** tool will be displayed and activated when you are in 2D view.*

In the **Draw** panel of the **Modify | Place Beam** contextual tab, you can use various sketching tools available in the list box to sketch a beam in your project. By default, the **Line** tool is chosen in this panel. To add more beam family types to your project, choose the **Load Family** tool from the **Mode** panel of the **Modify |Place Beam** contextual tab; the **Load Family** dialog box will be displayed. In this dialog box, for Imperial system, browse to **US Imperial > Structural Framing** folder location and then choose any of the sub-folders such as **Concrete**, **Light Gauge Steel**, **Precast Concrete**, **Steel**, and **Wood** or browse to **US Metric > Structural Framing** folder location and then choose any of the sub-folders such as **Concrete**, **Light Gauge Steel**, **Precast Concrete**, **Steel**, and **Wood** for Metric system. Next, select the family files from the chosen folder to load the desired beam types to the project view. After selecting the desired families, choose the **Open** button to close the **Load Family** dialog box and load the selected families into your project.

Note
After placing beams, the Flip Structural Framing ends arrow will be displayed which allows you to flip the start and end points of the beam.

In the **Properties** palette of beam, you can select a beam type from the **Type Selector** drop-down list. By default, the **W Shape 12X26** option in Imperial unit system or **UB- Universal Beam 305x165x40UB** in Metric unit system is selected in this drop-down list. In the **Properties** palette, you can also specify various instance and type parameters for a beam. To specify type parameters for a beam, choose the **Edit Type** button from the **Properties** palette; the **Type Properties** dialog will be displayed. In this dialog box, you can modify various type parameters of the beam. Next, in the project view, specify the start point and endpoint of the beam to add it. In the following sections, various instance and type parameters of beams are discussed.

Instance Parameters of Beam

In the **Properties** palette of a beam, you can specify different instance parameters that may be different for different families. Some of the instance parameters are discussed in the table next.

Parameter	Description
Reference Level	Specifies the level that constrains the beam.
z Justification	Specifies the z justification (vertical) for the beam cross-section. You can select the **Center**, **Top**, **Bottom**, or **Origin** option from the drop-down list displayed in its value field.
Structural Usage	Specifies the structural usage of a beam. You can select the **Girder**, **Horizontal Bracing**, **Joist**, **Other**, or **Purlin** option from the drop-down list in the value field.
y Justification	Specifies the y justification for the beam cross-section. You can select the **Center**, **Left,** or **Right** option from the drop-down list displayed in its value field.
Start Extension	Specifies the extension of structural framing at the starting, you can enter a value in the field corresponding to **Start Extension**, as a result the structural framing will extend at the start but the analytical model of the beam will not extend.
End Extension	Specifies the extension of structural framing at the end, you can enter a value in the field corresponding to **End Extension**, as a result the structural framing will extend at the end but the analytical model of the beam will not extend.

Structural Material	Specifies the material assigned to the beam. To change the material of the current beam type, choose the Browse button displayed in the **Value** field of this parameter; the **Material Browser** dialog box will be displayed. In this dialog box, you can specify settings to change the appearance and physical properties of the material to be assigned.

Apart from the parameters discussed in the previous table, there are other parameters available in the **Properties** palette of the beam. These parameters may differ depending upon the beam family type selected from the **Type Selector** drop-down list.

Type Parameters of the Beam

To specify type parameters, you need to invoke the **Type Properties** dialog box. To do so, choose the **Edit Type** button from the **Properties** palette of the beam. Note that the type parameters are different for the steel and concrete members. These parameters are discussed next.

Parameter	Description
b	Specifies the width of a concrete member.
h	Specifies the depth of a concrete member.
Section Area	Specifies the section area of a steel member.
Nominal Weight	Specifies the nominal weight of a steel member.
Flange Thickness	Specifies the width of flange width.

You can specify more type parameters in the **Type Properties** dialog box by clicking in their corresponding Value fields.

Modifying Beams

After adding beams in a project, you can modify them. To do so, select the beam that you want to modify; the **Modify | Structural Framing** contextual tab will be displayed. In this tab, you can use various options to modify the beam. You can also use the grip editing tools to increase the length of the selected beam. You can change the instance and type properties of a selected beam by using the **Properties** palette and the **Type Properties** dialog box.

Adding a Structural Beam System

In a project, you may require to place similar parallel beams in a specified area of a structure. In such a situation, you can use quickly the **Beam System** tool. This tool allows you to create a single structural framing element containing a series of parallel placed beams. You can use this tool to create a structural beam system either by picking the structural supporting elements such as beams and structural walls, or by sketching a border.

To create a structural beam system by picking a structural support, sketch the supporting elements that you require for the beam system. Next, invoke the **Beam System** tool from the **Structure** panel of the **Structure** tab; the **Modify | Place Structural Beam System** contextual tab will be displayed, as shown in Figure 5-22.

*Figure 5-22 Various options in the **Modify / Place Structural Beam System** tab*

In the **Beam System** panel of this tab, choose the **Sketch Beam System** tool; the **Modify | Create Beam System Boundary** contextual tab will be displayed. In the **Draw** panel of this tab, ensure that the **Boundary Line** tool is chosen and then choose the **Pick Supports** tool displayed in the list box next to the **Boundary Line** tool. On doing so, you will be prompted in the **Status Bar** to pick structural walls or beams to create the boundary lines for the beam system. In the drawing area, click on a wall or a beam that you want to define as the starting edge of the beam system. Note that the starting edge of the beam system defines the alignment of the beams that will be placed. For example, on clicking a wall, a magenta line along with a symbol of parallelism will be displayed at the center of the wall cross-section, refer to Figure 5-23. Next, click on the other walls that you want to include as a support for the system. Note that the sketched boundary for the beam system should be a closed boundary. After selecting the walls as supports for the beam system, you can specify various instance parameters for the beam system such as **Layout Rule**, **Fixed Spacing**, **Beam Type**, **Justification**, and more in the **Properties** palette.

Figure 5-23 Beams placed inside the boundary of a beam system

After specifying the various instance parameters, choose the **Finish Edit Mode** button from the **Mode** panel of the **Modify | Create Beam System Boundary** contextual tab; the **Modify | Structural Beam Systems** contextual tab will be displayed. Also, beams will be placed inside the defined boundary, refer to Figure 5-24. You can use various tools in the **Modify | Create Beam System Boundary** contextual tab to modify the created beam system, if required. You can also use the options in the **Options Bar**, displayed below the tab to change the size of the beams and edit the layout rules. Next, press ESC to exit the **Beam System** tool.

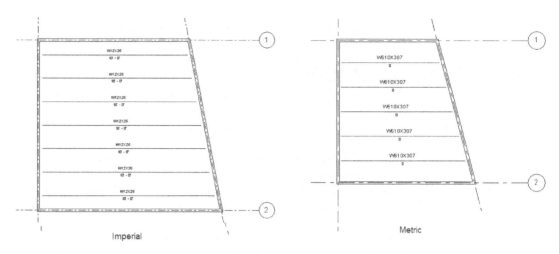

Imperial

Metric

Figure 5-24 Beams placed inside the boundary of a beam system

Alternatively, you can sketch the boundary of the beam system by choosing any of the sketching tools from the **Draw** panel of the **Modify | Create Beam System Boundary** contextual tab. In the next section, you will learn to add a beam system automatically in a closed loop of supporting elements.

Adding a Structural Beam System Automatically

You can add a beam system automatically inside a boundary enclosed by structural walls or beams. To do so, choose the **Beam System** tool from the **Structure** panel of the **Structure** tab; the **Modify | Place Structural Beam System** contextual tab will be displayed. In the **Beam System** panel of this tab, choose the **Automatic Beam System** tool, if not chosen by default, and then move the cursor to the structural members to which you want to add the beam system; the beam system will be highlighted in blue, as shown in Figure 5-25. Now click on the desired member; the beam system will be added inside the closed loop of supporting elements (walls or beams) already drawn.

Figure 5-25 The highlighted beam system

Note
The beam system will be aligned parallel to the structural member selected by you.

OPEN WEB STEEL JOISTS

In a structural project, the Open web steel joists or bar joists are very efficient structural members. The main purpose of placing the Open web steel joists is to provide support to roof and floor deck and transfer the imposed load to the beams and columns associated with it.

In a project, the Open web steel joists are not considered as structural steel as they are manufactured as proprietary structural steel members by various manufacturers that are recognized by Steel Joist Institute (SJI). The Steel Joist Institute specifies the standards for manufacturing of joists as well as designing and construction of joists.

The Open Web Steel Joist (OWSJ) is a lightweight steel truss that consist of parallel chords and a triangulated web system. The truss is designed to span between the bearings points. The Open Web Steel Joists system have various types: K Series Joists, LH and BLH Series Joists, and Joist Girders. In Autodesk Revit, you can add these joists by using the **Load Family** dialog box and then using the **Beam** tool from the **Structure** tab. The families that you can use for adding an Open web joist in Imperial system and Metric system are: **LH-Series Bar Joist**, **SLH-Series Bar Joist**, **G Joist Girder**, and **K- Series Bar Joist**, **M_ G Joist Girder**, **M_K- Series Bar Joist**, and **M_SLH-Series Bar Joist**.

Adding K Series Joist System

In a structural project, the K Series joist system is most commonly used to support roofs and floor decks. In this system, the depth can range from 8" to 30" (2'6") for Imperial system or for Metric system depth range from 200 to 700 mm. This system can be used economically to span up to 60'-0"(or 18288 mm). To add a K Series joist system, choose the **Load Family** tool from the **Load from Library** panel of the **Insert** tab; the **Load Family** dialog box will be displayed. In this dialog box, for Imperial system, browse to **US Imperial > Structural Framing > Steel** then select the **K-Series Bar Joist-Angle Web** file or for Metric system browse to **US Metric > Structural Framing > Steel** and then select the **M_K-Series Bar Joist-Angle Web** file from the list box. Next, choose the **Open** button; the **Specify Types** dialog box will be displayed. In this dialog box, select the desired family type from the **Family** area. In the **Types** area, select the type of sizes that are required and then choose the **OK** button; the selected file will be loaded in the current project. Next, select the structural plan view from the **Project Browser** and then choose the **Beam** tool from the **Structure** panel of the **Structure** tab; the **Modify | Place Beam** contextual tab will be displayed. In the **Properties** palette, you can select the **K-Series Bar Joist-Angle Web** type for Imperial or **M_K-Series Bar Joist-Angle Web** type for Metric from the **Type Selector** drop-down list. In the **Properties** palette, you can modify various instance properties of the Joist system. The instance properties of the joist system are same as that of beams. The instance properties of the beams has already been discussed in the previous sections of this chapter. To modify the type properties of the K-Series joist system, choose the **Edit Type** button from the **Properties** palette; the **Type Properties** dialog box will be displayed. In this dialog box, you can edit various type parameters such as **Web Thickness**, **Seat Length**, **Seat Depth**, **Chord Leg**, **Chord Thickness**, and **Depth**. The detailed representation of the parameters for the **K-Series Bar Joist -Angle Web 8K1** type is shown in Figure 5-26.

Figure 5-26 *The graphical representation of a K type joist system*

After editing the type properties in the **Type Properties** dialog box, choose the **OK** button to close it. Now, in the **Options Bar**, select an option from the **Placement Plane** drop-down list to specify a level in which the joist system will be placed. In the **Options Bar**, you can select an option from the **Structural Usage** drop-down list to specify the structural usage of the joist system. Also, you can select the **3D Snapping** and **Chain** check boxes in the **Options Bar** to activate snapping in 3D environment and the chain method, respectively. After specifying various options in the **Options Bar**, click at the desired point in the drawing area to specify the first bearing point to start creating the joist system; the joist system will be created at the specified point. Next, click on the other point to specify the other bearing of the joist system. On doing so, the joist system will be created between the two bearing points. Choose the **Modify** button from the **Modify | Structural Framing** contextual tab to exit the joist creation tool. To view the joist system in 3D view, choose the **Default 3D View** tool from the **View > Create > 3D View** drop-down. Figure 5-27 displays the 3D view of a joist system.

Note

The Steel joists are usually fastened to their supporting members by field welding.

Figure 5-27 *The 3-D view of a K-joist system supported between the walls*

TUTORIALS
Tutorial 1   Commercial Complex

In this tutorial, you will add foundations, foundation slab, and structural framing members to the *Commercial Complex* project created in Tutorial 1 of Chapter 4.

(Expected time: 1 hr 45 min)

Use the following project parameters and specifications:

1. Foundations:
    For Imperial   Types: **Pile Cap-2 : Pile 31"x 61"x 35"**
                          Pile Cap-4 : Pile 72"x 72"x 35"
                          Wall Foundation : Bearing Footing -36"x12"
    For Metric   Types: **M_Pile Cap-2 : Pile 800 x 1500 x 900mm**
                          M_Pile Cap-4 : Pile 1800 x 1800 x 900mm
                          Wall Foundation : Bearing Footing - 900 x 300mm

2. Foundation Slab:
    For Imperial   Type: **Foundation Slab : 12" Foundation Slab**
    For Metric   Type: **Foundation Slab : 300mm Foundation Slab**

3. Beams:
    For Imperial   Type: **Concrete-Rectangular Beam : 12 x 24**
    For Metric   Type: **M_Concrete-Rectangular Beam: 300 x 600mm**

4. Structural Floor:
    For Imperial   Type: **Generic 12"**
    For Metric   Type: **Generic 300mm**

5. File name to be assigned:
    For Imperial   *c05_Commercial-Complex_tut1.rvt.*
    For Metric   *M_c05_Commercial-Complex_tut1.rvt.*

    The following steps are required to complete this tutorial:

a. Open the *c04_Commercial-Complex_tut1.rvt* project file.
b. Load the isolated foundation families.
c. Create new types for isolated foundations.
d. Add isolated foundation.
e. Add foundation wall.
f. Add foundation slab.
g. Add beams.
h. Modify beams.
i. Add structural floor.
j. Save the project using the **Save As** tool.
k. Close the project using the **Close** tool.

Opening the Existing Project
In this section, you will open the project file created in Tutorial 1 of Chapter 4.

1. Choose **Open > Project** from the **File** menu; the **Open** dialog box is displayed.

2. In this dialog box, browse to the *C:\rst_2021\c04_rst_2021_tut* location and choose the project file *c04_Commercial-Complex_tut1.rvt* for Imperial unit system and *M_c04_Commercial-Complex_tut1.rvt* for Metric unit system. You can also download this file from *https://www.cadcim.com*. The path of the file is as follows: *Textbooks > Civil/GIS > Revit Structure > Exploring Autodesk Revit 2021 for Structure*.

3. Choose the **Open** button from the **Open** dialog box; the selected project file opens in the drawing window in the **Entry** structural plan view.

Loading Isolated Foundation Families
In this section, you will load the isolated foundation families to the current project.

1. Ensure that the **Entry** structural plan view is the current view in the drawing area. Choose the **Isolated** tool from the **Foundation** panel of the **Structure** tab; the **Modify | Place Isolated Foundation** contextual tab is displayed.

2. In this tab, choose the **Load Family** tool from the **Mode** panel; the **Load Family** dialog box is displayed.

3. In the **Load Family** dialog box, browse to folder location.
   For Imperial   **English Imperial > Structural Foundations**
   For Metric   **English Metric > Structural Foundations**

4. Press and hold the CTRL key and then click on the *Pile Cap-2 Pile.rfa* and *Pile Cap-4 Pile.rfa* files displayed in the **Structural Foundations** folder for Imperial or select *M_Pile Cap-2 Pile.rfa* and *M_Pile Cap-4 Pile* for Metric system; the files are highlighted indicating they have been selected.

5. Choose the **Open** button in the **Load Family** dialog box; the window closes and the highlighted family files are loaded in the project.

Creating New Types for the Isolated Foundation
In this section, you will create two new types of the isolated foundation.

1. In the **Properties** palette, ensure that the **Pile Cap-2 : Pile 31"x 71"x 35"** option for Imperial unit system or **M_Pile Cap-2 : Pile 800 x 1800 x 900mm** option for Metric unit system is selected from the **Type Selector** drop-down list.

2. Choose the **Edit Type** button from the **Properties** palette; the **Type Properties** dialog box is displayed.

3. Choose the **Duplicate** button in the **Type Properties** dialog box; the **Name** dialog box is displayed.

4. In the **Name** dialog box, enter the specified name in the **Name** edit box-
   For Imperial   **31" x 61" x 35"**
   For Metric   **800 x 1500 x 900**
   Next, choose the **OK** button; the **Name** dialog box is closed and the **Type Properties** dialog box is displayed.

5. In the **Type Properties** dialog box, select the desired option, if not selected by default, from the drop-down list in the **Value** field of the **Pile Type<Structural Foundations>** parameter.
   For Imperial   **Pile-Steel Pipe : 16" Diameter**
   For Metric   **M_Pile-Steel Pipe : 400mm Diameter**

6. Click in the **Value** field of the **Width** parameter and replace the existing value with **5' 1"** for Imperial unit system or **1500mm** for Metric unit system and press ENTER.

7. Click in the **Value** field of the **Clearance** parameter and replace the existing value with **1'** for Imperial or **300mm** for Metric and then press ENTER. Next, choose the **OK** button; the family is created.

8. Choose the **Edit Type** button from the **Properties** palette; the **Type Properties** dialog box is displayed. Select the **Pile Cap-4 Pile** option from the **Family** drop-down list and then select the desired option from the **Type** drop-down list, if not selected by default.
   For Imperial   **79" x 79" x 35"**
   For Metric   **2000 x 2000 x 900mm**

9. Choose the **Duplicate** button; the **Name** dialog box is displayed.

10. In the **Name** edit box of the **Name** dialog box, enter the specified value-
    For Imperial   **72" x 72" x 35"**
    For Metric   **1800 x 1800 x 900mm**
    Next, choose the **OK** button, the **Name** dialog box is closed and the **Type Properties** dialog box is displayed.

11. In the **Type Properties** dialog box, select the desired option, if not selected by default, from the drop-down list in the **Value** field of the **Pile Type<Structural Foundations>** parameter.
    For Imperial   **Pile-Steel Pipe : 16" Diameter**
    For Metric   **M_Pile-Steel Pipe : 400mm Diameter**

12. Click in the **Value** field corresponding to the **Width** and **Length** parameters and enter **6'** in Imperial or **1800mm** in Metric unit systems in each of them.

13. Click in the **Value** field corresponding to the **Clearance** parameter and enter **1' 3"** for Imperial or enter **380mm** for Metric to replace the existing value.

14. Choose the **OK** button; the **Type Properties** dialog box is closed.

Adding Isolated Foundations

In this section, you will add the isolated foundation types that you have created in the project.

1. In the **Properties** palette, select the option from the **Type Selector** drop-down list.
   For Imperial   **Pile Cap-4 Pile: 72"x 72"x 35"**
   For Metric   **M_Pile Cap-4 Pile: 1800 x1800 x900mm**

2. Choose the **At Columns** tool from the **Multiple** panel of the **Modify | Place Isolated Foundation** contextual tab.

3. Move the cursor and place it over the column located at the intersection of grid C and grid 2.

4. Click when the column is highlighted; a foundation with four piles and a pile cap is added at the center of the highlighted column.

5. Press and hold the CTRL key and repeat steps 3 and 4 to add foundation to all the internal columns. Refer to Figure 5-28 for the location of foundations.

Figure 5-28 *The 4-pile foundations added to all internal columns*

6. Release the CTRL key and choose the **Finish** button from the **Multiple** panel of the **Modify |Place Isolated Foundations > At Structural Column** contextual tab; the 4 pile foundation is added to the selected columns. Ignore if any warning message is displayed. Next, press ESC.

7. Choose the **Isolated** tool from the **Foundation** panel of the **Structure** tab to add the foundations to the remaining columns.

8. In the **Properties** palette, select the option from the **Type Selector** drop-down list.
    For Imperial   **Pile Cap -2 Pile : 31"x61"x35"**
    For Metric   **M_Pile Cap -2 Pile : 800 x1500 x900mm**

9. Choose the **At Columns** tool from the **Multiple** panel of the **Modify | Place Isolated Foundation** contextual tab.

10. Next, move the cursor and place it over the column located at the intersection of grid 1 and grid A; the column at the intersection of the grids is highlighted.

11. Click on the highlighted column; the foundation is added to the highlighted column.

12. Next press and hold the CTRL key and repeat steps 10 and 11 to add the foundation type to all the columns that do not have a foundation attached to them (except the columns at the intersection of grid C.1 and grid 3.1 and at the intersection of grid G.2 and grid 3.1), refer to Figure 5-29.

Figure 5-29 *The 2-pile foundations added to the columns*

13. Release the CTRL key, and choose the **Finish** button from the **Multiple** panel of the **Modify | Place Isolated Foundations > At Structural Column** contextual tab. Ignore, if any warning message is displayed. Next, press ESC.

14. Next, choose the **Isolated** tool from the **Foundation** panel of the **Structure** tab; the **Modify | Place Isolated Foundation** contextual tab is displayed.

15. In the **Properties** palette, ensure that the option is selected in the **Type Selector** drop-down list.

        For Imperial   **Pile Cap -2 Pile : 31"x61"x35"**
        For Metric   **M_Pile Cap -2 Pile : 800 x1500 x900mm**

16. Now place the cursor over the column at the intersection of grid C.1 and grid 3.1; both the grids at the intersection get highlighted.

17. Next, click on the highlighted grids; the selected foundation type is added to the column placed at the intersection of grid C.1 and grid 3.1. Ignore if any warning message is displayed.

18. Repeat steps 16 and 17 to add the foundation type to the column at the intersection of grid G.2 and grid 3.1. Ignore, if any warning message is displayed.

19. After adding the foundations, choose the **Modify** button from the **Select** panel of the **Modify|Place Isolated Foundation** contextual tab to exit the **Isolated** tool.

Adding the Foundation Wall
In this section, you will add the foundation wall to the structural walls in the project.

1.   Choose the **Wall** tool from the **Foundation** panel of the **Structure** tab; the **Modify | Place Wall Foundation** contextual tab is displayed.

2.   In the **Properties** palette, ensure that the **Wall Foundation : Bearing Footing - 36" x 12"** option in Imperial unit system or **Wall Foundation : Bearing Footing -900 x300mm** in Metric unit system is selected from the **Type Selector** drop-down list.

3.   Click on the structural wall located at grid B; the foundation wall of the selected type is added throughout the length of the wall, as shown in Figure 5-30.

Figure 5-30 *The foundation wall added to the structural wall located at grid B*

4.   Now, click on the remaining structural walls in the model; the foundation walls are added to all the structural walls in the project, as shown in Figure 5-31.

Figure 5-31   *The foundation walls added to all the structural walls in the project*

5.   Choose the **Modify** button from the **Select** panel to exit the **Wall** tool in the **Foundation** panel.

Adding the Foundation Slab

In this section, you will add foundation slab to the project.

1.   Invoke the **Structural Foundation: Slab** tool from **Structure > Foundation > Slab** drop-down; the **Modify | Create Floor Boundary** contextual tab is displayed.

2.   In the **Draw** panel of the **Modify | Create Floor Boundary** contextual tab, ensure that the **Boundary Line** tool is chosen, and then choose the **Rectangle** tool from the list box displayed next to it.

3.   In the **Options Bar**, click in the **Offset** edit box and replace the existing value with **6'** (for Imperial) or **1800mm** (for Metric). Next, press ENTER.

4.   Move the cursor and place it at the intersection of grid 1 and grid A and click when the **Midpoint** snap is displayed.

5.   Move the cursor down toward the right and place it at the intersection of grid I and grid 3.1, and click when the **Intersection** snap is displayed.

6.   Invoke the **Line** tool from the list box in the **Draw** panel of the **Modify | Create Floor Boundary** contextual tab.

7.   In the **Options Bar**, enter **3'** in Imperial unit or **900 mm** in Metric unit in the **Offset** edit box to replace the existing value.

8. Move the cursor and place it at the intersection of grid B and the right edge of the rectangle created previously, refer to Figure 5-32.

Figure 5-32 Intersection of grid B and the right edge of the rectangle created previously

9. Click when grid B and the right edge of the rectangle are highlighted and the **Intersection** snap is displayed.

10. Move the cursor toward the right and place it at the intersection of grid B and grid 5. Click when the **Midpoint and Horizontal** snap is displayed.

11. Move the cursor vertically down and place it at the intersection of grid G.1 and grid 5. Click when the **Midpoint and Vertical** snap is displayed.

12. Move the cursor horizontally left and place it at the intersection of grid G.1 and the right edge of the rectangle created.

13. Click when the **Intersection and Horizontal** snap is displayed. Next, press ESC.

14. In the **Modify** panel of the **Modify | Create Floor Boundary** contextual tab, choose the **Split Element** tool; the cursor changes into a pen symbol.

15. Place the cursor on the point marked **A**, refer to Figure 5-33, and click when the split symbol appears. On doing so, a blue dot is displayed at the point you clicked. Similarly, click at the point marked **B**, refer to Figure 5-33.

Line segment to be deleted

Figure 5-33 *Reference points for splitting the slab boundary and the line segment to be deleted*

16. Press ESC twice and select the split line between the points marked **A** and **B**, refer to Figure 5-33.

17. Press DELETE to remove the split line from the slab boundary.

18. Next, choose the **Finish Edit Mode** button from the **Mode** panel of the **Modify | Create Floor Boundary** contextual tab to finish the creation of the boundary of the foundation slab. Note that a warning message may be displayed at the bottom of the screen. Choose **OK** in the warning message box to ignore it.

19. In the **Properties** palette, select the **Foundation Slab : 12" Foundation Slab** option in Imperial unit system or **Foundation Slab : 150 mm Foundation Slab** option for Metric unit system from the **Type Selector** drop-down list. Ignore any warning message, if displayed.

20. Choose the **Modify** button from the **Select** panel of the **Modify | Structural Foundations** contextual tab to create the foundation slab.

Adding Beams

In this section, you will add beams to the **Second Floor** structural plan view of the project.

1. Double-click on the **Second Floor** sub-node under the **Structural Plans** head in the **Project Browser**; the **Second Floor** structural plan view becomes the current view.

2. Now, choose the **Beam** tool from the **Structure** panel of the **Structure** tab.

3. In the **Properties** palette, select the **Concrete-Rectangular Beam : 12x24** option for Imperial or **M_Concrete-Rectangular Beam: 300 x 600mm** option for metric from the **Type Selector** drop-down list.

4. In the **Options Bar,** ensure that the **Chain** check box is cleared. Now, move the cursor and place it at the intersection of grid 1 and grid A. Click at the intersection when the **Midpoint** snap is displayed.

5. Move the cursor to the right and place at the center of column. Click at the intersection when the **Midpoint and Horizontal** snap is displayed for the column placed at the intersection of grid A and grid 2. Notice that a beam is added between the intersections of grids.

6. Next, click when the **Midpoint** snap is displayed for the column placed at the intersection of grid 2 and grid A.

7. Move the cursor horizontally right and place it at the center point of the column placed at intersection point of grid A and grid 3. Click at the intersection when the **Midpoint and Horizontal** snap is displayed.

8. Repeat the procedure followed in steps 6 and 7 to add the remaining beams to the structural plan view. Refer to Figure 5-34 for the placement of beams. Note that while adding beams, a warning message may be displayed at the bottom of the screen. Choose the **OK** button to ignore the warning message box and close it.

Figure 5-34 The beams and other structural elements in the Second Floor structural plan view

Note
While referring to Figure 5-34 for the placement of beams, notice the tags on the beams to distinguish between beams and structural walls.

Tip
*In case, you want to show the tags of the beams then choose the **Tag on Placement** button from the **Tag** panel of the **Modify | Place Beam** contextual tab.*

9. Choose the **Modify** button from the **Select** panel of the **Modify |Place Beam** contextual tab to exit the **Beam** tool.

Modifying Beams

In this section, you will select all the instances of the beams in the project view and modify their instance properties.

1. Click on the beam placed at grid A between grid 1 and grid 2, and then right-click; a shortcut menu is displayed.

2. Choose **Select All Instances > Visible in View** from the shortcut menu, as shown in Figure 5-35; all beams in the project view area are selected.

Figure 5-35 *Choosing **Select All Instances > Visible in View** from the shortcut menu*

3. Now, press SHIFT key and then select the beams created on grids 4,5, B and G.1; these beams are removed from the selection.

4. In the **Properties** palette, specify the instance parameters as:
   For Imperial   Start Level Offset = **-1'**   End Level Offset = **-1'**
   For Metric   Start Level Offset = **-300mm**   End Level Offset = **-300mm**

5. Next, choose **Apply** in the **Properties** palette and then press ESC.

Adding a Structural Floor

In this section, you will add a structural floor to the project in the **Second Floor** structural plan view.

1. Ensure that the **Second Floor** sub-node under the **Structural Plans** node is highlighted in the **Project Browser**.

2. Invoke the **Floor: Structural** tool from the **Structure > Structure > Floor** drop-down.

3. In the **Properties** palette, select the **Generic 12"** option from the **Type Selector** drop-down list or **Generic 300mm** option in Metric unit system.

4. In the **Modify | Create Floor Boundary** contextual tab, ensure that the **Boundary Line** option is chosen in the **Draw** panel.

5. Choose the **Line** tool from the list box displayed right next to the **Boundary Line** tool.

6. In the **Options Bar**, ensure that the **Chain** check box is selected and then in the **Offset** edit box, replace the default value.

    For Imperial   **1'**
    For Metric   **300 mm**

7. Move the cursor and place it at the intersection of grid A and grid 1 and click when the **Endpoint** snap is displayed.

8. Move the cursor toward the right and place it at the intersection of grid A and grid 3. Click when the **Endpoint and Horizontal** snap is displayed.

9. Click on the other grid intersections in the following order:
    (C.1, 3); (C.1, 3.1); (D, 3.1); (D, 4); (C.1, 4); (C.1, 5); (F, 5); (F, 4); (E, 4); (E, 3.1); (G.2, 3.1); (G.2, 3); (I, 3); (I, 1); (G,1); (G, 2); (D, 2); (D, 1); and (A, 1)

Note
The grid intersection points are denoted by their intersecting grid lines. For example, (C.1, 3.1) represents the intersection point of grid C.1 and grid 3.1

After you click on the last grid intersection, the floor boundary is created, as shown in Figure 5-36.

Figure 5-36 Structural plan displaying the floor boundary

10. Choose the **Modify** tool from the **Select** panel to exit the current tool.

11. Choose the **Trim/Extend to Corner** tool from the **Modify** panel and then select the recently created line and the horizontal line starting from grid 1; the two lines get joined.

12. Next, choose the **Finish Edit Mode** button from the **Mode** panel of the **Modify | Create Floor Boundary** tab; the **Revit** message box is displayed.

13. Choose the **Modify** button from the **Select** panel of the **Modify | Floors** contextual tab to complete the floor creation.

Saving the Project

In this section, you will save the project file using the **Save As** tool.

1. Choose the **Save As > Project** option from the **File** menu; the **Save As** dialog box is displayed.

2. In this dialog box, browse to the *C:\rst_2021* location and create a folder with name *c05_ rst_2021_tut*. Open the *c05_rst_2021 _tut* folder and enter **c05_Commercial-Complex_tut1** for Imperial and **M_c05_Commercial-Complex_tut1** for Metric in the **File name** edit box.

3. Choose the **Save** button; the **Save As** dialog box closes and the project file is saved.

Closing the Project

1. Choose the **Close** option from the **File** menu.

The file is closed and this completes Tutorial 1 of Chapter 5.

Tutorial 2   Industrial Complex

In this tutorial, you will add foundation, foundation slab, and structural framing members to the Industrial Complex project created in Tutorial 2 of Chapter 4. Use the following project parameters and specifications: **(Expected time: 1 hr 45 min)**

1. Foundation:

For Imperial	Type:	**Footing - Rectangular : 72" x 48" x 18"**
For Metric	Type:	**M_Footing - Rectangular : 1800 x 1200 x 450mm**

2. Foundation Slab:

For Imperial	Type:	**Foundation Slab : 6" Foundation Slab**
For Metric	Type:	**Foundation Slab : 150mm Foundation Slab**

3. Beams:

For Imperial	Type:	**Concrete-Rectangular Beam : 12 x 24**
		W-Wide Flange : W14 X 30
For Metric	Type:	**M_Concrete-Rectangular Beam : 300 x 600mm**
		M_W-Wide Flange : W760 X 350

4. Structural Floor:

For Imperial	Type:	**LW Concrete on Metal Deck**
		1 1/2" Metal Roof Deck
For Metric	Type:	**160mm Concrete with 50mm Metal Deck**
		75mm Metal Roof Deck

5. File name to be assigned:

For Imperial	*c05_ Industrial-Complex_tut2.rvt.*
For Metric	*M_c05_ Industrial-Complex_tut2.rvt.*

The following steps are required to complete this tutorial:

a. Open the project file.

For Imperial	*c04_Industrial-Complex_tut2.rvt*
For Metric	*M_c04_Industrial-Complex_tut2.rvt*

b. Add foundations.
c. Add foundation slab.
d. Add beams.
e. Add structural floor.
f. Save the project using the **Save As** tool.
g. Close the project using the **Close** tool.

Opening the Existing Project

In this section, you will open the project file created in Tutorial 2 of Chapter 4.

1. Choose **Open > Project** from the **File** menu; the **Open** dialog box is displayed.

2. In this dialog box, browse to the *C:\rst_2021\c04_rst_2021_tut* location and then choose the *c04_Industrial-Complex_tut2.rvt* for Imperial or *M_c04_Industrial-Complex_tut2.rvt* for Metric project file. You can also download this file from *https://www.cadcim.com*. The path of the file is as follows: *Textbooks > Civil/GIS > Revit Structure > Exploring Autodesk Revit 2021 for Structure*.

3. Choose the **Open** button from the **Open** dialog box; the selected project file opens in the drawing window in the **Entry** structural plan view.

Adding Isolated Footing Foundations

In this section, you will add the isolated footing foundations to columns.

1. In the **Entry** structural plan view, choose the **Isolated** tool from the **Foundation** panel of the **Structure** tab; the **Modify | Place Isolated Foundation** contextual tab is displayed.

2. In the **Properties** palette, select the specified option from the **Type Selector** drop-down list if it is not selected by default.

    For English Imperial   **Footing - Rectangular : 72" x 48" x 18"**
    For English Metric   **M_Footing - Rectangular : 1800 x 1200 x 450mm**

3. Choose the **At Grids** tool from the **Multiple** panel of the **Modify | Place Isolated Foundation** contextual tab.

4. Next, move the cursor and place it over grid C and click when the grid is highlighted.

5. Press and hold the CTRL key, and select the grids marked 1, 2, 3, 4, 5, 6, 7, 8, 9, A', B', A, and B.

6. Release the CTRL key and choose the **Finish** button from the **Multiple** panel of the **Modify | Place Isolated Foundation > At Grid Intersection** contextual tab; the isolated foundations are added to the project view, refer to Figure 5-37. Ignore and close the warning message box if displayed.

7. Press ESC to finish the insertion of the isolated foundations and then exit from the **Isolated** tool.

8. Next, you need to delete the excess foundation added to the project view. To do so, move the cursor and place it toward the isolated foundation added at the intersection of the radial grids. For location of the excess foundation, refer to Figure 5-37. Click when the foundation is highlighted.

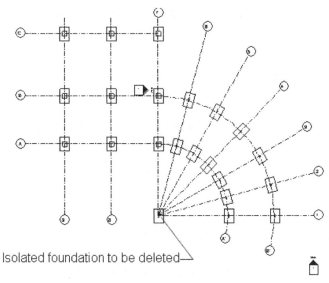

Figure 5-37 *Added isolated foundations*

9.   Press DELETE; the isolated foundation is deleted from the project.

Adding a Foundation Slab

In this section, you will add a foundation slab in the **Foundation Level** structural plan.

1.   Double-click on the **Foundation Level** node under the **Structural Plans** head in the **Project Browser** and then invoke the **Structural Foundation: Slab** tool from **Structure > Foundation > Slab** drop-down.

2.   In the **Properties** palette, select the option from the **Type Selector** drop-down list if not selected by default.

        For Imperial   **Foundation Slab : 6" Foundation Slab**
        For Metric   **Foundation Slab : 150mm Foundation Slab**

3.   In the **Draw** panel of the **Modify | Create Floor Boundary** contextual tab, ensure that the **Boundary Line** tool is chosen and then invoke the **Rectangle** tool from the list box displayed next to it.

4.   In the **Options Bar**, click in the **Offset** edit box. Replace the existing value in this edit box with **1'** for Imperial or **300mm** for Metric then press ENTER.

5.   Move the cursor and place it at the intersection of grid C and grid 9. Click when the **Midpoint** snap is displayed at the grid intersection.

Note
*If the **Intersection** snap is not displayed, you can right-click and choose **Snap Overrides** > **Intersection** from the shortcut menu displayed.*

6. Move down the cursor toward the right and place it at the grid intersection of grid C and grid 7. Click when the **Endpoint** snap is displayed at the intersection. Now, click on the other two grid intersections: (A, 7), and (A, 9).

7. Choose the **Finish Edit Mode** button from the **Mode** panel of the **Modify | Create Floor Boundary** contextual tab; the floor boundary is highlighted in blue.

8. Choose the **Modify** button from the **Select** panel of the **Modify| Structural Foundations** contextual tab to exit the **Foundation Slab** tool.

Adding Beams

In this section, you will add concrete and flange beams to the project view.

1. Double-click on the **Second Floor** node under the **Structural Plans** head in the **Project Browser**; the **Second Floor** structural plan view is displayed.

2. Invoke the **Beam** tool from the **Structure** panel of the **Structure** tab.

3. In the **Properties** palette, select the option from the **Type Selector** drop-down list.
         For Imperial   **Concrete- Rectangular Beam : 12 x 24**
         For Metric   **M_Concrete-Rectangular Beam : 300 x 600mm**

4. Choose the **On Grids** tool from the **Multiple** panel of the **Modify | Place Beam** contextual tab. Also, ensure that the **Tag on Placement** tool is selected in the **Tag** panel of this tab.

5. Select grid C by clicking on it; the beams of the selected type are added between the midpoint, as shown in Figure 5-38.

Figure 5-38 *Beams added at grid C*

6. Press and hold the CTRL key and select the grids A, B, 7, 8, and 9; the beams are added between the intersections, as shown in Figure 5-39.

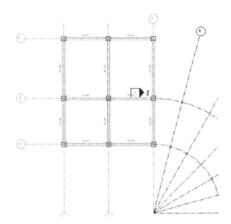

Figure 5-39 *Rectangular concrete beams added to the project*

7. Choose the **Finish** button from the **Multiple** panel of the **Modify | Place Beam > On Grid Lines** contextual tab.

8. In the **Properties** palette, select option from the **Type Selector** drop-down list.
   For Imperial   **W Shape : W14 X 30**
   For Metric   **M_W Shape : W760 X 350**

Note

*If the **M_W Shape** families are not loaded in the project then load them by choosing the **Load Family** tool from the **Mode** panel of the **Modify | Place Beam** contextual tab.*

9. Choose the **On Grids** tool from the **Multiple** panel of the **Modify | Place Beam** contextual tab.

10. Select grid 6; a beam of the selected type is added between the intersections of grid 6 with other grids.

11. Press and hold the CTRL key and select the grids 5, 4, 3, 2, 1, A', and B'; the flange beams are added between grids, as shown in Figure 5-40.

Figure 5-40 *Flange beams added to the project view*

12. Choose the **Finish** button from the **Multiple** panel of the **Modify | Place Beam > On Grid Lines** contextual tab. Press ESC to exit the **Beam** tool.

Adding the Structural Floors

In this section, you will add the structural floors to the project view.

1. Invoke the **Floor: Structural** tool from **Structure > Structure > Floor** drop-down; the **Modify | Create Floor Boundary** contextual tab is displayed.

2. In the **Properties** palette, click in the value field corresponding to the **Height Offset From Level** parameter and enter **19/4"** for Imperial or enter **120mm** for Metric and then press ENTER. Next, choose the **Edit Type** button; the **Type Properties** dialog box is displayed.

3. In the **Type Properties** dialog box, select required option from the **Type** drop-down list.
   For Imperial   **LW Concrete on Metal Deck**
   For Metric   **160mm Concrete with 50mm Metal Deck**

4. Choose the **OK** button to close the **Type Properties** dialog box.

5. In the **Draw** panel of the **Modify | Create Floor Boundary** contextual tab, choose the **Boundary Line** tool, if not chosen.

6. Invoke the **Rectangle** tool from the list box displayed next to the **Boundary Line** tool.

7. In the **Options Bar**, replace the existing value in the **Offset** edit box by entering 1' for Imperial or 300mm for Metric and press ENTER.

8. Move the cursor and place it at the intersection of grid 9 and grid C. Click when the **Endpoint** snap is displayed.

9. Next, move the cursor downward toward the right and place it at the intersection of grid A and grid 8.

10. Click when the **Endpoint** snap appears at the intersection.

11. Choose the **Finish Edit Mode** button from the **Mode** panel of the **Modify | Create Floor Boundary** contextual tab; the floor boundary is created, as shown in Figure 5-41 and is highlighted in blue color. Press ESC to exit the **Structural Floor** tool.

Figure 5-41 *The added structural floor*

12. Invoke the **Floor: Structural** tool from **Structure > Structure > Floor** drop-down; the **Modify | Create Floor Boundary** contextual tab is displayed.

13. In the **Draw** panel of the **Modify | Create Floor Boundary** contextual tab, choose the **Boundary Line** tool if not chosen by default.

14. Choose the **Pick Supports** tool from the list box displayed next to the **Boundary Line** tool chosen.

15. Place the cursor on the beam at grid 7 between grids A and B, as shown in Figure 5-42; the beam gets highlighted. Click on the highlighted beam to add the first edge of the structural floor.

Figure 5-42 *The selected beam highlighted*

16. Next, choose the **Pick Lines** tool from the list box in the **Draw** panel of the **Modify | Create Floor Boundary** contextual tab.

17. Move the cursor and place it over the beam located at grid B' between grids 6 and 7; the beam gets highlighted. Click on the highlighted beam.

18. Next, one by one, click on all the outer flange beams placed on grids B', 1, and A', to define the floor boundary. After you have clicked on all the outer flange beams, a floor boundary is created, as shown in Figure 5-43.

Figure 5-43 The structural floor boundary over the flanges

19. Choose the **Finish Edit Mode** button from the **Modify | Create Floor Boundary** contextual tab; floor is created, as shown in Figure 5-44.

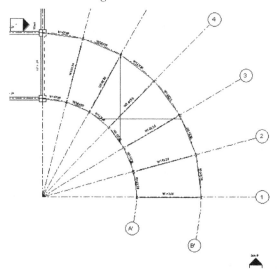

Figure 5-44 The structural floor created

20. In the **Properties** palette, select the option from the **Type Selector** drop-down list.
    For Imperial   **Floor : 1 1/2" Metal Roof Deck**
    For Metric   **Floor : 75mm Metal Roof Deck**

21. Press ESC to exit the **Structural Floor** tool.

Saving the Project

In this section, you will save the project file using the **Save As** tool.

1. Choose the **Save As > Project** option from the **File** menu; the **Save As** dialog box is displayed.

2. In this dialog box, browse to the *C:\rst_2021\c05_rst_2021_tut* location and enter **c05_Industrial-Complex_tut2** for Imperial or enter **M_c05_Industrial-Complex_tut2** for Metric in the **File name** edit box.

3. Choose the **Save** button; the **Save As** dialog box closes and the project file is saved.

Closing the Project

1. Choose the **Close** option from the **File** menu.

    The file is closed and this completes Tutorial 2 of Chapter 5.

Self-Evaluation Test

Answer the following questions and then compare them to those given at the end of this chapter:

1. _____ acts as an interface to transfer the load of a building structure to the earth strata.

2. _____ foundation is a footing that is attached to a wall.

3. The _____ instance parameter is used to specify the type of wall usage for the foundation.

4. _____ instance parameter is used to specify the distance of the top surface of structural floor from a level.

5. The _____ parameter is a read-only instance parameter which shows whether or not a foundation slab has been created from a mass object.

6. You can specify the distance at which the center of a foundation will be offset from the center of the host wall by using the _____ parameter.

7. An Isolated Foundation is a concrete slab placed under a column. (T/F)

8. A structural floor represents a floor deck or a floor slab. (T/F)

9. You can associate a material with an isolated footing foundation. (T/F)

10. Slab foundation does not transmit the load of a superstructure to the earth. (T/F)

Review Questions

Answer the following questions:

1. You can use the _____ parameter to specify whether a wall foundation remains continuous beneath the opening of a structural wall or not.

2. You can create an opening on the face of a structure by using the _____ tool from the **Structure** tab of the ribbon.

3. You can use the _____ tool to define a slope for a foundation slab.

4. In the **Properties** palette of a foundation slab, the instance parameters under the _____ head can be used to specify the creation and demolition phase.

5. In the **Properties** palette of a slab foundation, the **Structural Analysis** head contains the _____ parameter.

6. The _____ tool in the **Foundation** panel can be used to add a foundation slab to a structural model.

7. The **Structural** parameter specifies whether or not a foundation slab will have an analytical model. (T/F)

8. An isolated footing foundation is placed under a column. (T/F)

9. Shallow foundations transfer load from a building to the earth strata near the ground surface. (T/F)

10. In Autodesk Revit, you can add a bearing foundation to a structural model. (T/F)

EXERCISES
Exercise 1   Academic Institution

In this exercise, you will add foundations, beams, and structural floor to the project file created for Exercise 1 of Chapter 4, refer to Figures 5-45 and 5-46. Use the following project parameters and specifications: **(Expected time: 1 hr 15 min)**

1. Foundations: (To be added in the **Entry** structural plan view)
    For Imperial   Type: **Wall Foundation Bearing Footing : 36"x12"**
                           Footing Rectangular : 72"x48"x18"

For Metric   Type: **Wall Foundation Bearing Footing : 900 x 300**
                          M_Footing - Rectangular : 1800 x1200 x450mm

2. Beams: (To be added in the **Second Floor** structural plan view)
        For Imperial   Type: **Concrete-Rectangular Beam : 12x24**
        For Metric   Type: **M_Concrete-Rectangular Beam : 300 x600**

3. Structural Floor:
        For Imperial   Type: **3" LW Concrete on 2" Metal Deck**
                              1 1/2" Metal Roof Deck
        For Metric   Type: **160mm LW Concrete on 50mm Metal Deck**
                              75mm Metal Roof Deck

4. Project file to be used:
        For Imperial   *c04_Academic-Institution_exer1.rvt.*
        For Metric   *M_c04_Academic-Institution_exer1.rvt.*

5. File name to be assigned:
        For Imperial   *c05_Academic-Institution_exer1.rvt.*
        For Metric   *M_c05_Academic-Institution_exer1.rvt.*

6. For location and placement of beams, foundations and other structural elements, refer to
    Figure 5-45 and Figure 5-46.

*Figure 5-45 Structural plan view at the **Entry** level*

Figure 5-46 *Structural plan view at the **Second Floor** level*

Exercise 2   Factory Shed

In this exercise, you will add foundations, beams, and structural floor to the project file created in Exercise 2 of Chapter 4. Use the following project parameters and specifications:

(Expected time: 1 hr 45 min)

1. Project file to be used:

    For Imperial   *c04_Factory-Shed_exer2.rvt.*
    For Metric   *M_c04_Factory-Shed_exer2.rvt.*

2. Foundations:

    For Imperial   Type: **Footing - Rectangular : 72" x 48" x 18"**
    For Metric   Type: **M_Footing - Rectangular : 1800 x 1200 x 450mm**

3. Foundation Slab:

    For Imperial   Type: **Foundation Slab : 12" Foundation Slab**
    For Metric   Type: **Foundation Slab : 300mm Foundation Slab**

4. Beams:

For Imperial	Type: **Concrete-Rectangular Beam : 12 x 24**
	W-Wide Flange : W14 X 30
For Metric	Type: **M_Concrete-Rectangular Beam : 300 x 600mm**
	W-Wide Flange : W760 X 350

5. Structural Floor:

For Imperial	Type: **LW Concrete on Metal Deck**
	1 1/2" Metal Roof Deck
For Metric	Type: **160mm Concrete with 50mm Metal Deck**
	75mm Metal Roof Deck

6. File name to be assigned:

For Imperial	*c05_ Factory-Shed_exer2.rvt.*
For Metric	*M_c05_ Factory-Shed_exer2.rvt.*

Exercise 3   Residential Builiding

Download the *c05_residential_bldg_exer3* file from *s://www.cadcim.com*. The path of the file is as follows: *Textbooks > Civil/GIS > Revit Structure > Exploring Autodesk Revit 2021 for Structure*. In this exercise, you will add foundations, beams, and structural floor to the residential building project file. Refer to Figures 5-47 and 5-48 for the locations of beams, floors, and foundations in the project file. Use the following project parameters and specifications:

(Expected time: 1 hr)

1. Project file to be used:

For Imperial	*c05_residential_bldg_exer3.rvt.*
For Metric	*M_c05_residential_bldg_exer3.rvt.*

2. Foundations:

For Imperial	Type: **Footing - Rectangular : 72" x4 8" x 20"**
For Metric	Type: **M_Footing - Rectangular : 1800 x 1200 x 450mm**

3. Foundation Slab:

For Imperial	Type: **Foundation Slab : 6" Foundation Slab**
For Metric	Type: **Foundation Slab : 150mm Foundation Slab**

4. Beams:

For Imperial	Type: **Concrete-Rectangular Beam : 16 x 32**
For Metric	Type: **M_Concrete-Rectangular Beam : 400 x 800mm**

5. Structural Floor:

For Imperial	Type: **6" Concrete Floor**
For Metric	Type: **Insitu Concrete 225mm**

6. File name to be assigned:

For Imperial	*c05_ residential_bldg_exer3a.rvt.*
For Metric	*M_c05_ residential_bldg_exer3a.rvt.*

Figure 5-47 *Structural plan view at the* **Entry** *level*

Figure 5-48 *Structural plan view at the FL level*

Answers to Self-Evaluation Test

1. Foundation, **2.** Wall, **3. Structural Usage**, **4. Height Offset From Level**, **5. Related to Mass**,
6. Eccentricity, **7.** T, **8.** T, **9.** T, **10.** F

Chapter 6

Editing Tools

Learning Objectives

After completing this chapter, you will be able to:
- *Create a selection set of elements*
- *Move and copy elements*
- *Use the Cut and Paste tools*
- *Understand the use of the Rotate and Mirror tools*
- *Create an array of elements using the Array tool*
- *Group elements*
- *Use the Match, Align, Trim, Offset, and Delete tools*

In the previous chapters, you have learned to create structural elements such as structural walls, columns, and framing elements. In this chapter, you will learn about the editing process and the tools that are used to modify elements based on the design requirement. Some of the editing processes such as modifying type and instance properties, flipping orientation, and many more have already been discussed in the previous chapters. Also, you will learn to select and edit elements by using the object controls and editing tools such as **Move**, **Copy**, **Trim/Extend**, **Delete**, **Rotate**, **Mirror**, **Array**, **Align**, **Match**, and so on.

SELECTING ELEMENTS

Selecting elements in a drawing is an important and regular task needed for editing elements. Therefore, it is important to learn the basic and advanced methods of selection. Learning these methods will help you speed up the selection process as well as reduce the errors that may occur due to the wrong selection of elements.

In Revit Structure, you need to select the element or group of elements for editing. There are several methods that can be used to select the elements from a drawing. The method used to select an element may differ depending on the nature of selection. For instance, you may need to select a single element, multiple elements of different categories, multiple elements of same categories, and so on. These methods are discussed in detail next.

Selecting a Single Element

You can select a single element from a drawing by using the automatic highlighting feature. To select an element using this feature, move the cursor near or on the element to be selected; the outline of the desired element will be highlighted. After the element has been highlighted, you will notice that the description of the highlighted element is displayed in the Status Bar. Also, note that a similar description may appear along with the cursor as tooltip after a brief delay, as shown in Figure 6-1. Once the element has been highlighted, click on it to select it.

Figure 6-1 *Highlighted wall outline with the tooltip*

Note
In a project, if an element is selected in one view, it will remain selected in other views too.

When an element is selected, it becomes transparent and its color changes to blue, and also the temporary dimensions are displayed. You can modify the temporary dimensions to adjust the position of the element with respect to the adjacent elements. Additionally, when you select an element, a contextual tab consisting of editing tools is also displayed. You will also notice the selection count on the Status Bar. Selection count displays the number of elements selected.

In Revit Structure, you can also select multiple elements. Various methods to select multiple elements from a drawing are discussed next.

Selecting Multiple Elements

You can select multiple elements from a drawing in a number of ways, such as using the CTRL key, the TAB key, window selection method, and so on. The selection method used to select multiple elements depends on the user as well as the project requirement. Various methods for selecting multiple elements are discussed next.

Selecting Elements Using the CTRL Key

You can select multiple elements from a drawing by using the CTRL key. This method is used when you need to select multiple elements from the present selection set. To select multiple elements from a drawing, first select any one of the elements from the drawing area and then press and hold the CTRL key; a '+' symbol along with the cursor will appear. Next, move the cursor to the next element. When this element has been highlighted, click on it; the desired element will be added to the current selection set. If you need to add more elements to the current selection set, keep the CTRL key pressed and click on the elements to be added to the current selection set. However, if you have released the CTRL key and want to add another element to the current selection set, move the cursor to the desired element until the element has been highlighted. After the element has been highlighted, press and hold the CTRL key and then click on the desired element; the desired element will be added to the current selection set.

Selecting Structural Elements Using a Selection Box

You can select multiple elements of same or different categories simultaneously by drawing a selection box around them. To draw a selection box, place the cursor at one corner of the region where the elements to be selected are placed and then drag it diagonally toward the other side to form a rectangular boundary. When you drag the cursor from left to right, a rectangle is formed in continuous lines and the elements that are completely inside it are selected, refer to Figure 6-2. Alternatively, when you drag the cursor from right to left, a dashed rectangle appears and all items that are partially or fully inside it are selected.

Selecting Walls or Lines Using the TAB Key

You can use the TAB key to select walls, lines, or both the walls and lines that are joined together and form a chain. To select elements by using this method, first highlight any of the elements in the selection chain and then press the TAB key; all the elements that are joined to the highlighted element will be highlighted for selection. Click to select the elements. Figure 6-3 shows a wall chain selected by using the TAB key.

Figure 6-2 The selection box

Figure 6-3 The chain of walls selected

Note
The method of selection of elements using the TAB key has certain limitations. This method cannot be used if the walls are not properly joined together.

You can also use the TAB key to select multiple wall or line elements joined at a common endpoint. To select the elements using this method, first place the cursor on or near any wall or line; the wall or line will be highlighted, as shown in Figure 6-4. Next, press the TAB key; the next wall or line that is closest to the cursor will be highlighted, refer to Figure 6-5. In this figure, the cursor is positioned on the right side of the lower left wall and therefore is closest to the wall connected on the right. As a result, the wall connected on the right side also gets highlighted, refer to Figure 6-5. Now, you can click to select both the highlighted walls that are connected to a common endpoint. However, if you want to select all the walls connected at the common endpoint, press the TAB key; all the walls at the common endpoint will be highlighted, refer to Figure 6-6. Next, click to select the highlighted walls.

Figure 6-4 The first wall highlighted

Figure 6-5 *The second wall highlighted*   *Figure 6-6* *The third wall highlighted*

Selecting Elements Using the Select All Instances Option

In Revit Structure, you can select the elements of similar instances from a drawing. For example, if you need to select all instances of columns of the **Concrete-Rectangular-Column-24x30** type and change them to a different type, you can use the **Select All Instances** option. To use this option, first select any of the instances of the **Concrete-Rectangular-Column-24x30** type from the drawing area, refer to Figure 6-7. Next, right-click to display a shortcut menu. Choose **Select All Instances > Visible in View** from the shortcut menu; all elements of similar instances will be selected, refer to Figure 6-8. Alternatively, to select all instances from the drawing, select an element and then type **SA**. You can also select all instances of the selected element in the entire structural model. To do so, right-click and then choose **Select All Instance > In Entire Project** from the shortcut menu displayed.

Figure 6-7 *Selecting the first instance from the drawing area*   *Figure 6-8* *All instances of the element selected*

Selecting Elements Using the Advanced Selection Tools

In Autodesk Revit Structure, you can use the advanced selection tools for the selection and modeling process. These tools are available in the Status Bar. You can also invoke these tools from the **Modify** panel drop-down. Some of the advanced selection tools are discussed next.

Select Links Tool

 In a project, you may require to select an entire linked model or an individual element inside the linked model. To do so, choose the **Select Links** tool from the Status Bar and then select the element or the model.

Tip
To select an individual element in a model, place the cursor on it and then press the TAB key; the element gets highlighted. Click on the highlighted element to select it.

Select Underlay Element Tool

You can use the **Select Underlay Element** tool to select elements which are not a part of the current plan view. To do so, choose this tool from the Status Bar. Next, place the cursor on the underlaid element; the element gets highlighted. Next, click to select the highlighted element. You can disable this tool by choosing it again.

Select Pinned Element Tool

You can enable or disable the selection of the pinned elements in a model by using the **Select Pinned Elements** tool. To enable the selection of the pinned elements, choose this tool from the Status Bar.

Select Element by Face Tool

You can choose this tool to enable the selection of an element by face. To do so, choose the **Select Element by Face** tool from the Status Bar and then click at any point on the face of the element(s) such as wall or floor; the element will be selected. You can disable this tool by choosing it again.

Drag Elements on Selection Tool

You can choose the **Drag Elements on Selection** tool to drag an element without selecting it first. To do so, choose the **Drag Elements on Selection** tool from the Status Bar and then hover the cursor over the desired element such as wall or floor without selecting it; the element gets highlighted. Now, press and drag the mouse button; the element will be moved to the desired location.

Note
*It is recommended to disable the **Drag Elements on Selection** tool to avoid accidental displacement of the elements.*

Restoring a Selection

You can restore a selection which got cleared intentionally or unintentionally using several methods. One of the options for restoring the previous selection is to choose the **Modify** tool and then right-click in the drawing area to display a shortcut menu. Next, choose the **Select Previous** option from the shortcut menu to restore the previous selection. Alternatively, press CTRL+Left Arrow to restore the previous selection.

Selecting Elements Using the Filter Tool

In Revit Structure, you can use the **Filter** tool to refine the selection process by removing the elements of specific categories from the current selection set. Suppose a current selection set includes walls, structural foundations, structural columns, and beams, and you want to remove the elements of structural columns categories from the selection. You can do so by using the **Filter** tool. On using this tool, the walls, structural foundation, and beams will remain selected in the existing selection set. Figures 6-9 and 6-10 show the elements of different categories selected before and after using the **Filter** tool. Before using this tool, you need to select the elements from the drawing area. Next, invoke the **Filter** tool from the **Selection** panel of the **Multi-Select** tab; the **Filter** dialog box will be displayed along with a list of categories of the currently selected elements, refer to Figure 6-11. Alternatively, click on the filter icon displayed at the extreme right corner of the Status Bar to display the **Filter** dialog box.

Figure 6-9 Selected elements before using the **Filter** tool

Figure 6-10 Selected elements after using the **Filter** tool

Figure 6-11 The **Filter** dialog box

The **Category** column in the **Filter** dialog box displays all the element categories present in the selection set. The **Count** column displays the number of selected elements in each category. At the bottom of the dialog box, the **Total Elements** area displays the total number count of the elements currently selected.

In the **Filter** dialog box, the check boxes corresponding to the listed categories are selected by default. To exclude an element from a category, you can clear the check box corresponding to it. You can use the **Check All** or **Check None** button to select or clear all the check boxes in the element categories, respectively.

Note
*The **Total Selected Items** at the bottom of the **Filter** dialog box displays the count of the total number of elements selected. This count keeps on changing as you select or clear the check boxes.*

The Filter Icon

In Autodesk Revit Structure, you can see a filter icon along with a number located at the lower right corner of the interface on the Status Bar. The number displayed next to the **Filter** icon gives you a visual feedback of the number of currently selected elements.

MOVING STRUCTURAL ELEMENTS

In Revit Structure, you can move structural elements in the drawing area, independently or in association with other elements. To move a component independently, you can use the **Move** tool or drag the selected element. However, to move an element in association with other elements, you can use the options such as changing temporary dimensions, re-hosting elements, and so on. You can move a hosted component from one position to another. The methods used for moving an element are discussed next.

Moving Elements by Changing Temporary Dimensions

You can move an element by changing its temporary dimensions. The temporary dimensions for an element are displayed at the time you create or select the element. These dimensions are displayed in reference to a nearby element. To move an element, select it; its distance with respect to the nearby element will be displayed in the temporary dimensions. Click on the temporary dimension and enter a new value in the edit box to move the element to the desired location.

Moving Elements by Dragging

You can also move elements by dragging them to the desired location in the drawing area. To drag an element, select the element and place the cursor over it; the cursor will change into a move symbol and the color of the selected element will change. Next, click and hold the left mouse button and move the cursor toward the desired location. On doing so, an image of the selected element will move along with the cursor, as shown in Figure 6-12. When the element reaches desired location, release the left mouse button; the element will move to the new location. In case, you move a structural wall, the adjoining walls will extend with the moved wall. Figure 6-13 shows the adjustment of the adjoining walls when the selected wall is dragged to a new location. Note that some elements such as walls can be moved only in a particular direction. However, you can press the SHIFT key to remove this constraint. The rest of them can be moved in all directions. You can restrict the direction of movement of these elements by pressing the SHIFT key.

Figure 6-12 *Image of the selected element displayed along with the cursor symbol*

Figure 6-13 *The selected wall before and after dragging*

Dragging End-joined Components

Revit Structure provides you with the option to drag the end-joined components by using drag controls. You can drag and move more than two components simultaneously, provided they are joined. Note that this feature can be applied to the line based components only such as walls, beams, or braces.

To drag the joined elements, select one of the members of the joined elements from the drawing and right-click; a shortcut menu will be displayed. Choose **Select Joined Elements** from the shortcut menu; all the joined members will be highlighted and the circular drag controls will be displayed, refer to Figure 6-14. Next, move the cursor to the common joint; the **Drag Wall End** tooltip will be displayed. Drag the joint to a new location, as shown in Figure 6-14. You will notice that all walls joined to that common joint have been dragged.

Single wall selected   Adjoining walls also selected   Dragging the common join   Walls after being dragged

Figure 6-14 *The joined walls being dragged*

Doors and windows can be moved along their host walls. It can be done by picking and dragging them. When you move doors and windows, an opening is automatically created at the new location.

Moving Elements Using the Move Tool

Ribbon: Modify | (Elements or Components) > Modify > Move
Shortcut Key: MV

 You can also use the **Move** tool to move elements. The usage of the **Move** tool is similar to that of the tools used for dragging with the only difference that in case of the **Move** tool, the preview of elements is not displayed. This tool is more useful for moving the elements as it increases the accuracy of the position of the structural model by specifying the exact distance for moving the elements. To invoke the **Move** tool, select the element(s) from the drawing area; the **Modify | (Elements or Components)** contextual tab will be displayed. Next, choose the **Move** tool from the **Modify** panel. Alternatively, to invoke the **Move** tool, select the desired element and then type **MV**. On invoking the **Move** tool, the selected elements will be highlighted inside a dashed rectangle. The **Options Bar** shows three check boxes: **Constrain**, **Disjoin**, and **Multiple**. These check boxes are discussed in the table given next.

 Note
*The **Move** tool, like other editing tools such as **Copy**, **Rotate**, **Mirror**, **Array**, and **Scale**, is available only after a selection has been made. You can access these tools from the contextual tabs such as **Modify / Structural Columns, Modify / Structural Framing**. The name of the contextual tab will be based on the type of element or component selected.*

Name of the Check box	Description
Constrain	If this check box is selected, the movement of the selected element along with its collinear or perpendicular vectors will be restricted.

Disjoin	If this check box is selected, you can break an element from its associated elements and move it to a new location. For example, you can move a wall without moving the joined wall. You can also move the elements from their current host element to another host element. For example, you can easily move a door or window from one wall to another. The selection of this check box can be effectively used if the **Constrain** check box is cleared.
Multiple	The selection of this check box enables the creation of multiple copies of the elements by clicking at the desired location. It is enabled only when the copy of check box is selected. This check box is disabled by default.

After invoking the **Move** tool, click in the drawing area to specify the start point. Next, move the cursor to the desired location and click to specify the endpoint; the element will move to a new location. Alternatively, you can move the element by specifying distance. To do so, invoke the **Move** tool and specify the start point for the movement in the drawing area. Next, move the cursor away from the specified start point and toward the desired direction of movement; the image of the selected element will be displayed. Also, you will notice that a temporary dimension along with the image is displayed. Type a value to specify the distance; you will notice that the typed value is displayed in the edit box. To confirm the specified distance, press ENTER; the selected element will move by the specified distance.

COPYING STRUCTURAL ELEMENTS

In Autodesk Revit, you can copy structural elements to the drawing area by using the CTRL key, the **Copy** tool, the clipboard to copy-and-paste elements method, and the **Create Similar** tool. The methods of copying structural elements are discussed next.

Copying Elements Using the CTRL Key

Using the CTRL key for copying elements is the most commonly used method. To copy an element using this method, select the desired element and move the cursor over it; the move symbol will replace the existing cursor. Next, press and hold the CTRL key and the left mouse button. Then, drag the cursor away from the selected element or component at a desired direction; the image of the selected element will be highlighted and displayed. Also, the temporary dimensions with respect to the nearby elements will be displayed, refer to Figure 6-15. Now, you can release the CTRL key and the left mouse button, and then click on any temporary dimension to specify the position of the copied element. On clicking the temporary dimension, an edit box will be displayed. You can enter a value in the edit box to fix the position of the copied element or component in reference to the nearby element. After entering a value in the edit box, press the ESC key or double-click in the drawing area to finish copying elements or components.

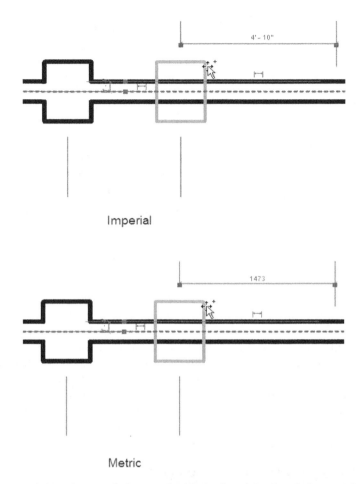

Figure 6-15 *The pasted elements highlighted and displayed along with their temporary dimension*

Copying Elements Using the Copy Tool

Ribbon: Modify | (Elements or Components) > Modify > Copy
Shortcut Key: CO

The usage of the **Copy** tool is similar to that of the **Move** tool. You can use the **Copy** tool to create a single or multiple copies of element(s). To use the **Copy** tool, select the element(s) that you want to copy from the drawing area; the **Modify | (Elements or Components)** contextual tab will be displayed. In this tab, invoke the **Copy** tool from the **Modify** panel; the selected element will be highlighted inside a rectangular dotted box. Next, click in the drawing area, preferably inside the rectangular dotted box to specify the start point of displacement for the element(s) to be copied. Next, move the cursor along the direction you want to copy the element(s). On doing so, the image of the rectangular dotted box will be displayed. Also, a temporary dimension in reference to the start point will be displayed. Now, you can either click at the desired location in the drawing area or use the temporary dimensions to specify the end position of the copied element(s) in reference to the selected element(s). After specifying the end position of the dotted rectangular box, you will notice that the copy of the selected element has replaced the dotted rectangular box and the temporary dimensions to align the copied element (s) will also be displayed at the same time. You can use the temporary dimensions of the copied elements to fix its horizontal and vertical distances. Next, press ESC to exit the selection mode. You can also use the **Copy** tool to copy element(s) multiple times. The method for copying elements multiple times is discussed next.

Creating Multiple Copies

You can create several copies of an element using the **Copy** tool. To do so, select the elements that you want to copy and then invoke the **Copy** tool. Select the **Multiple** check box in the **Options Bar**. Next, click in the drawing window to specify the start point. Move the cursor and click at the location where you want to create a copy. Each successive click will create a copy of the original element, refer to Figure 6-16. Alternatively, when the temporary dimensions are displayed, type the distance between the currently selected elements and the next element to create copies at a specified distance. The multiple copy option remains active until you choose some other tool or press the ESC key twice.

Figure 6-16 *Element copied multiple times*

Using the Create Similar Tool

| Ribbon: | Modify | (Elements or Components) > Create > Create Similar |
| Shortcut Key: | CS |

In a project, you can create and place similar type of elements at the required space. For this, you need to use the **Create Similar** tool. This tool will be available only after a selection has been made. Before using the **Create Similar** tool, select the element whose similar types you want to create and place in the drawing. Next, choose the **Create Similar** tool from the **Create** panel; the creation tool, similar to that of the element you have selected, will be invoked. Next, you can create the element of similar instance parameter as that of the selected element in the drawing area. For example, if you select a structural framing member from the drawing and then invoke the **Create Similar** tool, the **Modify | Place Beam** contextual tab will be displayed. By using the options in this tab, you can place a structural framing member of the same instance that you have selected from the drawing area. Alternatively, to invoke the

Create Similar tool, select the element and then right-click; a shortcut menu will be displayed. Next, choose the **Create Similar** option from the shortcut menu; the **Create Similar** tool will be invoked.

Copying Elements Using the Clipboard

In Revit Structure, you can use the functionality of cut, copy, and paste to speed up work and reduce the time required for creating new elements. These functions are generally called Clipboard operations and can be used to cut or copy one or more elements from the drawing area to the clipboard and then paste them in the drawing area of the same project or in another project. This method of copying elements is different from that of using the **Copy** tool. These tools and their usage are discussed next.

Cutting Elements from a Project

Ribbon: Modify | (Elements or Components) > Clipboard > Cut to Clipboard
Shortcut Key: Ctrl+X

The **Cut to Clipboard** tool is used to remove one or more elements from a project. The selected elements are copied on the clipboard where they remain until another selection has been pasted. When you cut and paste new elements to the clipboard, the existing selection is overwritten by a new one. You can then paste it in the same or another project. The **Cut to Clipboard** tool will be available only after a selection has been made. Select the elements or components from the drawing using any of the selection tools described earlier in this chapter and then invoke the **Cut to Clipboard** tool from the **Clipboard** panel of the contextual tab. Alternatively, press the CTRL+X keys. The selected elements will be removed from the project and pasted on the clipboard.

Copying Elements to the Clipboard

Ribbon: Modify | (Elements or Components) > Clipboard > Copy to Clipboard
Shortcut Key: Ctrl+C

You can create a copy of an element on the clipboard and retain the original ones in the current project. To copy an element, select the desired elements or components and then invoke the **Copy to Clipboard** tool from the **Clipboard** panel; copy of the selected elements will be created on the clipboard. Alternatively, to copy the desired elements or components to the clipboard, select them and then press the CTRL+C keys.

Pasting Elements from the Clipboard

Ribbon: Modify | (Elements or Components) > Clipboard > Paste drop-down
                     > Paste from Clipboard
Shortcut Key: Ctrl+V

In Revit Structure, once elements are copied, you can paste them in the drawing area of the current project or in another project by using any of the pasting options available in the **Paste** drop-down located in the **Clipboard** panel of the **Modify | (Elements or Components)** contextual tab. To display the options used for pasting elements, click on the **Paste** drop-down; a list of pasting tools will be displayed, as shown in Figure 6-17. The tools displayed in the drop-down are **Paste from Clipboard**, **Aligned to Selected Levels**, **Aligned to Selected Views**, **Aligned to Current View**, **Aligned to Same Place**, and **Aligned to Picked Level**. The different tools in the drop-down are discussed next.

Figure 6-17 Various pasting options

Using the Paste from Clipboard Tool

The **Paste from Clipboard** tool is used to paste one or more elements from the clipboard to the current or another project. This tool will be available only after the element(s) has been cut or copied . You can invoke the **Paste from Clipboard** tool from **Modify | (Elements or Components) > Clipboard > Paste** drop-down. On doing so, a preview box representing the pasted selection will be displayed with a temporary dimension and the original selection, refer to Figure 6-18. Notice that the original selection is displayed inside a rectangular dashed box. You can use the temporary dimension to fix the distance of the pasted selection from the original selection, or click on the desired location in the drawing area to place the pasted selection. Alternatively, you can press the CTRL+V keys to paste the copied element(s) with respect to the clipboard to the drawing area of the current project or another project. Once these elements have been pasted, they remain selected as a group in a dashed rectangular box and the **Modify | Model Groups** contextual tab is displayed. In this tab, there are other editing tools such as **Move, Copy, Rotate, Align**, and so on to modify the selected elements. In the **Options Bar**, you can choose the **Activate Dimensions** button to view the dimensions of the pasted elements from the nearby element(s). After pasting, choose the **Finish** tool from the **Edit Pasted** panel to return to the **Modify** tab (default mode). To quit the pasting operation even when the group of elements is selected, choose the **Cancel** button in the **Modify | Groups** contextual tab. On doing so, the recently pasted group of elements will be removed from the project and you will exit the **Paste** tool.

Imperial

Metric

Figure 6-18 *Pasted element shown in a preview box*

You can also edit the elements that you have pasted in the drawing area by changing the position of the individual element or changing the type properties of the elements while the **Modify | Groups** contextual tab is active. To do so, choose the **Edit Pasted Elements** tool from the **Edit Pasted** panel in the **Modify | Groups** contextual tab; the **Modify | Multi-Select** or **Modify | (Elements or Components)** contextual tab will be displayed and the elements, other than the pasted elements, will be inactive and appear fade. You can select an element from the pasted element and reposition them by using the tools available in the **Modify | Multi-Select** or **Modify | (Elements or Components)** contextual tab. As you select an element from the model group, the corresponding contextual tab will be displayed. For example, if you select a column, the **Modify | Structural Columns** contextual tab will be displayed. You can use various editing tools such as **Move** and **Copy** from the **Modify** panel of the contextual tab to reposition or realign the selected element. You can also rehost the element using various tools in the **Modify | Structural Columns** contextual tab.

Using the other Pasting Tools

After you cut or copy element(s) for pasting them to the clipboard, you can paste the copied or cut element(s) in various ways. For example, you can paste them on one level or multiple levels; in the current view or a specific view; at the same place over the original element or in an elevation/sectional view. To align the pasted elements, you need to click on the

Paste drop-down from the **Clipboard** panel of the **Modify | <Elements or Components>** contextual tab. On doing so, a drop-down list will be displayed with the following tools: **Aligned to Selected Levels**, **Paste from Clipboard**, **Aligned to Selected Views**, **Aligned to Current View**, **Aligned to Same Place**, and **Aligned to Picked Level**. By default, the **Aligned to Select Views** tool is inactive.

You can use the **Aligned to Selected Levels** tool to paste the copied elements to one or more levels. On choosing this tool from the drop-down list, the **Select Levels** dialog box will be displayed, as shown in Figure 6-19. In this dialog box, the names of the levels present in the structural model are displayed in a list box. You can select the individual level by clicking on it. You can use the CTRL key to select multiple elements. After selecting levels by their names, choose the **OK** button; the **Select Levels** dialog box will close and the selected elements will be pasted on the selected levels.

Figure 6-19 *The* ***Select Levels*** *dialog box*

You can invoke the **Aligned to Selected Views** tool to paste view-specific elements such as dimensions, tags, and texts to a similar type of view. The **Aligned to Current View** tool is used to paste the elements that are cut or copied from a different view and has to be pasted in the current view. Note that you can paste elements at the same place where you have copied them. To do so, you can use the **Aligned to Same Place** tool. The **Aligned to Picked Level** tool can be used to paste elements in an elevation or section view. Note that while using this tool, you need to copy and paste elements only in elevation or section view.

ROTATING STRUCTURAL ELEMENTS

Ribbon:	Modify | (Elements or Components) > Modify > Rotate
Shortcut Key:	RO

You can rotate elements in a project by using the **Rotate** tool. This tool is used to rotate the selected element(s) about a specified axis or point. You can rotate the selected elements about an axis perpendicular to the plan, elevation, or section view. In 3D view, elements rotate about an axis perpendicular to the current work plane. This tool will be available only after the elements have been selected.

To invoke the **Rotate** tool, select elements or components from the drawing area and then choose the **Rotate** tool from the **Modify** panel of the contextual tab displayed. Alternatively, you can type **RO**. On invoking the **Rotate** tool, a rotation symbol will be displayed at the center of the selected element(s). It represents the perpendicular axis or the center about which the elements will rotate. In the drawing area, you can drag the rotation symbol or use the **Place** button from the **Options Bar** to specify a different location as the center of rotation. If you want to place the center of rotation to its default location, choose the **Default** button from the **Options Bar**. Alternatively, you can snap the rotation symbol and drag it to the desired center of rotation.

Once the center of rotation has been specified, a line moving along the direction of the cursor is generated from the center of rotation. Click at the desired start point of the rotation to display a line indicating its direction. You can also use various object snap options to specify the start point of the rotation. Once the start point of the rotation has been specified, another line will rotate with the cursor to specify the endpoint. Also, you will notice that a preview box, indicating the selected elements, is rotating along with the selected elements. The element rotates to a new direction. When you move the cursor to the required angle and click to specify the second point of rotation. On rotating the entities, you will notice that a temporary angular dimension is displayed. You can enter the exact value of the angle of rotation to rotate the elements to the specified angle. When you invoke the **Rotate** tool, three options become available in the **Options Bar**, refer to Figure 6-20.

*Figure 6-20 Different rotation options in the **Options Bar***

Before rotating the entities, you can select the **Disjoin** check box to break the association between the selected elements and the other elements associated with them. For example, you can independently rotate a wall that is joined to other walls. The selection of the **Copy** check box enables you to create a rotated copy of the selected element without changing its original location. The **Angle** edit box can be used to rotate elements by a specific angle. You can enter the value of the angle of rotation in this edit box. On entering a value, the selected elements will rotate about the specified center of rotation with specified angle. For example, in the **Structural Plan** view, to rotate a horizontally aligned wall about its intersection point with the vertically aligned wall by 15 degrees, click on the horizontal wall to select it and then invoke the **Rotate** tool from the **Modify** panel of the **Modify | Walls** contextual tab. On doing so, the rotation symbol will be placed at the midpoint of the wall and a ray will be generated from it, as shown in Figure 6-21. Drag this symbol to the intersection of the two walls, as shown in Figure 6-22. The rotation symbol moves to the new location and the ray will be generated from this point. Next, move the cursor vertically upward such that it snaps to the vertical wall. To specify the start point of the rotation, click when the snap symbol is displayed. To create an angle of 15 degrees, move the cursor clockwise and click when the temporary dimension shows the desired angle value. As a result, the vertical wall will rotate about the specified center point. Alternatively, enter **15** for the new angle.

Figure 6-21 Ray generated at the midpoint of the wall

Figure 6-22 Rotation symbol dragged to the intersection of the wall

MIRRORING STRUCTURAL ELEMENTS

In Revit Structure, you can mirror elements and components to create design symmetry in a structural model. You can mirror elements using any of the following two tools: **Mirror - Pick Axis** and **Mirror - Draw Axis**. These tools can be chosen from the **Modify** panel of the contextual tab. To mirror elements or components in the structural model, first you need to select them from the drawing area; the contextual tab for the selected elements or components will be displayed. In the **Modify** panel of the contextual tab, choose any of these two tools: **Mirror - Draw Axis** and **Mirror - Pick Axis**. The selection of the tool depends on the project requirement. Note that when you invoke any of the tools, the **Options Bar** displays the **Copy** option. By default, this option is selected, and therefore enables you to create a mirrored copy of the elements. Clear the **Copy** check box if you do not require a copy. The two tools for mirroring elements or components are discussed next.

Mirror - Pick Axis Tool

Ribbon: Modify | (Elements or Components) > Modify > Mirror - Pick Axis
Shortcut Key: MM

The **Mirror - Pick Axis** tool can be used to mirror elements by selecting an element from the drawing to define the mirror axis. To mirror elements, select them from the drawing and then invoke the **Mirror - Pick Axis** tool from the **Modify** panel; the mirror symbol will appear with the cursor in the drawing area. Alternatively, you can type **MM** to invoke the **Mirror - Pick Axis** tool. Next, move the cursor over the element that will define the mirror axis and click when the appropriate object snap appears. Figure 6-23 shows beam, column, and wall elements selected for mirroring and the grid line **D** as the mirror axis. Figure 6-24 shows the elements created after mirroring.

> **Note**
> *Using the **Mirror-Pick Axis** tool, you can only select a line or a reference plane that the cursor can snap to. You cannot mirror elements about an imaginary axis created in the open space.*

Figure 6-23 Beams, columns, and walls selected for mirroring

Figure 6-24 Beams, columns, and walls mirrored on either side of the grid line D

Mirror - Draw Axis Tool

Ribbon:	Modify | (Elements or Components) > Modify > Mirror - Draw Axis
Shortcut Key:	DM

The **Mirror - Draw Axis** tool can be used to mirror an element or a component by creating a mirror line with the help of two points to define the mirror axis. This tool is represented by a pencil with a mirror symbol. To mirror elements, select the elements from the drawing and then choose the **Mirror - Draw Axis** tool from the **Modify** panel. You can also invoke this tool by typing **DM**. After invoking the tool, click in the drawing area to specify the start point of the mirror line; a ray will emerge from the specified point. Move the cursor to the desired location and click to specify the second point; the selected elements will be mirrored about the line that represents the mirror axis.

ARRAYING STRUCTURAL ELEMENTS

Ribbon:	Modify | (Elements or Components) > Modify > Array
Shortcut Key:	AR

The **Array** tool, which is used to create the copies of a selected element in a rectangular or radial pattern, will be available only after elements have been selected for an array. You can use any of the methods discussed earlier in this chapter to select an element. Revit Structure provides you the option of arraying multiple elements that are associated as a group. To invoke the **Array** tool, select the element(s) that you want to array and then choose the **Array** tool from the **Modify** panel of the contextual tab. Alternatively, you can type **AR** to invoke this tool. On invoking the **Array** tool, you will notice that various array options are displayed in the **Options Bar**. In the **Options Bar**, the **Group and Associate** check box is selected by default. As a result, the elements are copied as a group rather than individual elements. You can clear this check box so that the arrayed elements are not grouped. In the **Options Bar**, the **Linear** and **Radial** tools can be used to create two different types of arrays. The tools for creating different types of arrays are discussed next.

Linear Tool

The **Linear** tool is used to create an array of selected elements in a rectangular or linear pattern. When you invoke the **Array** tool, the **Linear** tool is also invoked by default in the **Options Bar**. As a result, various options which are available in the **Options Bar** to create an array are displayed according to the **Linear** tool. In the **Number** edit box, enter the number of copies you want to create. In the **Move To** area of the **Options Bar**, the **2nd** radio button is selected by default. As a result, you can click the cursor in the drawing area to specify the distance upto which the array will be created. Alternatively, select the **Last** radio button in the **Move to** area to specify the entire distance of the array. Click in the drawing area to specify the entire distance of the array. In the **Options Bar**, choose the **Activate Dimension** button to view various dimensions of elements. You can specify various options in the **Options Bar** before or during the creation of an array. After selecting the **2nd** radio button (if not selected by default) in the **Move To** area, click at any point in the drawing window to specify the start point of the array distance. As you move the cursor in the desired direction, a temporary dimension is displayed. You can either enter the value of the distance in that direction or simply move the cursor to the appropriate location and click. Revit Structure creates an array of the selected elements by calculating the distance and direction between the two specified points. After the second point is specified, you are prompted to enter the number of items for the array in an edit box. The number of items specified in the **Options Bar** will be displayed as the default value. You have the option of overriding it and specifying a new number. On specifying the number of items for the array, an array of the selected items will be created with the specified distance between each group of items. Figure 6-25 shows the selected elements and the distance specified between each element. The preview of the array to be created is shown in Figure 6-26.

Figure 6-25 *Specifying the distance between elements after selecting the **2nd** radio button from the **Options Bar***

Figure 6-26 *Preview of the array to be created*

You can select the **Constrain** check box in the **Options Bar** to restrict the movement of the cursor in orthogonal direction only. This helps in creating a horizontal or vertical linear array. You can select the **Last** radio button to create an array of elements between two points. Figure 6-27 shows the start point selected for specifying the array distance and the selected window to be arrayed. Move the cursor to the total distance that needs to be divided, as shown in Figure 6-28.

Figure 6-27 *Start point selected for the array*

Figure 6-28 *Specifying the endpoint to mark the total distance of the array*

As you click to specify the endpoint of the array distance, an edit box appears displaying the number of items in the array. You can specify the number in it, as shown in Figure 6-29, and press ENTER to complete the procedure. An array of the selected column created on the wall is shown in Figure 6-30.

Figure 6-29 *Specifying the array count in the edit box*

Figure 6-30 *The array of columns created on the wall*

Radial Tool

You can create radial arrays using the **Radial** tool available in the **Options Bar**. When you invoke this tool, the following setting options will be available in the **Options Bar**: the **Group and Associate** button, the **Number** edit box, and the **2nd** and **Last** radio buttons. These options are the same as those discussed for the **Linear** tool. The **Angle** edit box in the **Options Bar** is used to specify the angle about which the array is to be created. If the **2nd** radio button is selected in the **Move To** area, the angle specified in the **Angle** edit box will become the angle between each item, whereas if the **Last** radio button is selected from the **Move To** area, the number of items will be created by equally dividing the specified angle entered in the **Angle** edit box. Note that the procedure for creating a radial array is similar to that of rotating elements using the **Rotate** tool, which has been described earlier in this chapter. For arraying the selected elements radially, invoke the **Radial** tool from the **Options Bar**; a rotational symbol is displayed at the center of the selection. You can choose the **Place** button in the **Options**

Bar or drag the rotation symbol to a location that will be used as the center of the array. Figure 6-31 shows a semi-circular wall in which the rectangular column is selected for an array. The center of the semi-circular wall is specified as the center of the array. Next, click to specify the start point of the angle of the array. Select the **Last** radio button from the **Move To** area to specify the total angle of the array. Now, move the cursor radially and click to specify the end point of the angle, as shown in Figure 6-32; an edit box will be displayed, prompting you to enter the number of items to be created between the specified angles, as shown in Figure 6-33.

Figure 6-31 *Selecting the rectangular column to array radially over the semi circular wall*

Figure 6-32 *Specifying the endpoint to define the end angle of the array*

Imperial   Metric

Figure 6-33 *Specifying the array count for the radial array*

After specifying the number, press ENTER to complete the procedure. Figure 6-34 shows the resultant radial array of the rectangular columns. You will notice that the number of items is displayed in blue. You can click on it and enter a new value, if required. The two controls at the end of the arc can be used to resize it. The middle control can be used to modify the radius of the radial array, while the central control lets you drag it.

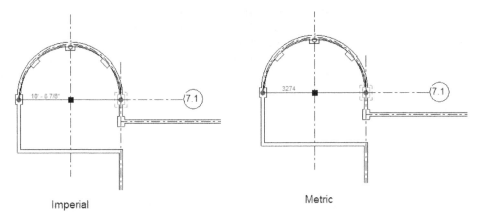

Imperial   Metric

Figure 6-34 *Preview of the arrayed rectangular columns*

Tip
Autodesk Revit displays an error message if the elements cannot be arrayed. For example, if the specified angle or the number of items do not fit into the length of the wall or overlap each other, a warning message will be displayed. This message box helps you modify the settings accordingly.

RESIZING ELEMENTS

Ribbon: Modify |(Elements or Components) > Modify > Scale
Shortcut Key: RE

In your project, you may need to resize or scale elements when required. To resize the elements in the project, you can use the **Scale** tool. This tool will help to modify the scale of a single element or a group of elements. This tool is only available for walls, lines, images, *.dwg* and *.dxf* imports, reference planes, and position of dimensions. To scale an element, select it from the drawing and then invoke the **Scale** tool from the **Modify** panel of the **Modify | (Elements or Components)** contextual tab. On doing so, the **Options Bar** will display two radio buttons: **Graphical** and **Numerical**. These radio buttons are selected to specify a method for scaling.

In the **Options Bar**, the **Graphical** radio button is selected by default. As a result, you can resize elements graphically. After selecting this radio button, you need to specify three points in the drawing area. The first point is used to specify the origin of scaling and the other two points define the scale vectors. Once the origin is specified, move the cursor and click to specify the length of the first vector. Then, move the cursor again and click to define the length of the second vector. Revit Structure will calculate the proportion of the two vectors and resize the selected element in the same proportion using the specified origin. The temporary dimensions displayed can also be used to resize the element to the desired scaling. For example, if the length of the first vector is **10'** for Imperial or **3048** mm for Metric and the second vector is **15'** for Imperial or **4572** mm for Metric, the selected element is resized **1.5** times. Figure 6-35 shows a **10'** for Imperial or **3048** mm for Metric long wall for which the left endpoint has been selected as the origin and the length of its final vector is **7'6"** in Imperial or **2286** mm in Metric. When you specify the length of the second vector as **15'** in Imperial or **4572** mm in Metric, as shown in Figure 6-36, Revit Structure calculates the proportion of the two vectors as 2 in this case and scales the wall length to **20'** in Imperial or **6096** mm in Metric. When the numeric value of the scaling is known, you can select the Numerical radio button from the Options Bar. After selecting the **Numerical** radio button, specify a numeric value in the **Scale** edit box. Next, you need to specify the origin of the scaling by clicking at the desired location in the drawing area. Revit Structure instantly will resize the element by the specified scaling proportion. For example, when you resize a **50'** long wall in Imperial or **15240** mm long wall in Metric by a numerical factor of **2.5**, its length is resized to **125'** for Imperial or **38100** mm for Metric systems.

Figure 6-35 *Structural wall selected for scaling with the origin at its left endpoint*

Figure 6-36 *Specifying the length of the second vector*

PINNING ELEMENTS

Ribbon: Modify | (Elements or Components) > Modify > Pin / Unpin
Shortcut Key: PN

Elements can be pinned to their position by using the **Pin** tool. To invoke the **Pin** tool, make a selection and choose this tool from the **Modify** panel. Alternatively, you can type **PN** to invoke the **Pin** tool. Once pinned, a graphical pushpin symbol will appear with the element, as shown in Figure 6-37, indicating that it is pinned and cannot be moved from its position. You can also pin the position with respect to other elements and groups. For example, you can pin the position of columns with the intersecting grid lines. Once pinned, column and grid lines cannot be moved without first unpinning their position. You can use the **Unpin** tool to unpin the position constraint for the pinned elements. Note that the **Unpin** tool will replace the **Pin** tool after an element has been pinned. You can click on the pin symbol to pin or unpin an element.

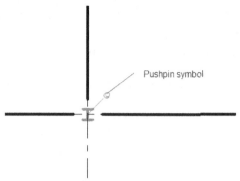

Figure 6-37 *The pushpin symbol displayed with the pinned column*

ALIGNING ELEMENTS

Ribbon: Modify > Modify > Align
Shortcut Key: AL

The **Align** tool is used to align elements collinearly. You can choose an element that acts as a reference line or a plane along which the other elements can be aligned. When you align elements, a padlock key will be displayed, representing the alignment constraint. Using this key, you can lock or unlock the alignment of the walls. Once you lock the alignment, walls move together. The **Align** tool can be used only in plan or elevation views that can be invoked from the **Modify** panel of the **Modify** tab. On doing so, a symbol will appear with the cursor. Now in the **Options Bar**, you can select the **Multiple Alignment** check box from the **Options Bar** to align a number of elements in a common line. While aligning walls, you can choose to align wall centerlines or wall faces by selecting an appropriate option from the **Prefer** drop-down list in the **Options Bar**.

After specifying the options from the **Options Bar**, you will be prompted to select the reference line or point for alignment. The reference line can be a grid line or can be referenced from the center or any face of an element. Move the cursor to the desired reference; the reference will be highlighted. Click on it; a dashed line will appear along the selected reference. This dashed line represents the reference line for alignment. Next, move the cursor over the element that you want to align; the reference of the element will be highlighted. For example, if you move the cursor over a rectangular concrete column, any of the central axes or edges may get highlighted. Click on the reference of the element when it gets highlighted; the selected element will be aligned with the reference line specified. After aligning the desired element, you will notice a padlock displayed along the reference line. You can click the padlock key to lock the alignment of these two walls. To align them to the third wall, select them as the reference line, as shown in Figures 6-38 through 6-41. These figures show the alignment of a column to the center of the structural wall.

Note
The pin symbol becomes invisible after invoking other tools. In such a case, the element or group must be selected to display the pin symbol.

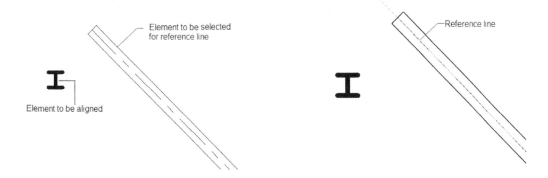

Figure 6-38 *Element to be selected for reference line and the element to be aligned*

Figure 6-39 *The reference line passing through the center of the selected structural wall*

Figure 6-40 *Vertical axis of the structural column selected for alignment*

Figure 6-41 *The aligned column with the structural wall with padlock displayed*

STEEL ELEMENT CUTTING TOOLS

Steel Element Cutting tools allow you to modify steel fabricated elements in a model. With these tools, you can create a cut, skewed cope, shorten, or create a contour cut on steel elements or plates. These tools are discussed in detail below.

Corner Cut

Ribbon:	Steel > Modifiers > Corner Cut

Corner Cut

This tool is used to create a corner cut on a structural plate. To create a corner cut, choose the **Corner Cut** tool from the **Modifiers** panel of the **Steel** tab and then click on the structural plate; a cut as per the default values in the Properties palette will be created and the **Modify|Modifiers** contextual tab will be displayed. In the **Properties** palette, you can select the type of cut you want to create by choosing the respective option from the **Type** drop-down list. You can select the **Straight** option from the **Type** drop-down list to create a straight cut at the edges. If the **Straight** option is selected, the **Side 1** and **Side 2** edit boxes will be displayed where cut values for two sides can be entered. You can select the **Concave** or **Convex** option from the **Type** drop-down list to create a curved cut at the edges.

On selecting any of these options, the **Radius** edit box will be displayed to specify the radius of the cut. Note that the corner cuts will be visible only when the detail level of the view is set to the **Fine** option. The options in the **Properties** palette for the **Corner Cut** tool are discussed next.

Parameter	Description
Type	Specifies the type of cut at the corner- convex, concave, or straight.
Side 1	(For straight cuts only) Specifies the length of the first side of the straight corner cut.
Side 2	(For straight cuts only) Specifies the length of the second side of the straight corner cut.
Radius	(For convex and concave cuts only) Specifies the segment length that calculates the convex or concave cut.

Cope Skew

Ribbon: Steel > Modifiers > Cope Skewed

Cope
Skewed

In Revit 2021, skewed cuts can be created on a steel framing elements. To create a cope skewed cut on a steel frame element, choose the **Cope Skewed** tool from the **Modifiers** panel of the **Steel** tab and then choose the frame element. On doing so, the cope skewed will be created on that element. The options in the **Properties** palette for the **Cope Skewed** tool are discussed next.

Parameter	Description
Cutback	Specifies the cutback distance of the cope planes from the end of the steel element.
Distance from axis	Specifies the offset distance of the cope planes along the z-axis.
Cross-section rotation	Specifies the angle of rotation of the cope planes around the steel element axis.
Around beam axis	When this check box is selected, the cross-section rotation is made around the steel element axis.
Plan rotation	Specifies the angle of rotation of the cope planes around its z-axis.
Tilt angle	Specifies the angle of rotation of the cope planes around its x-axis.
Radius	Specifies the radius for the convex or concave cut.
Boring out	When this check box is selected, the element is bored out by the radius value specified in the **Radius** parameter.

Shorten

Ribbon: Steel > Modifiers > Shorten

Shorten

The **Shorten** tool is used to shorten the start, end, top, or bottom of a steel beam, brace, or column to accommodate the geometry necessary for steel fabrication of elements. To shorten a steel framing element, choose the **Shorten** tool from the **Modifiers** panel of the **Steel** tab and then click on the steel framing element; the cut will be placed at the point where you click on the element. Note that you can not change its position once you have created it. The options in the **Properties** palette can be used to vary the properties of the **Shorten** tool. You can increase the length of the cut by entering required value in the **Length** edit box. If you specify a negative value in the **Length** parameter, then the length of the element will extend. To create a diagonal cut along height or width, you can assign angle values in the **Angle along height** or **Angle along width** edit box, respectively . Note that the modifications done through the **Shorten** tool will be visible only when the detail level of the view will be set to the **Fine** option.

Contour Cut

Ribbon: Steel > Modifiers > Contour Cut

Contour
Cut

In Revit 2021, contour cuts can be created on the face/s of steel framing elements or plates. To create a contour cut, choose the **Contour Cut** tool from the **Modifiers** panel of the **Steel** tab and then select the face of the steel element on which you want to sketch the contour cut; the **Modify | Create Contour** contextual tab will be displayed. You can use the sketch tools from the **Draw** panel of the **Modify | Create Contour** contextual tab to draw the shape of the contour. After drawing the contour cut on the steel fabricated material, choose **Finish Edit Mode** from the **Mode** panel of the **Modify | Create Contour** contextual tab; a contour cut will be created in the steel element. The instance properties of the contour cut will be available in the **Properties** palette. Plates and contour cuts will be only visible when the detail level of the view is set to the **Fine** option. Note that contour cuts will only be created on planar faces and once created, you cannot modify their position.

STRUCTURAL STEEL CONNECTIONS

Parametric tools are used to create connections between steel elements to accurately modify their geometry. With parametric tools, you can create cope, miter cut, saw cut at flange, saw cut at web, cut through, and cut by at the intersection of steel elements. These tools are discussed in detail next.

Cope

Ribbon: Steel > Parametric Cuts > Cope

Cope

In Revit 2021, you can create cope only between intersecting structural beams. To create a cope, choose the **Cope** tool from the **Parametric Cuts** panel of the **Steel** tab. Next, select the intersecting elements to cope and press ENTER; a cope will be created and the sub-connection between the framing elements will be displayed as a dashed-lined box, refer to Figure 6-42. Select the sub-connection box to modify the instance values in the **Properties** palette. Note that the steel fabrication cope cuts will be visible only when the detail level of the view is set to the **Fine** option.

Figure 6-42 *The Sub-connection created by using the **Cope** tool*

Miter

Ribbon:	Steel > Parametric Cuts > Miter

You can create a miter cut at the juncture of two steel elements. To create a parametric miter cut, choose the **Miter** tool from the **Parametric Cuts** panel of the **Steel** tab. Next, select the steel element to cut and press ENTER; the miter cut will be created and the sub-connection between the elements will be displayed as a dashed-lined box, refer to Figure 6-43. Select the sub-connection box to modify the instance properties displayed in the **Properties** palette. Note that the steel fabrication miter cuts are only visible when the detail level of the view is set to the **Fine** option.

Figure 6-43 *The sub-connection created by using the **Miter** tool*

Saw cut - Flange

Ribbon:	Steel > Parametric Cuts > Miter > Saw cut - Flange

Saw cut - Flange

In Revit 2021, you can create a connection between the flanges of two or more steel beams. To create a connection between the beams, choose the **Saw cut - Flange** tool from the **Miter** drop-down in the **Parametric Cuts** panel of the **Steel** tab. Next, select the steel elements and press ENTER; the connection is created between the flanges of the selection beams. The sub-connection between the elements will be displayed as a dash-lined box. You can modify the instance and type properties from the **Properties** palette.

Saw cut - Web

Ribbon:	Steel > Parametric Cuts > Miter > Saw cut - Web

Saw cut - Web

In Revit 2021, you can create a connection between the flanges of two or more steel beams. To create a connection between the beams, choose the **Saw cut - Web** tool from the **Miter** drop-down in the **Parametric Cuts** panel of the **Steel** tab. Next, select the steel elements and press ENTER; the connection is created between the webs of the selection beams. The sub-connection between the elements will be displayed as a dash-lined box. You can modify the instance and type properties from the **Properties** palette.

Cut Through

Ribbon:	Steel > Parametric Cuts > Cut Through

Cut Through

You can create a contour cut that allows a structural element to pass through an intersecting element with a weld in between. To create a parametric cut, choose the **Cut Through** tool from the **Parametric Cuts** panel of the **Steel** tab. Select the intersecting steel elements and then press ENTER; a cut through will be created at the intersection of the steel elements. The weld between the elements will be displayed as a cross symbol, as shown in Figure 6-44. You can modify its instance properties from the **Properties** palette.

Cut By

Ribbon:	Steel > Parametric Cuts > Cut By

Cut By

You can create a contoured cut along the shape of two or more intersecting elements. To create a parametric cut, choose the **Cut By** tool from the **Parametric Cuts** panel of the **Steel** tab. Select the intersecting steel elements and press ENTER; a cut will be created at the intersection. The sub-connection between the elements will be displayed as a dash-lined box. You can modify the properties of the connection from the **Properties** palette.

*Figure 6-44 The cross symbol formed by using the **Cut Through** tool*

MATCHING TYPE PROPERTIES

Ribbon: Modify > Clipboard > Match Type Properties
Shortcut Key: MA

In Revit Structure, you can use the **Match Type Properties** tool to copy the properties of a source element and transfer them to another element belonging to the same family. For example, you can select two walls and then match second wall's properties with the first wall.

Invoke the **Match Type Properties** tool from the **Clipboard** panel of the **Modify** tab. On doing so, you will notice that as you move the cursor in the drawing window, a paint brush will be attached to the cursor. To select an element to match, move the paint brush near the element and click. The empty paint brush will change into a filled one indicating that the element type has been selected. To match another element of the same family, move the dropper over it and click; the dropper will become empty again indicating that the element type has been changed. In case of walls, the matching wall type does not change the instance parameters. Revit Structure provides option for matching multiple family elements to a selected element of the same family.

TRIMMING AND EXTENDING ELEMENTS

In Revit Structure, you can use various tools to trim or extend one or more elements to a boundary defined by the element of the same type. You can also use the tools to extend or trim (if the elements intersect) the non-parallel elements to create a corner. These tools can be used to create corners, and trim or extend a reference line or a wall to another reference line or wall. You can use these tools with walls, lines, beams, or braces. In Autodesk Revit Structure, you can trim and extend elements by using three tools: **Trim/Extend to Corner**, **Trim/Extend Single Element**, and **Trim/Extend Multiple Elements**. The three tools are discussed next.

Trim/Extend to Corner Tool

Ribbon: Modify > Modify > Trim/Extend to Corner
Shortcut Key: TR

The **Trim/Extend to Corner** tool is used to extend a wall or a beam to another wall or beam, or trim any extended portion at the apparent intersection to form a corner. For example, to extend the vertical structural wall to the horizontal structural wall such that the left portion of the horizontal structural wall is retained, use the **Trim/Extend to Corner** tool, refer to Figure 6-45. You can invoke the **Trim/Extend to Corner** tool from the **Modify** panel of the **Modify** tab. Next, select the horizontal structural wall which is to be trimmed or extended. If you want to retain its left portion then click anywhere on the structural wall on the left region of the apparent intersection, as shown in Figure 6-46. To select the next structural wall to be trimmed or extended, move the cursor near the vertical wall. As you move the cursor, you will notice that a dashed line is displayed indicating that the corner will be formed, as shown in Figure 6-47. When you click on the vertical structural wall, it extends and the horizontal wall is trimmed to form the desired corner, as shown in Figure 6-48.

Figure 6-45 Horizontal wall to be trimmed with the extended vertical wall

Figure 6-46 Selecting the first wall to trim/ extend on the side to be retained

Figure 6-47 Selecting the second wall to be trimmed/extended

Figure 6-48 Trimmed and extended walls

Trim/Extend Single Element Tool

Ribbon: Modify > Trim/Extend Single Element

The **Trim/Extend Single Element** tool enables you to extend or trim an element by defining a reference line or boundary. Using this tool, you can trim a wall or extend a wall to another wall without creating a corner at the intersection. You can also select the desired side of the wall to be retained. For example, you can use this tool to trim the vertical wall at its intersection with the horizontal wall so that the lower portion of the vertical wall is retained. To do so, invoke the **Trim/Extend Single Element** tool from the **Modify** tab, and then to retain the lower portion of the horizontal wall, move the cursor near it until the lower edge of the horizontal wall is highlighted, as shown in Figure 6-49. Next, click on the highlighted edge to select the boundary. Move the cursor to the lower side of the vertical wall and click anywhere on this wall to retain the lower portion. On doing so, the vertical wall will be trimmed at the specified boundary, as shown in Figure 6-50.

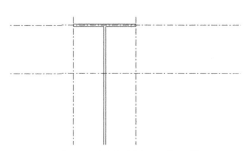

Figure 6-49 *Selecting the edge of the wall to specify the boundary*

Figure 6-50 *Trimmed wall*

Trim/Extend Multiple Elements Tool

Ribbon: Modify > Trim/Extend Multiple Elements

The **Trim/Extend Multiple Elements** tool is used to extend or trim a number of elements by using a common boundary or edge. The common boundary or edge can be defined by clicking on an element. After specifying the boundary, select the elements to be extended or trimmed; Revit Structure will extend or trim them at the defined boundary. For example, you may want to extend and trim multiple vertical and inclined walls by using the horizontal wall as the boundary defining element such that the lower portions of the walls are retained. For this, invoke the **Trim/Extend Multiple Elements** tool from the **Modify** tab; you will notice that a symbol appears along with the cursor. Next, move the cursor and place it on the lower edge of the wall and click when the edge is highlighted. On doing so, the lower edge of the horizontal wall will be defined as the cutting boundary and will be highlighted, as shown in Figure 6-51. Next, move the cursor and place it on the lower portion of the middle vertical wall; it will be highlighted, as shown in Figure 6-52. Next, click to trim the wall at the specified boundary. Similarly, you can click on the inclined wall at its lower portion to trim it. Without exiting the **Trim** tool, move the cursor near the vertical wall which you want to extend, and click when the dashed line appears, as shown in Figure 6-53. The wall will extend to the horizontal wall, as shown in

Figure 6-54. In this way, you can extend or trim multiple building elements to a specified boundary. Alternatively, you can trim walls by drawing a selection set and selecting the length of the elements to be trimmed.

Figure 6-51 *Selecting the lower edge of the horizontal wall*

Figure 6-52 *Placing the cursor on the lower portion of the middle wall*

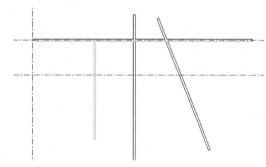

Figure 6-53 *Selecting the wall to extend*

Figure 6-54 *The selected wall extended*

> **Tip**
> *While selecting walls or lines for extending and trimming, ensure that the portion of the element to be retained is clicked. In trimming, the portion of the element on the other side of the intersection is removed.*

OFFSETTING ELEMENTS

Ribbon:	Modify > Modify > Offset
Shortcut Key:	OF

In Autodesk Revit, you can use the **Offset** tool to offset elements based on your project requirement. This tool is used to create the copy of a selected element at a specified distance from the original element. You can select a single element or multiple elements. The selection can be made even after invoking this tool. By default, Revit Structure creates the copy of a selected element while creating an offset. To invoke the **Offset** tool, choose it from the **Modify** panel of the **Modify** tab. Alternatively, you can type **OF** to invoke this tool. On invoking the **Offset** tool, you will notice that the **Copy** check box is displayed in the **Options**

Bar. By default, this check box is selected. As a result, you can create a copy of the element at the offset distance. Clear the **Copy** check box if you do not need a copy of the element. The **Options Bar** also displays two radio buttons: **Graphical** and **Numerical**. The use of these radio buttons is discussed next.

Select the **Graphical** radio button and then select the elements. Next, click in the drawing area to specify the start point of the offset distance. On doing so, a preview image of the selected element will be displayed. Next, click again to specify the second point; the selected element will be copied at the distance and direction defined by two specified points. As you move the cursor to specify the second point, the temporary dimension will be displayed. To specify the exact offset distance, move the cursor in an appropriate direction and enter the offset value in the edit box, as shown in Figure 6-55. Figure 6-56 shows the offset element that is created. The **Numerical** radio button of the **Offset** tool provides you the flexibility to create an offset by specifying the offset distance in the **Offset** edit box of the **Options Bar**. Note that the value you specify in the edit box must be a positive number. After specifying the offset distance, if you move the cursor near the element, a preview image profile of the selected element at the specified offset distance will be displayed in the form of a dashed line. At this stage, you can change the offset distance. You will notice that as you move the cursor over the element, the preview image flips the sides. To select a chain of elements, press the TAB key when the preview image is displayed; all the connected elements will be selected and the preview will change accordingly. Figure 6-57 shows the connected wall profile with its preview offset image. When you see the preview image on the desired side, click to offset the walls; the offset will be created at the distance specified in the **Offset** edit box in the **Options Bar**. Figure 6-58 shows the wall profile created by offsetting it.

Note
You can offset elements only in the same work plane. You cannot offset the elements created as in-place families.

Wall created after offsetting

*Figure 6-55 Specifying the offset distance on selecting the **Graphical** radio button*

*Figure 6-56 Offset wall created at the specified distance on selecting the **Graphical** radio button*

Figure 6-57 *Previewing the offset and selecting a chain of walls using the TAB key*

Figure 6-58 *Walls created at the specified offset distance*

DELETING ELEMENTS

Ribbon: Modify | (Elements or Components) > Modify > Delete
Shortcut Key: DE

 You can use the **Delete** tool to remove the selected elements from a project. On doing so, the deleted elements will permanently be removed and will not be pasted on the clipboard. The tool is available only after the elements have been selected. To invoke the **Delete** tool, select the element that you want to delete and then choose it from the **Modify** panel of the contextual tab. Alternatively, you can press the DELETE key or enter **DE** to invoke the **Delete** tool.

GROUPING ELEMENTS

Ribbon: Structure > Model > Model Group drop-down > Create Group

Grouping elements helps you to represent a number of elements as a single entity. Once grouped, these elements can be modified individually. For example, you can move or copy the grouped elements as a single unit. Each instance of the group acts as a single unit and any modification done in the group is reflected in all its instances.

For example, you may create a group with a collection of beams and then create its multiple instances. When you modify the beam type in one group, the change will reflect in all the instances of that group. In a project, you can create three types of groups for the elements in the model. These types are: Model Groups, Detail Groups, and Attached Detail Groups. You can create groups either by selecting the elements first and then grouping them, or by creating the groups first and then adding elements to the group. To create a group, invoke the **Create Group** tool from the **Create** panel of the **Modify** tab; the **Create Group** dialog box will be displayed. In this dialog box, enter the name of the group in the **Name** edit box.

Next, in the **Group Type** area, you can select the **Model** or **Detail** radio button. You can select the **Model** radio button to create a model group or select the **Detail** radio button to create a detail group. Now, choose the **OK** button to close the **Create Group** dialog box. However, if you invoke the **Create Group** tool after selecting the elements, you would need to name the group first and then you can add elements in the group. In the next sections, you will learn various methods and techniques to create, modify, and place groups in a project.

Creating Groups by Selecting Elements

In a project, you can create a group by selecting only the model elements from the project views or using the **Group Editor**. To create groups of elements, select the elements to group and then choose the **Create Group** tool from the **Create** panel of the **Modify | Multi-Select** contextual tab; the **Create Model Group** dialog box will be displayed. Alternatively, after selecting the elements to be grouped, choose the **Create Group** tool from **Structure > Model > Model Group** drop-down; the **Create Model Group** dialog box will be displayed.

In the **Create Model Group** dialog box, specify the name of the group in the **Name** edit box and choose the **OK** button; the name of the created group will be automatically displayed under the **Group** heading in the **Project Browser**. The default name of a model group is **Group 1** and the number in it increments as more groups are created. You can rename a group by selecting and right-clicking on its name and choosing **Rename** from the shortcut menu.

Note
While creating a group, if you have selected any one element type, the corresponding Modify | (Elements / Components) contextual tab will be displayed instead of the Multi-Select tab.

Creating Groups Using the Group Editor

This option allows you to create groups prior to the selection of the elements. You can create the **Model** group or the **Annotation** group based on the requirement and later on, select the elements from the project views and add them to the group. To do so, choose the **Create Group** tool from **Structure > Model > Model Group** drop-down; the **Create Group** dialog box will be displayed. In this dialog box, specify the name of the group in the **Name** edit box. The **Group Type** area in this dialog box displays two radio buttons, **Model** and **Detail**. Specify the type of group by selecting the **Model** or **Detail** radio button and then choose the **OK** button; the screen will turn into the edit mode with a yellow background and the **Edit Group** panel will be displayed in the **Structure** tab. Figure 6-59 shows the options in the **Edit Group** panel.

Figure 6-59 The options in the Edit Group panel

In the **Edit Group** panel, you can choose the **Add** button to add elements into a group. On choosing the **Add** button, the add (+) symbol will appear with the cursor. You can select the elements from the project view to group them. If there are no elements in the project view, you can create the elements using different tools from the **Structure** panel in the **Structure** tab. The elements will be automatically grouped. You can remove the elements from the existing group, attach details, and even view properties of the group using the respective buttons from the toolbar. Choose the **Finish** button after adding elements to the group to finish editing.

Creating a Detail Group

Revit Structure allows you to group all detail lines, fill regions, and the detail components separately. To group detail components, select them in the drawing and choose the **Create Group** tool from **Annotate > Detail > Detail Group** drop-down; the **Create Detail Group** dialog box will be displayed. Specify the name of the detail group in the **Name** edit box and choose the **OK** button; the name of the detail group will be displayed in **Groups > Detail** head in the **Project Browser**.

You can create a new group by duplicating an existing group. You can also modify the group without affecting the parent group. To create a duplicate group, select the group to be duplicated in the **Project Browser** and right-click; a shortcut menu will be displayed. Choose **Duplicate** from the shortcut menu; a new group will be added in the **Project browser** under the parent group. You can rename the group, if required.

Alternatively, to create a duplicate group, select the group of which the duplicate is to be created from the drawing area; the **Modify| Detail Groups** contextual tab is displayed. Choose the **Type Properties** tool from the **Properties** panel of this tab; the **Type Properties** dialog box is displayed. Choose the **Duplicate** button from the dialog box; the **Name** dialog box will be displayed. Name the group in the **Name** edit box of this dialog box and choose the **OK** button; the **Name** dialog box will be closed. Now, choose the **OK** button in the **Type Properties** dialog box; the dialog box will be closed and the group will be added to the **Project Browser** with a new name.

Placing Groups

Once a group is created, you can easily place its instances in the project by dragging the group from the **Project Browser**. Select the required **Detail** or **Model** group from the **Project Browser**, drag and drop it at the desired location in the drawing area, and then click to place it. Alternatively, to place a model group, choose the **Place Model Group** tool from **Structure > Model > Model Group** drop-down; the **Modify | Place Group** contextual tab will be displayed. Select the required group from the **Type Selector** drop-down list and click in the drawing area to place the model group.

Alternatively, to place a detail group, choose the **Place Detail Group** tool from **Annotate > Detail > Detail Group** drop-down; the **Modify | Place Group** contextual tab will be displayed. Now, select the desired detail group from the **Type Selector** drop-down list and click in the drawing area to place the detail group.

Modifying Groups

You can modify a group by ungrouping it. To modify a group, select it from the drawing; the **Modify | Model Groups** contextual tab will be displayed. The **Group** panel of this tab displays the **Edit Group**, **Ungroup**, and **Link** buttons. On choosing the **Ungroup** button, the elements in the selected group will be disassociated and ungrouped. Using the **Edit Group** button, you can add or remove elements from the group and also attach details to it. When you choose this button, the screen will enter into the edit mode displaying the **Edit Group** panel, refer to Figure 6-59. The **Add** and **Remove** buttons can be chosen to add and remove elements from the group, respectively. After editing, choose the **Finish** button to complete the modifications. The **Cancel** button provides the option of discarding the modifications and returning to the **Modify | Model Groups** contextual tab. You can use different editing tools on the grouped elements such as **Move**, **Copy**, **Mirror**, **Cut**, **Paste**, **Rotate**, and so on.

Excluding Elements from a Group

You can exclude elements from a group if some elements of the group overlap with the elements of the other group while placing them together. To exclude an element from a group, place the cursor over the element that you want to exclude. Next, press TAB to highlight it, and click; a blue color icon will be displayed. When you place the cursor on the icon, a tooltip will be displayed prompting you to click on the icon to exclude the selected element. Click on the icon and press ESC; the element will be excluded from the group, and will not be displayed in the drawing. Alternatively, to exclude an element from the group, select the element in the drawing as explained above and right-click; a shortcut menu will be displayed. Choose **Exclude** from the shortcut menu; the element will disappear from the drawing and will be excluded from the group. The elements that are excluded will not be visible in the drawing and will not be included in the schedule. To restore the excluded elements in the group, place the cursor over the desired group and right-click; a shortcut menu will be displayed. Choose **Restore All Excluded** from the shortcut menu; the elements will be restored in the group and will be displayed in the drawing.

Saving and Loading Groups

To save groups, choose **Save As > Library > Group** from the **File** menu; the **Save Group** dialog box will be displayed. Select the group to be saved from the **Group To Save** drop-down list and then save it using either the same name as the group name or enter a new name in the **File name** edit box. The group(s) will be saved with the assigned name with *.rvt* extension in case of a project file, or *.rfa* extension in case of a family file.

EDITING ELEMENTS

In Autodesk Revit, you can use editing tools to modify the elements so as to enhance their properties. Some of the editing tools are discussed in detail next.

Applying and Removing Coping

Coping is a process which is used to attach steel members of a model such as beams and columns together. This is basically applied to those beams which are intersecting each other, as shown in Figure 6-60. The **Apply Coping** tool is used to attach the beams to the girders on which they rest. You can apply and then remove copings between the structure steel members.

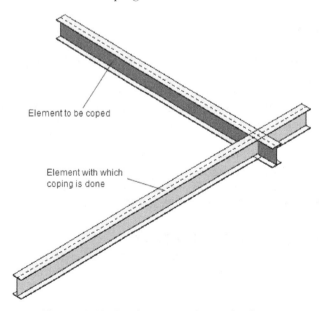

Figure 6-60 *Two beams crossing each other*

Choose the **Apply Coping** tool from the **Cope** drop-down of the **Geometry** panel; the cursor will change to cross hairs and will prompt you to select the element to be coped, refer to Figure 6-60. Select the first element and then next element with which coping is to be done. The two beam members will get coped, as shown in Figure 6-61.

Note
*Once two elements cope with each other, the **Coping Distance** parameter will be displayed in the **Properties** palette. You can change the value of the **Coping Distance** parameter as desired.*

You can remove the coping between the beams by choosing the **Remove Coping** tool from the **Cope** drop-down of the **Geometry** panel and then select the two beams from which coping is to be removed.

Figure 6-61 *The beams after applying coping*

Joining and Unjoining Elements

The **Join Geometry** tool allows you to create joins between two or more host elements which share common face such as columns and walls. To join the geometries, choose the **Join Geometry** tool from the **Join** drop-down of the **Geometry** panel. On doing so, the join geometry tool gets attached with the cursor and prompts you to select the geometry to be joined. First, select the geometry to be joined, as shown in Figure 6-62, and then select the geometry with which it is to be joined, as shown in Figure 6-63. The geometries get joined, as shown in Figure 6-64.

Figure 6-62 *Select first entity to be joined*

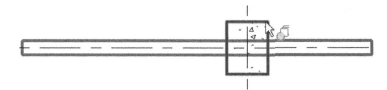

Figure 6-63 *Select second entity to be joined*

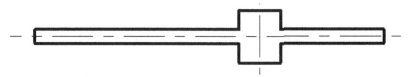

Figure 6-64 *First entity gets joined with the second*

Similarly, you can unjoin the geometries from the drawing. To unjoin the geometries, choose the **Unjoin Geometry** tool from the **Join** drop-down of the **Geometry** panel. On doing so, the tool gets attached with the cursor and prompts you to select the geometries to be removed. Select both geometries one by one and the joins will be removed.

SPLITTING FACE

You can use the **Split Face** tool to divide the face of an element such as wall or an architectural column. This tool allows you to divide the face into different regions for application of different materials. To apply the split on the face, choose the **Split Face** tool from the **Geometry** panel of the **Modify** tab. On doing so, a cube gets attached with the cursor and you are prompted to select a wall of whose face is to be splitted. Select a wall to split the face, as shown in Figure 6-65; the **Modify | Split Face > Create Boundary** contextual tab will be displayed.

Figure 6-65 *Selecting the face to be split*

In this tab, you can select the required tool to sketch the geometry from the **Draw** panel, as shown in Figure 6-66 and then choose the **Finish Edit Mode** button; the face get split from the selected face, as shown in Figure 6-67. Now, you can apply separate material to the split face.

Figure 6-66 *The geometry created on the selected face*

Figure 6-67 *The created geometry gets split from the selected face*

TUTORIALS

Tutorial 1   Commercial Complex

In this tutorial, you will rotate some of the structural foundations and columns of the *Commercial Complex* project created in Tutorial 1 of Chapter 5. Further, you will copy beams, columns, and floor in the **Second Floor** structural plan view and paste them on the **Roof** level, using the **Filter** tool. Use the following project parameters and specifications:

(Expected time: 45 min)

1. Rotation Angle: **90°**
2. Elements to be copied to level: columns, beams, and structural floor
3. File name to be assigned:
    For Imperial   *c06_Commercial-Complex_tut1.rvt*
    For Metric   *M_c06_Commercial-Complex_tut1.rvt*

The following steps are required to complete this tutorial:

a. Open Tutorial 1 of Chapter 5.
b. Rotate structural foundations (at the **Entry** level).
c. Rotate columns (at the **Entry** level).
d. Copy and paste columns, floors, and beams.
e. Save the project using the **Save As** tool.
f. Close the project using the **Close** tool.

Opening the Existing Project
In this section, you will open the project file created in Tutorial 1 of Chapter 5.

1. Choose **Open > Project** from the **File** menu; the **Open** dialog box is displayed.

2. In this dialog box, browse to *C:\rst_2021\c05_rst_2021_tut* location and then choose the *c05_Commercial-Complex_tut1.rvt* for Imperial *or M_c05_Commercial-Complex_tut1.rvt* for Metric project file. You can also download this file from *https://www.cadcim.com*. The path of the file is as follows: *Textbooks > Civil/GIS > Revit Structure > Exploring Autodesk Revit 2021 for Structure*.

3. Choose the **Open** button from the **Open** dialog box; the selected project file opens in the drawing window in the **Second Floor** structural plan view.

Rotating the Structural Foundations
In this section, you will select some of the structural foundations in the **Entry** project view and rotate it.

1. Double-click on the **Entry** node in the **Structural Plans** head in the **Project Browser** to open the corresponding structural floor plan view.

2. Place the cursor on the structural foundation located at the intersection of grid 3.1 and grid C.1; the structural foundation is highlighted, as shown in Figure 6-68.

3. Click on the highlighted foundation to select it.

4. Choose the **Rotate** tool from the **Modify** panel of the **Modify | Structural Foundations** contextual tab; a dashed preview box is displayed around the selected foundation.

Figure 6-68 *The structural foundation highlighted*

5. In the **Options Bar**, click on the **Angle** edit, enter **90** and then press ENTER; the selected structural foundation is rotated by 90 degrees about its center, refer to Figure 6-69.

Figure 6-69 *The structural foundation rotated*

6. Place the cursor on the structural foundation located at the intersection of grids 3.1 and G.2. Click to select the highlighted structural foundation.

7. Repeat the procedure followed in steps 4 and 5 to rotate the selected structural foundation.

8. Choose the **Modify** tool from the **Select** panel to exit the selection.

Rotating Columns

In this section, you will rotate some of the structural columns in the structural model.

1. Place the cursor over the column located at the intersection of grid 4 and grid D; the column is highlighted, as shown in Figure 6-70. Click on the highlighted column to select it.

Figure 6-70 *The structural column highlighted*

2. Choose the **Rotate** tool from the **Modify** panel of the **Modify | Structural Columns** contextual tab; a dashed preview box is displayed around the structural column.

3. In the **Options Bar**, click in the **Angle** edit box and enter **90**. Press ENTER; the selected column is rotated 90 degrees about its center.

4. Next, repeat the procedure followed in steps 1 to 3 to rotate the columns located at the following grid intersections: (4, E); (5, D); and (5, E). After rotating the desired columns, the structural plan view at the **Entry** level appears as shown in Figure 6-71.

Figure 6-71 *The structural plan view at the **Entry** level*

Copying and Pasting Structural Columns, Floors, and Beams

In this section, you will select structural columns and beams in the **Second Floor** structural plan view and then copy and paste them at the **Roof** level. To select the beams and columns, you will use the **Filter** tool.

1. Double-click on **Second Floor** in the **Structural Plans** head in the **Project Browser** to open the corresponding structural floor plan view.

2. Place the cursor between grids A and 1, as shown in Figure 6-72.

3. Now, press and hold the left mouse button and drag the cursor diagonally down and place it between grid I and grid 5.1, as shown in Figure 6-73. On dragging the cursor down, a selection window emerges and all the elements including grids enclosed inside the selection box are highlighted.

Figure 6-72 *Placing the cursor to select the start point of the selection window*

4. Release the left mouse button; all the elements in the selection box are selected.

5. Choose the **Filter** tool from the **Selection** panel of the **Modify | Multi-Select** contextual tab; the **Filter** dialog box is displayed.

6. In the **Filter** dialog box, choose the **Check None** button; all the check boxes in the **Category** column are cleared.

Figure 6-73 Placing the cursor to select the endpoint of the selection window

7. Now, select the following check boxes in the **Category** column: **Floors**, **Structural Columns**, **Structural Framing (Girder)**, and **Structural Framing (Other)**.

8. Choose **Apply** and then **OK**; the **Filter** dialog box closes.

9. Invoke the **Copy to Clipboard** tool from the **Clipboard** panel of the **Modify | Multi-Select** contextual tab; the selected elements are copied to the clipboard.

10. Next, choose the **Aligned to Selected Levels** tool from **Modify | Multi-Select > Clipboard > Paste** drop-down; the **Select Levels** dialog box is displayed.

11. Click on the **Roof** option in this dialog box and then choose **OK**; the selected elements are copied to the **Roof** level. Ignore warning message, if any.

12. Choose the **Modify** tool from the **Select** panel to exit the selection.

Adding Beams to the Roof Level
In this section, you will add beams to the columns that are projected to the **Roof** level.

1. Double-click on the **Roof** node under the **Structural Plans** head in the **Project Browser**.

2. Invoke the **Beam** tool from the **Structure** panel in the **Structure** tab.

3. In the **Properties** palette, ensure that the **Concrete-Rectangular Beam: 12 x 24 (M_Concrete-Rectangular Beam: 300x600** for metric) option is selected in the **Type Selector** drop-down list.

4. Now, using the **Beam** tool that is already invoked, add beams between the following grid intersections:
   (G.1,4) and (E,4); (E,4) and (D,4); (D,4) and (B,4); (B,4) and (B, 5); (B,5) and (D, 5); (D,5) and (E, 5); (E,5) and (G.1, 5); and (G.1,5) and (G.1, 4)

5. Next, choose the **Modify** tool from the **Select** panel and then select the beams created in the previous step by using the CTRL key, and in the **Properties** palette, replace the existing values in the value fields of the **Start Level Offset** and **End Level Offset** parameters with **-1'** for Imperial (**-300mm** for Metric).

6. Choose the **Modify** tool to exit from the current selection.

Saving the Project

In this section, you will save the project file using the **Save As** tool.

1. Choose the **Save As > Project** option from the **File** menu; the **Save As** dialog box is displayed.

2. In this dialog box, browse to the *C:\rst_2021* location and create a folder with name **c06_rst_2021_tut**. Next, open the created folder and enter **c06_Commercial-Complex_tut1** for Imperial and **M_c06_Commercial-Complex_tut1** for Metric unit system in the **File name** edit box.

3. Choose the **Save** button; the **Save As** dialog box closes and the project file is saved.

Closing the Project

1. Choose the **Close** option from the **File** menu.

The file is closed and this completes Tutorial 1 of Chapter 6.

Tutorial 2   Industrial Complex

In this tutorial, you will rotate some of the structural foundations and columns of the *Industrial-Complex* project created in Tutorial 2 of Chapter 5. Further, you will copy beams, columns and floor in the **Second Floor** structural plan view and paste them on the **Roof** level using the **Filter** tool. You will also mirror the structural elements at different levels. Use the following project parameters: **(Expected time: 45 min)**

1. Rotation Angle: **90°**

2. Elements to be copied to **Roof** level: columns, beams, and floor

3. File name to be assigned:

   For Imperial   *c06_Industrial-Complex_tut2.rvt.*
   For Metric   *M_c06_Industrial-Complex_tut2.rvt*

The following steps are required to complete this tutorial:

a. Open the project file.
       For Imperial   *c05_Industrial-Complex_tut2.rvt*
       For Metric   *M_c05_Industrial-Complex_tut2.rvt*
b. Copy and paste structural elements.
c. Rotate structural foundations and columns.
d. Delete structural columns and foundations.
e. Mirror structural elements at different levels.
f. Adjust the height of the column and the offset of the beams.
g. Save the project using the **Save As** tool.
h. Close the project using the **Close** tool.

Opening the Existing Project
In this section, you will open the project file created in Tutorial 2 of Chapter 5.

1. Choose **Open > Project** from the **File** menu; the **Open** dialog box is displayed.

2. In this dialog box, browse to the *C:\rst_2021\c05_rst_2021_tut* location and choose the *c05_Industrial-Complex_tut2.rvt* for Imperial *or M_c05_Industrial-Complex_tut2.rvt* for Metric project file. You can also download this file from *httpss://www.cadcim.com*. The path of the file is as follows: *Textbooks > Civil/GIS > Revit Structure > Exploring Autodesk Revit 2021 for Structure*.

3. Choose the **Open** button from the **Open** dialog box; the selected project file opens in the drawing window in the **Second Floor** structural plan view.

Copying and Pasting the Structural Elements
In this section, you will select the columns, beams, and floor displayed in the **Second Floor** structural plan view, copy them to the clipboard, and then paste them to the **Roof** level.

1. Ensure that the **Second Floor** node is selected in the **Structural Plans** head in the **Project Browser**.

2. Place the cursor between grid 9 and grid C, refer to Figure 6-74. Now, press and hold the left mouse button and drag the cursor down diagonally, and place it in the area bounded by grid 7 and grid A', refer to Figure 6-75. On dragging the cursor down, a selection window emerges from the start and all the elements that are enclosed completely inside the selection box get highlighted.

3. Next, release the left mouse button to specify the endpoint of the selection box; all elements inside the selection box are selected.

Figure 6-74 *The start point of the selection box*   *Figure 6-75*   *Specifying the endpoint of the selection box*

4. Choose the **Filter** tool from the **Selection** panel of the **Modify | Multi-Select** contextual tab; the **Filter** dialog box is displayed. In this dialog box, choose the **Check None** button, and then select the following check boxes: **Floors**, **Structural Columns**, and **Structural Framing (Girder)**, refer to Figure 6-76.

Figure 6-76   *The **Filter** dialog box displaying the selected check boxes*

5. In the **Filter** dialog box, choose **Apply** and then **OK** to apply the filter to the selection and close the **Filter** dialog box.

6. Invoke the **Copy to Clipboard** tool from the **Clipboard** panel of the **Modify| Multi-Select** contextual tab.

7. Next, invoke the **Aligned to Selected Levels** tool from **Modify| Multi-Select > Clipboard > Paste** drop-down; the **Select Levels** dialog box is displayed, as shown in Figure 6-77.

*Figure 6-77 The **Select Levels** dialog box*

8. In this dialog box, click on the **Roof** option and choose **OK**; the **Select Levels** dialog box is closed. The selected elements are copied and pasted at the **Roof** level. Ignore warning message if any.

9. Next, choose the **Modify** tool from the **Select** panel to exit from the current selection.

Rotating Structural Foundations and the Columns

In this section, you will rotate some of the structural columns and foundations.

1. Double-click on the **Entry** node under the **Structural Plans** head in the **Project Browser**.

2. Place the cursor over the structural column located at the grid intersection (A',3); the structural column is highlighted.

3. Click to select the highlighted structural column.

4. Next, press and hold the CTRL key and click on the structural foundation located at the same grid intersection; the structural foundation is added to the selection.

5. Now, release the CTRL key and choose **Modify > Rotate** from the **Modify | Multi-Select** contextual tab. Notice that a preview box in dashed line is displayed around the selected elements.

6. In the **Options Bar**, type **90** in the **Angle** edit box and press ENTER; the selected column and the structural foundation are rotated by 90 degrees.

7. Repeat steps 2 to 6 and rotate columns and foundations at the following grid intersections: (B',3); (B',2); and (A',2).

Note

While selecting the column and foundation, first you will select the column and then the structural foundation using the CTRL key.

After rotating the desired structural foundations and columns, choose the **Modify** tool from the **Select** panel to exit the selection mode.

Deleting Columns and Structural Foundations

In this section, you will delete some of the structural columns and foundations.

1. Place the cursor over the column at the grids intersection (A',1); the structural column is highlighted.

2. Click to select the structural column.

3. Press and hold the CTRL key and select the structural foundation located at the same grid intersection.

4. Next, click on the column and then click on the structural foundation located at the grid intersection (B',1).

5. Release the CTRL key and choose **Modify > Delete** from the **Modify | Multi-Select** contextual tab; the selected elements are deleted from the project.

Mirroring the Structural Elements at Different Levels

In this section, you will mirror the left section of the structural model using grid 4 as mirror axis.

1. Double-click on the **Foundation Level** node under the **Structural Plans** head in the **Project Browser**.

2. Now, place the cursor between grid C and grid 9, as shown in Figure 6-78. Press and hold the left mouse button and drag the cursor downward and place it between grid 7 and grid A', as shown in Figure 6-79.

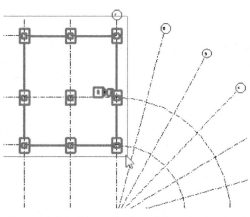

Figure 6-78 The start point of the selection box   *Figure 6-79* The endpoint of the selection box

3. Release the left mouse button; the elements within the selection box are selected.

4. Choose the **Filter** tool from the **Selection** panel of the **Modify| Multi-Select** contextual tab; the **Filter** dialog box is displayed.

5. In the **Filter** dialog box, clear the **Foundation Span Direction Symbol** check box.

6. Choose **Apply** and then the **OK** button; the filter is applied to the selection and the **Filter** dialog box is closed.

7. Now, choose the **Mirror - Pick Axis** tool from the **Modify** panel of the **Modify | Multi- Select** contextual tab. Notice that the mirror symbol appears with cursor. Move the cursor and place it over grid 4; grid 4 is highlighted.

8. Click at the highlighted grid; the selected elements are mirrored along grid 4. Ignore warning message if any.

9. Now, double-click on the **Second Floor** node under the **Structural Plans** head in the **Project browser**.

10. Next, create a selection box similar to that created using steps 2 and 3, refer to Figures 6-78 and 6-79.

11. Choose the **Filter** tool from the **Selection** panel of the **Modify | Multi-Select** contextual tab; the **Filter** dialog box is displayed.

12. In the dialog box, choose the **Check None** button and then select the following check boxes: **Floors** and **Structural Framing (Girder)**.

13. Choose **Apply** and then **OK** from the **Filter** dialog box; the filter is applied to the selection and the **Filter** dialog box is closed.

14. Now, repeat steps 7 and 8 to mirror the selected elements.

15. Double-click on the **Roof** node under the **Structural Plans** head in the **Project Browser**.

16. Next, create a selection box similar to that created using steps 2 and 3.

17. Choose the **Filter** tool from the **Selection** panel of the **Modify |Multi-Select** contextual tab; the **Filter** dialog box is displayed.

18. In the dialog box, ensure that the following check boxes: **Floors**, **Structural Columns**, and **Structural Framing (Girder)** are selected.

19. Choose **Apply** and then **OK** from the **Filter** dialog box; the filter is applied to the selection and the **Filter** dialog box is closed.

20. Now, repeat steps 7 and 8 to mirror the selected elements, as shown in Figure 6-80. After mirroring the selected elements, choose the **Modify** tool from the **Select** panel to exit the selection mode. Ignore, if a warning message is displayed.

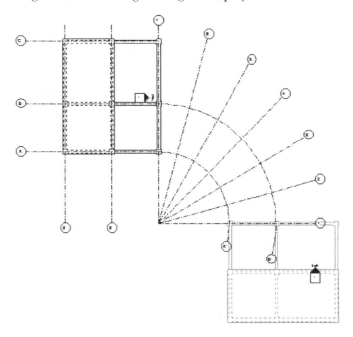

Figure 6-80 *The mirrored structural elements*

Adjusting the Height of Columns and Offset of Beams
In this section, you will adjust the height of the columns and also offset the beams.

1. Place the cursor over the column located at the grid-intersection (C,7). Click when it is highlighted.

2. Next, right-click and choose **Select All Instances > Visible in View** from the shortcut menu displayed; all the rectangular concrete columns displayed in the **Roof** structural plan view are selected.

3. In the **Properties** palette, click in the value field of the **Base Offset** parameter and replace the existing value with **0** for Imperial unit system or Metric unit system. Choose the **Apply** button from the **Properties** palette to apply the modified parameter to the selected columns.

4. Double-click on the **Second Floor** node under the **Structural Plans** head in the **Project Browser**.

5. Move the cursor and place it over the column located at the grid intersection (B',6). Click when it is highlighted.

6. Right-click and choose **Select All Instances > Visible in View** from the displayed shortcut menu; all the W Shapes columns displayed in the **Second Floor** structural plan view are selected.

7. In the **Properties** palette, click in the value field corresponding to the **Top Offset** parameter and delete the existing value. Next, enter **-5"** for Imperial or **-127mm** for Metric. Choose the **Apply** button in the **Properties** palette to apply the modified parameter to the selected columns.

8. Next, place the cursor on the beam located at grid intersection (B',5) and (A',5). Click when it is highlighted.

9. Right-click and then choose **Select All Instances > Visible in View** from the shortcut menu displayed; all the W Shapes beams displayed in the **Second Floor** structural plan view are selected.

10. In the **Properties** palette, click in the value fields of the **Start Level Offset** and **End Level Offset** parameters and replace the existing value **-5"** in Imperial system or **-127mm** in Metric system. Choose the **Apply** button in the **Properties** palette to apply the modified parameter to the selected columns.

Saving the Project

In this section, you will save the project file using the **Save As** tool.

1. Choose **Save As > Project** option from the **File** menu; the **Save As** dialog box is displayed.

2. In this dialog box, browse to *C:\rst_2021\c06_rst_2021_tut* and enter **c06_Industrial-Complex_tut2** for Imperial or **M_c06_Industrial-Complex_tut2** for Metric in the **File name** edit box.

3. Now, choose the **Save** button; the **Save As** dialog box closes and the project file is saved.

Closing the Project

1. Choose the **Close** option from the **File** menu.

    The file is closed and this completes Tutorial 2 of Chapter 6.

Self-Evaluation Test

Answer the following questions and then compare them to those given at the end of this chapter:

1. You can use the _____ tool to select the elements of similar instances in a drawing.

2. The _____ tool is used to refine a selection process by removing the elements of specific categories from the current selection set.

3. The _____ tool is used to create and place the copies of same type of a selected element or a group at specified points.

4. The _____ tool is used to paste the copied elements to one or more levels.

5. The _____ tool enables you to extend or trim a number of elements using a common boundary or edge.

6. You can offset elements in your project by using the _____ tool.

7. The _____ tool is used to copy the properties of a source element and transfer them to another element belonging to the same family.

8. You can select multiple elements from the drawing area by using the CTRL key. (T/F)

9. In Autodesk Revit, you can trim and extend elements in your project by using a single tool. (T/F)

10. You cannot create a copy while rotating the elements using the **Rotate** tool. (T/F)

Review Questions

Answer the following questions:

1. You can use the _____ key to select multiple wall or line elements joined at a common endpoint.

2. The _____ tool is used to resize elements.

3. The _____ tool is used to lock a model at one place.

4. For the current view of a structural model, you can select elements of similar instances by using the _____ tool.

5. You can use the _____ tool to mirror elements by sketching the mirror line in the drawing area.

6. The _____ tool is used to extend or trim an element by defining a reference line or boundary.

7. You can use the **Copy to Clipboard** tool to create a copy of the selected elements on the clipboard and retain the original ones in the current project. (T/F)

8. The **Match Type Properties** tool can be used to copy the properties of a source element and transfer them to another element belonging to a different family. (T/F)

9. The **Offset** tool is used to create a copy of an element at a specified distance in reference to the selected element. (T/F)

10. You can paste elements at the same place from where you have copied them. (T/F)

EXERCISES

Exercise 1   Academic Institution

In this exercise, you will mirror the structural model created in Exercise 1 of Chapter 5. You will define grid 10 as mirror axis. Further, you will copy the structural floor, beams, and columns to the **Roof** level. Use the following project parameters and specifications:

(Expected time: 1 hr)

1. Use the **Second Floor** structural plan view to mirror the floor and beams.

2. Use the **Entry** structural plan view to mirror the foundations.

3. File name to be assigned: *c06_Academic-Institution_exer1.rvt*.

4. Copy the structural floor, beams, and columns displayed in the **Second Floor** view and paste it at the **Roof** level.

5. For reference of the mirror line, refer to Figures 6-81 and 6-82.

Figure 6-81 *The mirrored structural elements at the **Second Floor** level*

Figure 6-82 *The mirrored structural elements at the **Entry** level*

Exercise 2   Factory Shed

In this exercise, you will mirror the structural model created in Exercise 2 of Chapter 5. You will define grid 1 as mirror axis. Further, you will copy the structural floor, beams, and columns to the **Roof** level. Use the following project parameters:

(Expected time: 1 hr)

1. Use the **Second Floor** structural plan view to mirror floor and beams.

2. Use the **Plinth** structural plan view to mirror foundations.

3. File name to be assigned:
   For Imperial   *c06_Factory-Shed_exer2.rvt.*
   For Metric   *M_c06_Factory-Shed_exer2.rvt.*

4. For the reference of the mirror line, refer to Figures 6-83 and 6-84.

Figure 6-83 *The mirrored structural elements at the **Second Floor** structural plan view*

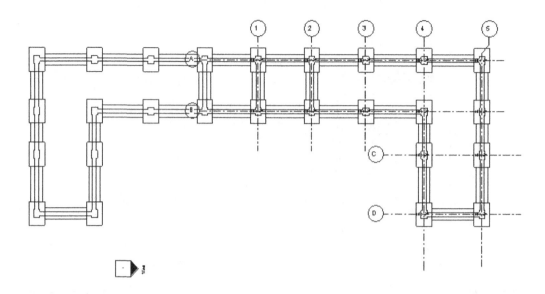

Figure 6-84 *The mirrored structural elements at the **Plinth** structural plan view*

5. Copy the structural floor, beams, and columns displayed in the **Second Floor** view and paste it at the **Roof** level.

Exercise 3   Residential Building

Download the *c06_residential_bldg_exer3* file from *https://www.cadcim.com*. The path of the file is as follows: *Textbooks > Civil/GIS > Revit Structure > Exploring Autodesk Revit 2021 for Structure*. In this exercise, open the *c06_residential_bldg_exer3* file in Imperial unit system or *M_c06_residential_bldg_exer3* file in Metric unit system and copy the structural floors, columns, and beams displayed in the **Second** structural floor plan to Third and Roof levels. Further, you will mirror the entire model keeping grid D.1 as the mirror axis.

(Expected time: 1 hr)

Use the following specifications to complete the exercise:

1. In the **Second** structural floor plan, copy the structural floor, columns, and beams and paste them to **Third** and **Roof** level view.

2. Use the **North** elevation view to mirror the entire model. For reference of the mirror line, refer to Figure 6-85.

Figure 6-85 *The* **North** *elevation view of the Residential Building project displaying the grid D.1 as mirror line*

3. File name to be assigned:

        For Imperial   *c06_residential_bldg_exer3a*.

        For Metric   *M_c06_residential_bldg_exer3a*

Answers to Self-Evaluation Test

1. Select All Instances, 2. Filter, 3. Paste from Clipboard, 4. Aligned to Selected Levels, 5. Trim/Extend Multiple Elements, 6. Offset, 7. Match Type Properties, 8. T, 9. T, 10. F

Chapter 7

Documenting Models and Creating Families

Learning Objectives

After completing this chapter, you will be able to:
- *Add permanent dimensions*
- *Convert temporary dimensions into permanent dimensions*
- *Modify a dimension and its parameters*
- *Add tags to project*
- *Add beam annotations to a project*
- *Understand family creations*

In the previous chapters, you learned how to add structural grids, columns, framing members, and various other structural elements to a project. In this chapter, you will learn how to document a project and prepare it as a working drawing by using various tools and techniques in Revit. To document a model, you need to place dimensions to the structural plan view, add text notes and place tags to columns, beams, and structural elements wherever required. In this chapter, you will also learn about various dimensioning terms and tools, tools for placing text notes, and placing tags and beam annotations in your project.

DIMENSIONING

Dimensions play a crucial role in the presentation of a project. Although the structural model of a project can convey what the appearance or design of the model would be, yet to materialize it at the site, there must be information and statistics regarding each element involved in the model. Since the design of a project is used for the actual construction of the project, it is essential to describe each element of the project in terms of actual measurement parameters such as length, width, height, angle, radius, diameter, and so on. All these information can be added to a project by using dimensions. In most cases, information conveyed through dimensions is as important as the project view itself. The dimensions added in the project view ensure that the project drawings in the view are read and interpreted in an appropriate manner. Adding dimensions also help in avoiding the discrepancies that may creep in between the elements used for the generation of the building drawings. In a structural project, you can add dimensions based on the actual dimensions of the elements to be created. In other words, they are as truthful as the project elements themselves. The units used in the dimensions play an important role in describing the detailing that is required to complete a project. For example, the use of fractional inches in the dimensions indicates the amount of detailing required while generating a design. It also reflects the extent of detailing and the precision required to complete a project. Therefore, dimensions are used not only for specifying the sizes of elements, but also for instructing the persons involved in the project, such as cost estimators, project managers, site engineers, contractors, supervisors, and so on.

In Revit, you can create two types of dimensions for an element: temporary dimension and permanent dimension. Temporary dimensions appear while creating or selecting an element, but they do not appear in project views. On the other hand, permanent dimensions appear in the views in which they are created and describe the size or distance. In Revit, you can add the dimensions denoting the length of a wall, distances between rebars, distance between columns, arc length of a curved beam, angle between columns and braces, spot elevation of the top of a slab, and so on. While dimensioning a model, you can change various type parameters of the dimensions such as its size, color, and so on by using the **Type Properties** dialog box. In the next section, you will learn about various entities in a dimension, various types of dimensions, adding dimensions to a project, and modifying the added dimensions.

Types of Dimension

In Revit, you can use two types of dimension: temporary and permanent. By default, the units specified at the start-up of a project for temporary and permanent dimensions are used as the default units. Unlike temporary dimensions, the permanent dimensions are view-specific. It means if you change the view of a project, the permanent dimensions will not be visible.

Using Temporary Dimensions

Revit displays temporary dimensions around the component or element when you place or sketch it in a view. The dimension that appears dynamically while drawing or placing an element is called temporary dimension. This type of dimension is not view-specific and appears in any view while drawing or selecting an element. Temporary dimensions help you position elements at the desired location and references. While sketching the lines of desired length at the desired angle instantly, temporary dimensions can help you speed up your drafting work.

Temporary dimension appears only in three situations. First, when you draw an element; second, when you select an element; and third, when you select or place a component in a project.

When you place a component in a project, temporary dimension becomes a useful tool to guide the exact placing of the component with respect to a fixed element or a component. While placing a component, the temporary dimensions are displayed at the nearest perpendicular element or component with a predefined snap increment setting. This helps in placing a component in a drawing properly. Figure 7-1 shows temporary dimensions displayed while adding a structural column to a project view.

Figure 7-1 *Temporary dimensions displayed while placing a structural column*

While using a temporary dimension, you can set the point of reference of the element being placed. To change the settings of the temporary dimension, invoke the **Temporary Dimensions** tool from **Manage > Settings > Additional Settings** drop-down; the **Temporary Dimension Properties** dialog box will be displayed, as shown in Figure 7-2. This dialog box contains two areas: **Walls** and **Doors and Windows**.

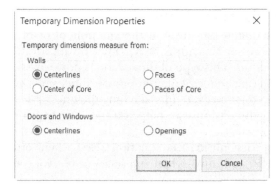

Figure 7-2   *The options in the **Temporary Dimension Properties** dialog box*

In the **Walls** area of the **Temporary Dimension Properties** dialog box, you can select any one of the four radio buttons, namely **Centerlines**, **Center of Core**, **Faces**, and **Faces of Core** to set the reference point for displaying temporary dimensions of walls. To change the point of reference for placing doors and windows, you can select any of the two options, namely **Centerlines** and **Openings** from the **Doors and Windows** area of the **Temporary Dimension Properties** dialog box. These settings help you set the references of walls, doors, and windows for temporary dimensions while creating or placing elements or components in a model.

Entities in a Dimension

Before using the dimensioning tools, it is important to understand various entities in a dimension. Figure 7-3 shows the terms used for various entities in a dimension. In the next section, these entities are discussed briefly.

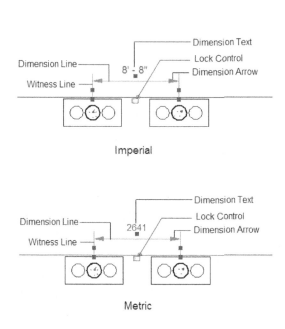

Figure 7-3 *Various entities in a permanent dimension*

Dimension Line

The dimension line in a dimension indicates the distance or angle being measured. By default, the dimension line has tick marks at both ends and the dimension text is placed along the dimension line. Note that in case of angular or radial dimension, the dimension line will be an arc.

Dimension Text

The dimension text represents the actual measurement (dimension value) between the selected points. You cannot modify this value but can add prefixes or suffixes to it. Note that the dimension text value is automatically updated when the size of an element is modified.

Dimension Arrows

Dimension Arrows are added at the intersection of the dimension line and witness line. As drafting standards differ from company to company, Revit allows you to select tick marks from a range of in-built symbols.

Witness Lines

Witness lines are generated from a selected element and extend toward the dimension line. Generally, they are generated perpendicular to the dimension line. You can move the witness lines to a desired location by using the witness line drag controls. Alternatively, you can move the witness lines by first selecting the desired dimension and then moving the cursor and placing it above the witness line control; the color of the witness line control will change and at the same time, a tool tip displaying **Move Witness Line** text will also be displayed. Note that the tooltip will only be displayed if the setting in the **Options** dialog box (Refer to Chapter 2) permits so. Next, right-click to display a shortcut menu. In the shortcut menu, choose the **Move Witness Line** option; an additional witness line will appear. Move this witness line and click at the desired reference point for the new location; the selected dimension will change to a new value and the desired witness line will move to a new location.

You can add an extra witness line to the existing dimension. To do so, select the desired dimension and then right-click; a shortcut menu will be displayed. In this shortcut menu, choose the **Edit Witness Line** option; an additional witness line with a dimension line will emerge from any of the witness lines of the selected dimension. Next, click on the desired reference; a dimension will be added in extension to the selected dimension. Figures 7-4 and 7-5 show the addition of a witness line to an existing dimension.

Imperial   Metric

Figure 7-4 *Additional witness line emerging from the dimension*

Imperial   Metric

Figure 7-5 *Witness line added to the desired dimension*

Note
*The **Edit Witness Lines** option will be displayed when you choose permanent dimension in the
Modify / Dimensions contextual tab.*

Tip
*You can also edit witness lines by selecting the dimension and then choosing the **Edit Witness
Lines** tool from the **Witness Lines** panel of the **Modify / Dimensions** contextual tab.*

Adding Permanent Dimensions

Permanent dimensions are added for a specific measurement. In Revit, you can access various
dimension tools from the **Dimension** panel in the **Annotate** tab, as shown in Figure 7-6. You
can choose appropriate dimension type and dimension tool to add dimensions to an element.
The dimensioning tools are discussed next.

Figure 7-6 *Various dimensioning tools in the **Dimension**
panel of the **Annotate** tab*

Aligned Tool

Ribbon:	Annotate > Dimension > Aligned

The **Aligned** tool is used to dimension two orthogonal references or points such as
wall-ends. To do so, invoke this tool from the **Dimension** panel; the **Modify | Place
Dimensions** contextual tab will be displayed. To change the type of the
aligned dimension, select an option from the **Type Selector** drop-down list in the
Properties palette. Next, to set the snap point of the cursor for dimensioning, select
an option from the first drop-down list on the left in the Options Bar, refer to Figure 7-7. For
example, if you select the **Wall centerlines** option from the drop-down list, the cursor if placed
above the wall will snap to the centerline of the wall. Select the **Individual References** option
from the **Pick** drop-down list. Place the cursor at a reference point on an element; the
reference point will be highlighted. Next, left-click to specify the reference point and then place

the cursor on the required location of the next reference point and click. As you move the cursor upward, a dimension line will appear. Move the cursor away from the component and left-click again; a permanent aligned dimension will appear, refer to Figure 7-8. The **Aligned** tool can also be used to dimension the center of the arc wall and other walls or lines. If you select **Entire Walls** from the **Pick**: drop-down list in the **Options Bar**, the **Options** button will be activated. Choose the **Options** button; the **Auto Dimension Options** dialog box will be displayed. Select the check boxes in the dialog box. Now, you can dimension the openings, doors, windows, and the intersecting walls simultaneously. You can also define the references for dimensioning by choosing the **Centers** and **Widths** radio buttons. Click on the wall that you want to dimension and then move the cursor away from the wall. Next, click in the drawing area; the walls, doors, and openings will be dimensioned separately based on the settings specified in the **Auto Dimension Options** dialog box.

Figure 7-7 Various options in the Options Bar for the Aligned tool

Figure 7-8 Dimension created using the Aligned tool

Linear Tool

Ribbon: Annotate > Dimension > Linear

The **Linear** tool is used to dimension straight elements and distances. It measures the shortest distance between any two specified points. To measure a distance, invoke this tool from the **Dimension** panel. On doing so, the **Modify | Place Dimensions** contextual tab will be displayed. From the **Properties** palette, click on the **Type Selector** drop-down list and select an option to assign a type to the linear dimension that you want to create. After selecting this option, select the first point by clicking at the appropriate location. After selecting the first point, select the second point of reference for the dimension; the dimension line appears. You can now move the cursor to the desired location and click to place the dimension. The dimension thus created will display various parameters controls. You can invoke any other tool or press ESC to exit the **Linear** tool. A linear dimension will be created, as shown in Figure 7-9.

Figure 7-9 *Dimension created using the **Linear** tool*

Angular Tool

Ribbon:	Annotate > Dimension > Angular

The **Angular** tool is used to dimension an angle. It is also used to create a dimension arc (dimension line in the shape of an arc with arrows on both ends) to indicate the angle between two non-parallel elements, as shown in Figure 7-10. To dimension an angle, invoke the **Angular** tool from the **Dimension** panel; the **Modify | Place Dimension** contextual tab will be displayed. From the **Properties** palette, click on the **Type Selector** drop-down list and select an option. Next, move the cursor, click on the first reference, and then click on the other reference. On doing so, the angular dimension between the selected references will be displayed. Next, click on an appropriate place to locate the dimension displayed. Figure 7-10 shows an angular dimension between two structural walls.

Figure 7-10 *Dimension created using the **Angular** tool*

Radial Tool

Ribbon:	Annotate > Dimension > Radial

The **Radial** tool is used to dimension the radius of a circular profile, as shown in Figure 7-11. To do so, invoke the **Radial** tool from the **Dimension** panel; the **Modify | Place Dimensions** contextual tab will be displayed. In the **Properties** palette of this tab, click on the **Type Selector** drop-down list and select an option from the list of types displayed. After selecting an option, move the cursor near the profile and click when the appropriate snap option appears; a center mark along with the dimension will automatically be generated. Move the cursor and place the dimension.

Figure 7-11 *Dimension created using the* ***Radial*** *tool*

Diameter Tool

Ribbon: Annotate > Dimension > Diameter

⊘ Diameter   The **Diameter** tool is used to dimension the diameter of a circular arc profile. The dimension text generated by Autodesk Revit has a prefix ø which indicates a dimension. To create a dimension, invoke this tool from the **Dimension** panel; the **Modify | Place Dimensions** contextual tab will be displayed. Place the cursor on the curve of a circle or arc, and then click; a temporary dimension displaying the diameter of the curve will be displayed. Move the cursor along the dimension line, and click to place the diametric dimension.

Arc Length Tool

Ribbon: Annotate > Dimension > Arc Length

⌒ Arc Length   The **Arc Length** tool is used to dimension a curved wall or a curved beam based on its overall length. To dimension a curved wall, invoke this tool from the **Dimension** panel; the **Modify | Place Dimensions** contextual tab will be displayed. In the **Properties** palette, select the dimension type from the **Type Selector** drop-down list. Next, move the cursor near the arc wall and click to specify the radial point. Select the start and end reference points between which the arc length is to be measured. Move the cursor away from the arc wall or beam and click; the arc length dimension will be created, as shown in Figure 7-12.

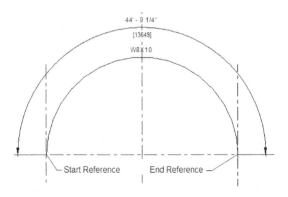

Figure 7-12 *Dimension created using the* ***Arc Length*** *tool*

Spot Elevation Tool

Ribbon: Annotate > Dimension > Spot Elevation

 The **Spot Elevation** tool is used to display the elevation at a point in the drawing area. Spot elevations display the elevation level of a point with respect to the base level. They can be placed in a plan, elevation, or 3D view. You can add spot dimensions on non-horizontal and non-planar surfaces. You can use the spot elevation to specify the elevation level of points on a floor, ramp, road, topographical surface, stairs, and other features. To place a spot elevation at a point, invoke the **Spot Elevation** tool from the **Dimension** panel; the **Modify | Place Dimensions** contextual tab along with the **Options Bar** will be displayed. The **Leader** check box is selected by default in the **Options Bar**. As a result, a leader will be displayed along with the spot dimension placed in the drawing. You can clear the check box, if you do not need the leader to be displayed along with the spot dimension in the drawing. In the Options Bar, the **Shoulder** check box is also selected by default. As a result, a shoulder line will be displayed along with a leader line in the spot dimension to be placed. You can clear the **Shoulder** check box to remove the shoulder line from the leader line. In the **Relative Base** drop-down list of the Options Bar, you can select an option to specify the base level for the spot elevations created using the relative type. By default, the **Relative Base** drop-down list is disabled. This drop-down list will be enabled on selecting a relative type of spot elevation. To add a spot elevation of relative type, select an option from the **Type Selector** drop-down list. The options available in **Type Selector** drop-down list are: **Spot Elevations : Target (Relative)**, **Spot Elevations : Beam (Relative)**, **Spot Elevations : Crosshair (Relative)**, or **Spot Elevations : No Symbol (Relative)** and so on. In the Options Bar, select an option from the **Display Elevations** drop-down list to control the display value(s) of the spot elevation to be placed in the project. For example, you can select the **Top & Bottom Elevations** option to display the elevation of the top and bottom faces of an element. In Figure 7-13, you can see the spot elevation of a column. It displays the elevations of top and bottom faces. Next, to place spot elevation in the drawing, move the cursor near any edge of an element; the edge will be highlighted and the desired spot elevation of the highlighted edge will be displayed. Now, you can click on the highlighted edge to place the spot elevation. After clicking once, you may require to click two times in the drawing area to define suitable points for the leader line and the shoulder line.

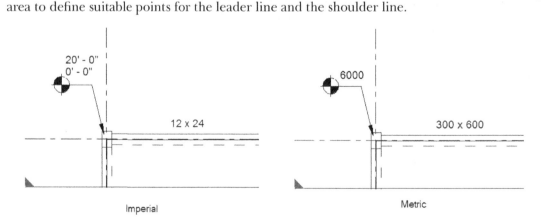

Figure 7-13 *The spot elevation of the column displayed*

Note
*The placement of the shoulder line and the leader line in the spot elevation depends on the options that you select from the **Shoulder** and **Leader** drop-down lists in the Options Bar.*

Spot Coordinate Tool

Ribbon:	Annotate > Dimension > Spot Coordinate

The **Spot Coordinate** tool is used to display coordinates of a point (Northing and Easting) of a point in a project. You can place spot coordinates on floors, walls, toposurfaces, and boundary lines in a project. Spot coordinates can also be placed on non-horizontal surfaces and non-planar edges.

To place spot coordinates, invoke the **Spot Coordinate** tool from the **Dimension** panel; the **Modify | Place Dimensions** contextual tab will be displayed. The options and the properties for the spot dimension will be displayed in the Options Bar and the **Properties** palette, respectively. In the Options Bar, you can select the **Leader** and **Shoulder** check boxes to control the display of shoulder and leader along with the spot coordinate dimension. By default, both the check boxes are selected. As a result, leader and shoulder will be displayed along with spot coordinate dimension. To turn off the display of the shoulder and leader, clear the **Shoulder** and **Leader** check boxes. After specifying options from the Options Bar, you can select the type of spot coordinate dimension from the **Type Selector** drop-down list in the **Properties** palette. You can select any of these two options: **Horizontal** and **Horizontal (w- Elevation)** from this drop-down list. Select the **Horizontal** option if not selected by default in the **Type Selector** drop-down list to align the text in the spot coordinate horizontally with respect to the current work plane. Refer to Figure 7-14 to see a horizontal type spot dimension placed.

Figure 7-14 Horizontal type spot coordinate dimension placed

Alternatively, select the **Horizontal (w-Elevation)** option from the **Type Selector** drop-down list to add a spot coordinate dimension along with its elevation. Adding spot coordinates with this type will help you to know the coordinates of a desired point along with its elevation in reference to a predefined base. To add a spot coordinate dimension with the **Horizontal (w-Elevation)** type selected, place the cursor on the point whose spot coordinates you want to display; the point will be highlighted and its spot coordinate dimension will appear. Click on the highlighted point, and then click twice to place the leader and shoulder of the spot coordinate dimension. Figure 7-15 shows a **Horizontal (w-Elevation)** spot coordinate dimension placed

Figure 7-15 *Horizontal (w-Elevation) type spot coordinate dimension placed*

Spot Slope Tool

Ribbon:	Annotate > Dimension > Spot Slope

The **Spot Slope** tool is used to specify the slope of an edge or a face of an element at a point in a drawing. You can display the spot slope dimension in a plan, elevation, section, or in a 3d view. To add the spot slope at a point in the drawing, choose the **Spot Slope** tool from the **Dimension** panel; the **Modify | Place Dimension** contextual tab will be displayed. In the Options Bar, you can set the representation type for the spot slope dimension that you will place in the drawing. You can set an arrow or a triangle as the representation type for the spot slope dimension. Note that the **Arrow** option is selected by default in the **Slope Representation** drop-down list. You can select the **Triangle** option from the **Slope Representation** drop-down list to set the representation type of the spot slope dimension as a triangle. After setting the desired representation type, you can enter a suitable value in the **Offset from Reference** edit box in the Options Bar. This will specify the offset distance of the slope symbol and the dimension text from the point referred for the dimension of the slope. By default, **1/16"** is displayed for the Imperial system or **1.5 mm** for the Metric system in the **Offset from Reference** edit box in Options Bar. After setting the options in the Options Bar, you can place the cursor on a sloping edge of a model element or a sloping face. As you place the cursor at a point, the slope dimension at that point appears. Click at the desired point to place the slope dimension and then click again to fix the vertical alignment of the slope dimension. Figure 7-16 shows the slope dimensions of an inclined beam and an inclined slab.

Figure 7-16 *Elevation of a structural model displaying the slope dimensions in different slope representation*

Note

*While using the **Spot Slope** tool if you click on one of the faces of a flat slab or on the straight edge of a beam, the **No Slope** text will be displayed at the point you clicked on.*

Modifying Dimension Parameters

You can modify the parameters of a dimension such as text font of a dimension, gap of witness line from element, and so on to achieve the desired dimension style. To do so, select the required dimension from the drawing; the contextual tab corresponding to the selected dimension type will be displayed. For example, for linear dimension, the **Modify | Dimensions** contextual tab will be displayed, and for the spot elevation dimension, the **Modify | Spot Elevations** contextual tab will be displayed. In this tab, you can use various editing tools from the concerned panel, if required. While the desired dimension is selected, the properties of the selected dimension will be displayed in the **Properties** palette. Figure 7-17 shows the **Properties** palette of the selected linear dimension. In this palette, there are various instance parameters that can be modified from their respective heads. The appearance of these parameters depends upon the type of dimension selected in the drawing area. In the **Properties** palette, you can change the type properties of the selected dimension. To do so, choose the **Edit Type** button from the **Properties** palette; the **Type Properties** dialog box will be displayed, as shown in Figure 7-18. In the **Type Properties** dialog box, you can also create a new dimension style with the parameters most suitable to the project by using the **Duplicate** button. Various type parameters and their usage are discussed next.

Using the **Leader Type** parameter, you can specify the type of line to be drawn for the leader. You can select the **Arc** or **Line** option from the drop-down list displayed on clicking on the value field corresponding to it. You can specify the type of tick mark for the leader by selecting an option from the value field in the **Value** column corresponding to the **Leader Tick Mark** parameter. You can specify the condition for the display of the leader. To do so, select an option from the drop-down list in the value field in the **Value** column corresponding to the **Show Leader When Text Moves** parameter. For the **Tick Mark** parameter, you can select the mark type to be used as the tick mark. Select the desired mark from the drop-down list in the value column. The **Line Weight** parameter is used to specify the line weight or thickness for the dimension line. You can select the value ranging from 1 to 16, depending on the desired thickness. The **Tick Mark Line Weight** parameter sets the thickness of the tick mark line. The **Dimension Line Extension** parameter is used to specify the distance by which the dimension line can be extended to the point where it intersects with the witness line. In the **Equality Text** parameter under the **Other** head, you can change the default label from **EQ** to a different text description for the dimension type. This custom label will be displayed for all equality texts created with this dimension type. Apart from various dimension settings, you can also set various parameters for the dimension text such as **Text Size**, **Text Offset**, and so on. After modifying the parameter(s), choose the **Apply** button to apply the changes.

Figure 7-17 *The **Properties** palette displaying various properties of the linear dimension type*

Figure 7-18 *The **Type Properties** dialog box*

Locking Permanent Dimensions

When you add a permanent dimension, a lock control symbol is displayed. I` also appears when you select a permanent dimension. This symbol can be used to lock or unlock the dimension of an element. When the symbol is unlocked, you can modify the extent of the dimension. In such cases, the dimension is also modified along with the element. When you lock a dimension, the element corresponding to it is also locked along with it. This means you cannot modify its dimension value. You can, however, move the element along with dimension. Once the dimension is locked, you must unlock it to change its value.

Converting Temporary Dimensions into Permanent Dimensions

As discussed in the earlier sections of this chapter, temporary dimensions appear while creating various structural elements such as grids, walls, columns, beams, and other structural elements. They can be used to specify the size and location of an element in the structural model. You can move or resize an element by clicking on the temporary dimension and entering a new value. When you create an element, a conversion control symbol is also displayed along with the temporary dimension, as shown in Figure 7-19. When you click on this symbol, temporary dimension is converted into a permanent dimension, as shown in Figure 7-20.

Figure 7-19 *The conversion control symbol displayed in the selected temporary dimension*

Figure 7-20 *Temporary dimension converted into a permanent dimension*

TEXT NOTES

Text notes are important parts of a project detail. They not only help in adding the specification of various structural elements but also in conveying the specific design intent. Revit provides a variety of options to add text notes to a structural model detail view by using the **Text** tool. Various options to add and modify a text in a model view are discussed next.

Adding Text Notes

Ribbon:	Annotate > Text > Text

In Revit, text notes are view-specific entities. You can add different text notes to different views. Generally, text notes are added to the plan view, section view, callout view, or in drafting view. The selection of a view in which the text notes are added depends on the project requirement. To add a text note to a desired view, invoke the **Text** tool from the **Text** panel; the **Modify | Place Text** contextual tab will be displayed, as shown in Figure 7-21.

Figure 7-21 *Various options in the **Modify / Place Text** tab*

In this tab, you can use the tools in the **Leader** panel to control the writing format of the text note to be added in the project view. For instance, using the text note, you can attach a straight leader line that has a single segment or double segments. Alternatively, you can also attach a curved leader line to a text note. If you insert a text note into project view, no leader will be attached to the text note because the **No Leader** tool is chosen by default in the **Leader** panel. To attach a straight leader line with one segment, choose the **One Segment** tool from the **Leader** panel. You can choose the **Two Segments** tool or the **Curved** tool from the **Leader** panel to attach a double segment straight leader line or a curved leader line to the text note. Figure 7-22 illustrates the usage of the leader options discussed earlier. After choosing the desired option for the display of the leader line, you can choose various tools from the **Leader** panel to locate the leader line in reference to the text note. For instance, you can place the leader line on the left of a text note at three different places: top left, middle left, or bottom left corner of the text note. To do so, choose the **Leader at Top Left**, **Leader at Middle Left**, or **Leader at Bottom Left** tool respectively, from the **Leader** panel. Similarly, you can place the leader line on the right of the text note. To do so, choose the **Leader at Top Right**, **Leader at Middle Right**, or **Leader at Bottom Right** tool from the **Leader** panel. By default, the **Leader at Top Left** and **Leader at Bottom Right** tools are chosen from the **Leader** panel. As a result, the leader will be attached to the text note at the top left corner or at the bottom right corner, depending on the side the leader is placed on. After setting the options for the placement of leader, you can set the alignment of the text to be inserted. To do so, you can choose any of the three tools, namely **Align Left**, **Align Center**, or **Align Right**, from the **Alignment** panel. The **Align Left** tool is chosen by default in this panel. As a result, the text will be aligned on the left margin in the text box. You can choose the **Align Center** tool to align the text evenly between the left margin and the right margin of the text box. You can choose the **Align Right** tool to align the text to the right margin of the text box.

After setting the desired options for placing the leader line and the text alignment, move the cursor near the desired location and click to add the text note. On doing so, a leader will emerge from the location you have clicked on, if the settings for the leader allow the display of leader. You may need to click once or twice depending upon the option chosen for the leader. After specifying the leader, if required, click to display a text box along with a text symbol. After the text box has been displayed, you can add the desired text in it. Note that before adding text in the text box, you can set various text formatting options from the **Font** panel. You can use the **Bold**, **Italics**, or **Underline** tool, or their combinations to make the text as specified. After setting the options for the text formatting, you can write the desired text in the text box.

Figure 7-22 Illustration showing various options of a leader in a text note

While entering text in a text box, you may need to formatting options like numbering or bulletting sentences. To format a paragraph, choose any of the five options from the **Paragraph** panel. The options displayed in the menu are **None**, **Bullets**, **Numbers**, **Lowercase Letters**, and **Uppercase Letters**. After writing text in the text box, click outside the text box in the drawing area; the text note with drag controls will be highlighted. After entering the text in the text box, you can check the spellings as well. To do so, choose the **Check Spelling** tool from the **Text** panel of the **Modify | Place Text** contextual tab; the **Check Spelling** dialog box will be displayed, as shown in Figure 7-23. In this dialog box, the **Context** area displays the context or sentence in which the word(s) is misspelt. The **Not in Dictionary** edit box displays the word that is misspelt in the context displayed in the **Context** area. The **Change to** area displays a list box containing the words suggested to replace the misspelled word. You can click on the suitable word in the list box and then choose the **Change** button to replace the misspelt word with the suggested word. On doing so, the **Revit** message box will be displayed, informing you that the spell-check operation has completed. Choose the **Close** button and press ESC twice to exit the text editing option.

Note
*In the **Context** area of the **Check Spelling** dialog box, the misspelled word is displayed in boldface.*

*Figure 7-23 The **Check Spelling** dialog box*

Editing Text Notes

You can set the properties of a text note before creating it or edit them later. When you select a text note, its controls are displayed. You can use these controls to edit the text note parameters. The controls consist of one blue dot on each side of the text box that represents the stretch controls that can be used to modify the size of the text box. The rotation controls are also placed at the top right corner of the text box. You can use it to rotate the text box The location of the leader arrow-head remains in its original position and only the text box is rotated. The leader tail automatically adjusts to the rotated text box. You can also drag the location of the leader elbow and leader head by using the drag control dots. The drag control is used to change the location of the text box.

As you select the text note, the **Modify | Text Notes** contextual tab is displayed. In this tab, you can use various editing tools such as **Copy**, **Mirror**, **Rotate**, **Array**, and so on to edit and arrange the text note. The alignment of the text note can be modified by choosing appropriate alignment tool from the **Format** panel. In this panel, you can choose the **Add Left Side Straight Leader** or **Add Right Side Straight Leader** tool to add a leader to the left or right side of the text note. You can select the **Remove Last Leader** option from the **Format** panel to remove the leader that is added last to the text note. To modify a text note, click inside the text box and then select the text note. Next, enter the new note. You can also modify the instance properties of the text note such as text font and text size. To do so, you can use various parameters in the **Properties** palette. In this palette, the value assigned to the **Horizontal Align** parameter is used to specify the horizontal text alignment of the selected text. To change the value assigned to the **Horizontal Align** parameter, click on the value column corresponding to it and select the desired alignment option from the drop-down list displayed. The **Arc Leaders** instance parameter is used to specify whether or not an arc leader should be attached to a text. The value column of this parameter displays a check box, which is cleared by default. You can select this check box to attach an arc leader to a text.

You can also edit the type properties of a text using the **Properties** palette. To do so, choose the **Edit Type** button from the **Properties** palette; the **Type Properties** dialog box will be displayed, as shown in Figure 7-24. In this dialog box, you can edit the font of a text by clicking in the value field in the **Value** column corresponding to the **Text Font** parameter and then selecting the required text font from the drop-down list displayed. The **Text Size** parameter is used to specify the size of the text note. The **Tab Size** parameter is used to set the tab spacing used in text notes. The tab spacing can be inserted by pressing the TAB key. You can also select the check boxes for the **Bold**, **Italic**, and **Underline** parameters to set the format of the text note.

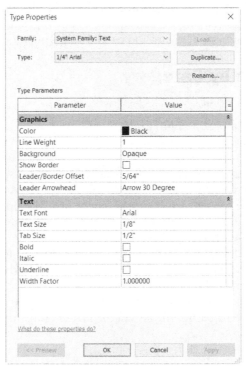

*Figure 7-24 The **Type Properties** dialog box for the selected text*

The **Type Selector** drop-down list in the **Properties** palette of the selected text note displays the available text types. You can select the appropriate type from the available text types before creating text notes. Alternatively, you can select a text note that was created earlier and then select the new text type from the **Type Selector** drop-down list to replace the old text type. You can also use the **Copy to Clipboard** and **Paste Aligned** tools from the **Modify | Text Notes** contextual tab to copy the text notes from one level to multiple levels.

ADDING TAGS

You can easily add tag to various elements in a structural model. A tag is a useful annotation that assists in identifying elements in a drawing. While designing complex structural models using Revit, tags play an important role in arranging various elements in schedules. You can then add necessary description for each tagged element in a tabular form.

Revit provides various tools to add and edit tags. When you open a default template file, the tags of a certain category of elements are pre-loaded. Therefore, when you add the elements such as columns and beams to a model, Revit automatically tags them. For the other elements, you need to load their respective tags from the Revit library. Like other annotations, tags are also view-specific and therefore they appear only in the view they have been created in. You can control the visibility of tags by choosing the **Visibility/ Graphics** tool from the **Graphics** panel of the **View** tab. On doing so, the **Visibility/Graphics Overrides for <current view >** dialog box will be displayed. In this dialog box, the **Annotation Categories** tab contains the list of tag categories such as **Analytical BraceTags**, **Analytical BeamTags**, **Analytical Column Tags**, **Analytical Floor Tags**, **Structural Annotations**, **Structural Column Tags**, **Structural Framing Tags**, **Structural Rebar Tags**, and so on. You can select appropriate check boxes to control the visibility of each category of tags. The method used for tagging an element is discussed next.

Tagging Elements by Category

Ribbon: Annotate > Tag > Tag by Category

To attach a tag to an element based on its category, choose the **Tag by Category** tool from the **Tag** panel; the Options Bar displays the parameters related to the placement and orientation of the tag. In the Options Bar, you can select the **Horizontal** or **Vertical** option from the drop-down list displayed on the left to specify the direction of the text in the tag. You can use the **Leader** check box to enable or disable the display of a leader with the tag. On selecting this check box, the options in the drop-down list displayed on the right of the **Leader** check box will be enabled. You can select two options from this drop-down list: **Attached End** and **Free End**. If you select the **Attached End** option from the drop-down list, you will not be able to move the end of the leader with the tag away from the element category it is attached to. On selecting the **Attached End** option from the drop-down list, an edit box on its right will be enabled. In this edit box, you can specify the length of the leader or the distance of the tag from the attached element. If you select the **Free End** option from the drop-down list, you can move the end of the leader away from the element it is attached to.

Loading the Tags

By default, Revit loads tags for certain categories of elements such as structural area reinforcement, structural beam systems, structural columns, structural foundation, and so on. To display the tags that are loaded in the project, choose the **Loaded Tags And Symbols** tool from the expanded **Tag** panel of the **Annotate** tab. On doing so, the **Loaded Tags And Symbols** dialog box will be displayed. This dialog box displays the category-wise list of the tags loaded in the project, refer to Figure 7-25.

In case the category of element to be tagged does not have its corresponding tag already loaded, choose the **Load Family** button from the **Loaded Tags And Symbols** dialog box; the **Load Family** dialog box will be displayed. You can select various categories of tags from the **US Imperial > Annotations** or **US Metric > Annotations** folder path based on your requirement. The **Preview** area of the **Load Family** dialog box displays preview image of the selected tag, as shown in Figure 7-26. Select an appropriate tag from the list and choose the **Open** button to load it into the project. On doing so, the desired tag will be added to the list of loaded tags for the corresponding element category in the **Tags** dialog box.

Figure 7-25 The **Loaded Tags And Symbols** *dialog box*

Figure 7-26 Preview of the selected tag in the **Load Family** dialog box

Another way of loading the tags is to invoke the **Tag By Category** tool and select the element to be tagged. If you select an element that does not have a tag already loaded, the **No Tag Loaded** message box will be displayed, as shown in Figure 7-27. This message box shows that you have not loaded a tag for the selected object type. Choose the **Yes** button in this message box; the **Load Family** dialog box will be displayed. In this dialog box, choose the category of the element to be tagged and then choose the required type of tag; the tag will be loaded. After loading the tag if you move the cursor near the element, Revit will display the preview image of the tag. Move the cursor to the desired location and click when the tag appears; the tag will be placed. Then, select different elements of the same category and tag them individually. When you select a tag, its controls will be displayed, as shown in Figure 7-28. The move control displayed with the tag is used to move the tag to some desired location. The leader elbow control is used to adjust the leader. The '?' control is used to enter text for the label of the tag. When you add a label, Revit displays a message box, informing you that you are changing the type parameter of the tag and that it could affect many elements. Choose **Yes** in the message box to continue working in the project; the value entered will appear as the label in the tag.

*Figure 7-27 The **No Tag Loaded** message box*

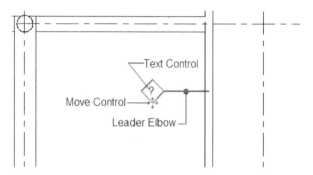

Figure 7-28 The selected tag with its control

Tagging All Elements in a View

You can tag all the elements visible in the current view. You can do so by using the **Tag All** tool. So, to tag all elements, choose this tool from the **Tag** panel; the **Tag All Not Tagged** dialog box will be displayed, as shown in Figure 7-29. This dialog box has two radio buttons: **All objects in current view** and **Only selected objects in current view**. By default, the **All objects in current view** radio button is active, and the **Only selected objects in current view** radio button is inactive. If you have selected an object before invoking the **Tag All Not Tagged** dialog box only then the **Only selected objects in current view** radio button gets activated. The selection of the **All objects in current view** radio button ensures that all the objects present in the current view are tagged, provided that their categories are selected in the **Category** column of the **Tag All Not Tagged** dialog box. The table displayed below the radio buttons shows the listing of category tags of all elements present in the current view and their corresponding loaded tags.

*Figure 7-29 The **Tag All Not Tagged** dialog box*

 Tip
*You can load tags for multiple categories of components by holding down the CTRL key and selecting multiple tags from the drop-down list in the **Loaded Tags** column of the **Tags** dialog box.*

 Note
*If a category of elements you wish to tag does not appear in this list, you need to load the corresponding tag family and then use the **Tag All** tool.*

From the table displayed in the **Tag All Not Tagged** dialog box, select a desired category. The **Leader** check box can be used to add a leader to them. You can also select the orientation and length of the leader in this dialog box. Choose **Apply** to apply the settings to the current view. For example, you can tag all structural framing members in a layout plan view by using the **Tag All** tool, as shown in Figure 7-30.

Figure 7-30 *All structural framing members tagged using the **Tag All** tool*

Beam Annotations

Ribbon:	Annotate > Tag > Beam Annotations

In Revit, you can place tags, annotations, and spot elevations on all or selected beams in the current views by using the **Beam Annotations** tool. To do so, invoke this tool from the **Tag** panel; the **Beam Annotations** dialog box will be displayed, as shown in Figure 7-31. This dialog box contains two areas: **Placement** and **Annotation location and type**. The options in these two areas are discussed next.

Figure 7-31 *The **Beam Annotations** dialog box*

Placement Area

The options in the **Placement** area are used to specify the placement of beam annotations in the current view. In this area, the **All beams in current plan view** radio button is selected by default. As a result, Revit annotates all beams present in the current view. By default, the **All selected beams in current plan view** radio button in the **Placement** area remains inactive. You can select this radio button to annotate the beams selected in the current view. To make this radio button active, select the beams that you want to annotate before invoking the **Beam Annotations** tool.

In the **Placement** area of the **Beam Annotations** dialog box, the **Remove existing beam tags and spot elevations** check box is cleared by default. As a result, Revit will not place new annotations on the beams that have already been annotated. You can select the **Remove existing beam tags and spot elevations** check box to replace the existing beam tags and spot elevation in the beam with the new ones. You can choose the **Settings** button to specify the offset distances of annotation tags and spot elevations from the beam. On choosing this button, the **Placement Settings** dialog box will be displayed, as shown in Figure 7-32. In this dialog box, the image displayed illustrates various settings for the offsets of the tag in reference to the beam. In the **Horizontal End Offset** area that is marked **1**, you can enter a suitable value in the edit box displayed inside it to specify the offset distance of tags or spot elevations from their points of attachment.

*Figure 7-32 The **Placement Settings** dialog box*

Similarly, you can specify the settings for the vertical offset distance of the tags or spot elevations from their attachment points. To do so, you can use various settings displayed inside the **Vertical Offset** area, marked **2**, in the **Placement Settings** dialog box. In the **Vertical Offset** area, the **Default Offset** radio button is selected by default. As a result, "3/8" for Imperial system or 9.25mm for Metric system is set as the value for the vertical offset distance. To override the default value for the vertical offset distance, select the radio button below the **Default Offset** radio button in the **Vertical Offset** area; the edit box next to it will become active. You can enter a positive value less than 360000" for Imperial system or 9144000mm for Metric system in the edit box. After specifying the desired offset distances for the beam annotations, choose the **OK** button; the **Placement Settings** dialog box will be closed and the settings will be designated to the beam annotations.

Note
The values entered for horizontal and vertical distances represent the drawing scale to be used in the project.

Annotation location and type Area

The options in the **Annotation location and type** area are used to specify the annotation type and location for the beam annotations to be placed in a beam in the current view. This area has two tabs: **Level beams in plan** and **Sloped beams in plan**. The **Level beams in plan** tab is chosen by default. This tab displays the image of a level beam in the plan. This image is surrounded by six text boxes: three above it and three below it. The text box displayed at the top left of the image displays the type of structural framing tag or spot elevation used to annotate the beam at its start end. This text box will be inactive and displays the **<Start>** text inside it.

To assign a suitable spot elevation or structural framing tag type for the spot elevation or tag, choose the button displayed next to it; the **Select Annotation Type** dialog box will be displayed, as shown in Figure 7-33. In this dialog box, the **None** radio button is selected by default. As a result, no structural framing tag or spot elevation will be displayed at the top left corner of the beam. In the **Select Annotation Type** dialog box, you can select the **Structural Framing Tag** radio button to add a structural framing tag at the top left corner of the beam. On doing so, the **Structural Framing Tag** area will be displayed, refer to Figure 7-34. In this area, you can click on the **Type** drop-down list and select

*Figure 7-33 Partial view of the **Select Annotation Type** dialog box*

a desired type for the structural framing tag from the list. If the desired type is not available in this list, select the **Load Structural Framing Tag** option from the drop-down list; the **Beam Annotation** window will be displayed. Choose the **Clos**e button in this window; the **Load Family** dialog box will be displayed. In this dialog box, browse to **US Imperial > Annotations > Structural** or **US Metric > Annotations** folder path based on your requirement and select the **Structural Framing Tag-w-Start Reactions** file. Choose the **Open** button in the **Load Family** dialog box; the selected tag family will be added to the **Type** drop-down list.

Alternatively, you can select the **Spot Elevation** radio button in the **Select Element to Place** area to add a spot elevation at the top left corner of the beam (start end of the beam). On selecting the **Spot Elevation** radio button, the **Spot Elevation** area will be displayed in the **Select Annotation Type** dialog box, as shown in Figure 7-35. In the **Spot Elevation** area, you can click on the **Type** drop-down list to select the desired type for the spot elevation.

*Figure 7-34 The **Structural Framing** **Tag** area*

*Figure 7-35 The **Spot Elevation** area*

By default, the **Beam Elevation (Project)** is selected in the drop-down list. As a result, the spot elevation of the beam will be calculated from the lowest level of the project. Alternatively, you can select the **Beam Elevation (Relative)** option from the **Type** drop-down list to display the spot elevation relative to the selected level in the project. On selecting the **Beam Elevation (Relative)** option from the **Type** drop-down list, the **Relative Base** drop-down list will be enabled. In this drop-down list, you can select the desired level to specify the reference level for the spot elevation of the beam. From the **Type** drop-down list in the **Spot Elevation** area, you can also select the **<Create /modify types>** option. On selecting this option, the **Beam Annotation - Loading Spot Elevation Types** message box will be displayed, as shown in Figure 7-36.

*Figure 7-36 The **Beam Annotation-Loading Spot Elevation Types** message box*

This message box will inform that a type will be added to the **Type** drop-down list only when spot elevations are allowed to rotate with the components to which they are attached. Next, choose the **Close** button from the message box; the **Type Properties** dialog box will be displayed. In this dialog box, select the check box corresponding to **Rotate with Component parameter**. In the **Type Properties** dialog box, you can set other parameters to change the display of various elements in the spot elevation. After specifying the desired parameters in the **Type Properties** dialog box, choose the **OK** button; the dialog box will be closed. Also, you will notice that a new type of spot elevation has been added to the **Type** drop-down list. In the **Spot Elevation** area, you can select various options from the **Display Elevation** drop-down list to specify the location of the measured elevation on the beam. From the **Display Elevation** drop-down list, you can select any of the four options: **Actual (Selected) Elevation**, **Bottom Elevation**, **Top & Bottom Elevation**, and **Top Elevation**. The **Actual (Selected) Elevation** option will be selected by default from the **Display Elevation** drop-down list. As a result, when the beam is annotated, the spot elevation will display the actual spot elevation of the location line of the beam with respect to the base level. Alternatively, you can select any of the remaining three options available in the **Display Elevation** drop-down list to specify the type of spot elevation to be displayed. In the **Select Annotation Type** dialog box, you can select the **Do not place when value is equal to** check box to prevent the spot elevation from being displayed for certain elevation values. As you select the **Do not place when value is equal to** check box, the edit box below it gets activated. You can enter a value in this edit box to specify elevation for which the spot elevation will not be displayed for the beam. By default, **0"** for metric system or **0.00 mm** for Metric system is displayed in the edit box. After specifying the desired options in the **Select Annotation Type** dialog box, choose the **OK** button; the **Select Annotation Type** dialog box will close and you will return to the **Beam Annotations** dialog box.

In the **Level beams in plan** tab of the **Beam Annotations** dialog box, you can choose other buttons located at the top and bottom of the image of the beam and specify the desired tag using the **Select Annotation Type** dialog box.

In the **Beam Annotations** dialog box, you can choose the **Sloped beams in plan** tab to assign the tags to the sloping beams displayed in the plan view. The options in this tab are similar to that discussed for the **Level beams in plan** tab. After specifying various parameters and options in the **Beam Annotations** dialog box, choose the **OK** button; the beam annotations will be displayed in the view at the locations specified in the **Beam Annotations** dialog box, refer to Figure 7-37.

Note
*On selecting the **Remove existing beam tags and spot elevations** check box in the **Beam Annotations** dialog box, the existing beam tags and spot elevations will be removed from the beam locations in the plan view and the annotations in the beams will be placed as per the settings in the **Beam Annotations** dialog box.*

Imperial

Metric

Figure 7-37 *The beam annotations displayed in a structural plan view*

CREATING FAMILIES

Revit family is defined as a collection of parametric components or elements having similar graphical representation, utility, and common parameters. By nature, all the elements used in Revit are family-based. A Revit family has a wide range of collections starting from a wall to a window and extends up to two-dimensional annotations or symbols required for your project. In Revit, each family inherits the character of a specific type. A type is a member of Revit family that consists of certain parameters known as **Type Parameters**. These parameters are constant for identical types. For example, the **C-Channel-Column** family can have different types such as **C-Channel-Column C12x30**, **C-Channel-Column C15x40**, and others. You can access these types from the **Type Selector** drop-down list.

In Revit, families are useful tools as they are driven by the Revit parametric change engine. This engine helps to reflect the changes made in a family throughout the project. You can edit the parameters of a family after you have created it in a project using the **Revit Family Editor**. The **Revit Family Editor** is an interface that allows you to create or make changes in a family. At the same time, it helps you add or modify specific parameters of your model while defining it as a family type.

While creating a project, you may need to define a family inside another family. This type of family is called nested family. For example, if you are creating a truss family, you can create another family inside it for the profiles of the members inside it. The use of nested family adds details to the family you have created.

In Autodesk Revit, there are three types of families: System families, In-place families, and Standard component families. These families are differentiated on the basis of their creations and utilities in a project.

The System families include the most common building components that are frequently used in a project such as walls, floors, roofs, and ceilings. You cannot create a new system family of your own, but you can create duplicate families and modify their properties as per your need. The In-place families are project-specific, therefore, you can use them when you need to create a unique component for a specific project. For example, you may need to design a unique table, featuring curved edges and material finishes specific to the flooring of a dining area. In such a case, you can use the In-place families for creating the table. Also, you can save this table for further use. In Revit, the Standard component families are the basic components that are commonly used in a building design. These families are not project-specific. Whenever a need arises, you can download these families from common libraries. You can place the Standard component families in a project template, so that they can be used whenever you start a new project. Revit allows you to load the required family of door, window, and so on from the in-built Revit library. To do so, choose the **Load Family** tool from the **Load from Library** panel in the **Insert** tab; the **Load Family** dialog box will be displayed. Select the required file for the family from the appropriate folder and then choose **Open**; the family will be loaded into the project.

In Revit, you can save a selected family or all families loaded in the current project or template to a location on your system or to a network location. To save a family loaded in the current project, choose **Save As > Library > Family** from the **File** menu; the **Save Family** dialog box will be displayed. In this dialog box, browse to a folder location to save the family file. Next, in the **File name** edit box, enter the name of the file and then select an option from the **Family to save** drop-down list to specify a family or all families loaded in the project. Next, choose the **Save** button; the selected family will be saved at the specified location. Note that in-place families and system families, such as walls, and patterns cannot be saved. Revit also enables you to create your own customized families and then use them in a project. There are two methods that you can use to create a family. These methods are discussed next.

Creating In-Place Families

This method is used to create custom families such as the furniture for reception and workstations in a building model. You can create a family while working on a project. The family created is saved within the project and gets updated according to the changes made in the project.

To create an In-Place family, choose the **Model In-Place** tool from **Structure >Model > Component** drop-down; the **Family Category and Parameters** dialog box will be displayed. In the **Family Category** area, select an option from the **Filter list** drop-down list to filter the list of categories that will be displayed in the list box displayed below it. Double-click on the required category from the list box; the **Name** dialog box will be displayed. In this dialog box, enter a name for the family in the **Name** edit box and then choose the **OK** button; the sketch mode will be invoked and the options in the **Create** tab will be displayed. Sketch the reference planes and set the work plane to help you sketch the geometry for the family using the required sketching tools from the **Model** panel and the **Forms** panel. After creating the massing geometry, choose the **Finish Model** button from the **In-Place Editor** panel; a family will be created. After creating the geometry of a family, you can assign materials to the family and create family types with different dimensions.

Creating a Family Geometry in the Family Editor

As discussed earlier, the Family Editor environment provides tools to create family geometry. To create a new family, choose **New > Family** from the **File** menu; the **New Family - Select Template File** dialog box will be displayed. In this dialog box, select the *Generic Model.rft* file (commonly used) from the **English_I** folder [for Metric the *Metric Generic Model.rft* file (commonly used) from the **English** folder] and choose the **Open** button; the family interface will be displayed, as shown in Figure 7-38.

Figure 7-38 *The family interface*

Note
Some of the family templates files that you can use for creating structural elements are: **Structural Stiffner.rft**, **Structural Trusses.rft**, **Structural Column.rft**, **Structural Foundation.rft**, *and so on.*

In the Family Editor environment, the **Create** tab contains tools to create family geometry. These tools can be used to create family geometries in solid or in void form.

To create a solid form, invoke the **Extrusion / Blend / Revolve / Sweep / Swept Blend** tool from the **Forms** panel of the **Create** tab. These tools are used to create different solid forms. Similarly, to create a void form, choose the **Void Extrusion / Void Blend / Void Revolve / Void Sweep / Void Swept Blend** tool from the **Void Forms** drop-down in the **Forms** panel. You can create a family geometry using any of these family tools or a combination of the **Solid** and **Void** tools depending on the family geometry to be created. Various tools used to create a solid or a void geometry are explained in the next sections.

Creating an Extrusion

Ribbon: Create > Forms > Extrusion

The **Extrusion** tool is used to create family geometry by adding height to any sketched profile. You can invoke this tool from the **Forms** panel in the **Create** tab of the ribbon in the Family Editor. On doing so, the **Modify | Create Extrusion** contextual tab will be displayed. In this tab, you can select options to sketch an extrusion profile and create a family geometry. Figure 7-39 shows different options in the **Modify | Create Extrusion** contextual tab.

*Figure 7-39 Different options in the **Modify / Create Extrusion** tab*

To create an extrusion, first you need to define the work plane. To do so, select the **Set** tool available in the **Work Plane** panel of the **Modify | Create Extrusion** contextual tab. After specifying the work plane, you can invoke the **Reference Plane** tool in the **Datum** panel of the **Create** tab to draw reference planes for locating exact points to sketch a profile. To sketch 2D profile to be extruded, you can invoke a sketching tool, depending on the shape of the profile, from the **Draw** panel of the **Modify | Create Extrusion** contextual tab. Note that the profile must be a closed loop. In the **Properties** panel, choose the **Properties** tool to display the **Properties** palette if not displayed by default. In this palette, you can specify the start and end levels of extrusion and other properties. The **Extrusion Start** instance parameter in the **Properties** palette indicates the start or bottom level of extrusion from the base level. The **Extrusion End** parameter indicates the top level of extrusion. The difference between these two parameters is calculated as the depth of the extrusion. You can also enter its value in the **Depth** edit box of the Options Bar. Autodesk Revit assumes the depth of extrusion from the base level. After sketching the profile, choose the **Finish Edit Mode** button from the **Mode** panel to finish the sketch of the profile for extrusion.

If you want to create a high-rise building, invoke the **Extrusion** tool from the **Forms** panel. In the Options Bar, you can specify the height of extrusion in the **Depth** edit box and also if required, select the **Chain** check box if not selected by default. Next, in the **Draw** panel of this tab, the **Line** tool (invoked by default) can be used to sketch the extrusion profile. You can also use other sketching tools available in the **Draw** panel to sketch the profile. Sketch the base using temporary dimensions, as shown in Figure 7-40. After the profile is completed, choose the **Finish**

Edit Mode button to extrude the sketched profile up to the specified depth. The building mass created can be seen in the 3D view, as shown in Figure 7-41.

Figure 7-40 Sketch of a building profile to be extruded

*Figure 7-41 Family geometry created by using the **Extrusion** tool*

Creating a Revolved Geometry

Ribbon:	Create > Forms > Revolve

The **Revolve** tool is used to create solid geometry by revolving a profile about an axis. This tool can also be used to create shapes such as domes, donuts, cylinders, and so on. To create a revolved geometry, invoke this tool from the **Forms** panel; Autodesk Revit enters the sketch mode and the **Modify | Create Revolve** contextual tab will be displayed, as shown in Figure 7-42.

*Figure 7-42 Options in the **Modify / Create Revolve** tab*

In the **Draw** panel, the **Boundary Line** tool is chosen by default. As a result, various sketching tools used to sketch the profile of the revolved geometry are displayed in a list box in this panel. Before invoking any of the sketching tools, you need to set the work plane. To do so, choose the **Create** tab, and then choose the **Set** tool from the **Work Plane** panel; the **Work Plane** dialog box will be displayed. In this dialog box, you can use various options to specify the required work plane for sketching the profile of the revolved geometry. After selecting the required plane, you can sketch the profile of the revolved geometry.

To sketch this profile, invoke the **Modify | Create Revolve** contextual tab. Now, you can use various sketching tools from the list box in the **Draw** panel. The sketched profile must be a single closed loop or multiple closed loops that do not intersect. After defining the profile, you need to define the axis about which the profile will revolve. To do so, invoke the **Axis Line** tool from the **Draw** panel; two tools, **Line** and **Pick Lines**, will be displayed. The **Line** tool is used to draw a line that can be used as an axis and the **Pick Lines** tool is used to pick a line or an edge to define the axis of revolution. After completing the sketch and defining the axis of revolution, choose the **Finish Edit Mode** button from the **Modify | Create Revolve** contextual tab; the **Modify | Revolve** contextual tab will be displayed and the revolved geometry will be created.

In the **Modify | Revolve** contextual tab, you can change the instance property of a revolved geometry in the **Properties** palette. In this palette, you can set the start and end angles of revolution. The default values for these two parameters are 0-degree and 360-degree, respectively.

If you want to create a dome, you can sketch the profile and define the axis for it, as shown in Figure 7-43. Before you start the sketch, you need to set the work plane that is perpendicular to the horizontal plane. The resultant revolved family geometry with the axis and its profile is shown in Figure 7-44. Figure 7-45 shows an example of the revolved geometry in which the **End Angle** and **Start Angle** parameters in the **Properties** palette have been assigned the values 180.000° and 0.000°, respectively.

Figure 7-43 *Sketching a closed profile for a revolved geometry*

Figure 7-44 *Family geometry created by using the **Revolve** tool*

Figure 7-45 *Revolved geometry created by revolving the profile at an angle of 180 degrees*

> **Tip**
> *In Autodesk Revit, you can quickly edit the revolve angle of a revolved geometry by selecting the geometry from the drawing and then changing the temporary angular dimension displayed in the geometry.*

Creating a Sweep

Ribbon: Create > Forms > Sweep

The **Sweep** tool is used to create a family feature by selecting a profile along a sketched path. To create a family feature by sweeping a profile, invoke the **Sweep** tool from the **Forms** panel; the sketch mode will be invoked and the **Modify | Sweep** contextual tab will be displayed, as shown in Figure 7-46. The **Sketch Path** tool in the **Sweep** panel of the **Modify | Sweep** contextual tab is used to sketch the path to be used for extrusion. On invoking this tool, the **Modify | Sweep** contextual tab will be replaced by the **Modify | Sweep > Sketch Path** contextual tab which contains tools to draw path.

*Figure 7-46   Options in the **Modify / Sweep** tab with its tools*

Using the tools from the **Draw** panel, you can sketch an open or closed profile path of desired shape. After sketching the path, choose the **Finish Edit Mode** button from the **Mode** panel; the **Modify | Sweep** contextual tab will be displayed. In this tab, you can sketch a profile or load a profile for the sweep geometry. To sketch a profile, choose the **Edit Profile** tool from the **Sweep** panel in the **Modify | Sweep** contextual tab; the **Go To View** dialog box will be displayed. In this dialog box, select an appropriate view and sketch the profile using different sketching tools. After sketching the profile, choose the **Finish Edit Mode** button from the **Mode** panel; the **Modify | Sweep > Edit Profile** contextual tab will be displayed. In this tab, choose the **Finish Edit Mode** button from the **Mode** panel; a sweep geometry will be created. Figure 7-47 shows an example of a 2D path with a sketched profile and Figure 7-48 shows the resulting family shape.

Figure 7-47   Sketching the profile and the 2D path for creating a sweep

*Figure 7-48   Family geometry created by using the **Sweep** tool*

Autodesk Revit also provides in-built profiles that can be used in projects. These profiles are available in the **Profile** drop-down list in the **Sweep** panel of the **Modify | Sweep** contextual tab. You can also choose the **Load Profile** button from the **Sweep** panel and access additional profiles in the **Profiles** subfolder in the **US Imperial** folder (for Metric **US Metric** folder). You can modify the properties, such as **Structural** and **Mechanical**, of the sweep profile. To do so, select the family created by the **Sweep** tool; the **Modify | Sweep** contextual tab will be displayed. In this tab, choose the **Edit Sweep** tool from the **Mode** panel; the properties of the sweep model will be displayed in the **Properties** palette. In this palette, click on the value field corresponding to the **Part Type** parameter under the **Mechanical** head; a drop-down list will be displayed. You can select an option from the displayed drop-down list to specify a part type for the sweep model. In the **Properties** palette, select the check box corresponding to the **Can host rebar** parameter to allow the sweep mass to host rebar for structural detailing.

Creating a Blend

Ribbon: Create > Forms > Blend

Using the **Blend** tool, you can create a family geometry by blending or linking two profiles. To create a family geometry using this tool, invoke it from the **Forms** panel; the **Modify | Create Blend Base Boundary** contextual tab will be displayed. The tools in this tab are used to create and edit a blend. Figure 7-49 shows various tools in the **Modify | Create Blend Base Boundary** contextual tab.

*Figure 7-49 Different tools in the **Modify / Create Blend Base Boundary** contextual tab*

After setting the work plane, you can sketch the base profile using different sketching tools available in the **Draw** panel. In the **Properties** palette, you can specify values in the value fields of the **First End** and **Second End** instance parameters to set the height of the blend geometry. After completing the base profile, choose the **Edit Top** option from the **Mode** panel in the **Modify | Create Blend Base Boundary** contextual tab to display the **Modify | Create Blend Top Boundary** contextual tab. Using the options in this tab, you can sketch the profile of the top of the blend geometry in any work plane. The depth of the blend geometry can be specified in the **Depth** edit box available in the Options Bar.

The **Edit Vertices** tool in the **Mode** panel of the **Modify | Create Blend Top Boundary** contextual tab will be available only after both the base and top profiles are sketched. This tool enables you to specify the connectivity between the vertices of their profiles. After sketching both the profiles, choose the **Finish Edit Mode** button from the **Mode** panel to create the blend geometry. Figure 7-50 shows two circular profiles being sketched as the base and top profiles. The resulting geometry is shown in Figure 7-51.

Figure 7-50 Sketching the base and top profiles to create a blend geometry

Figure 7-51 Resulting shape after blending the base and top profiles

Creating a Swept Blend

Ribbon: Create > Forms > Swept Blend

 The solid swept blend geometries are created by using the **Swept Blend** tool. This tool has combined features of the **Sweep** and **Blend** tools. A geometry created using the **Swept Blend** tool consists of a path and two different profiles drawn at the either end of the path.

To create a swept blend geometry, choose the **Swept Blend** tool from the **Forms** panel; the screen will enter into the sketch mode and the **Modify | Swept Blend** contextual tab will be displayed, as shown in Figure 7-52.

*Figure 7-52 Different options in the **Modify / Swept Blend** tab*

The **Modify | Swept Blend** contextual tab contains various tools to sketch and edit the path and profiles of a solid swept blend geometry. Figure 7-53 shows graphical representation of the solid swept blend geometry.

To create the geometry, first you need to sketch the 2D path. To do so, choose the **Sketch Path** tool from the **Swept Blend** panel; the sketch mode will be invoked. You can use various sketching tools in the **Draw** panel to sketch the 2D path. Next, choose the **Finish Edit Mode** button from the **Mode** panel of the **Modify | Swept Blend > Sketch Path** contextual tab. Alternatively, you can define the 2D path for the solid swept blend geometry by choosing the **Pick Path** tool from the **Swept Blend** panel and then selecting an existing open curve or the edges of elements. The desired 2D path is always an open geometry consisting of single segment. Once you have sketched or picked the 2D path, you need to define a profile at either end. Choose the **Select Profile 1** tool from the **Swept Blend** panel and then choose the **Edit Profile** tool from the **Edit** panel; the **Go To View** dialog box will be displayed. Choose required option from this dialog box and then choose the **Open View** button; the view will change based on the option chosen and the **Modify | Swept Blend > Edit Profile** contextual tab will be displayed. Sketch the first profile at the end of the 2D path where you can see the reference plane with a red dot prominently displayed by using appropriate sketching tools from the **Draw** panel. Next, to finish the sketching of the first profile, choose the **Finish Edit Mode** button from the **Mode** panel of the **Modify | Swept Blend > Edit Profile** contextual tab. Similarly, you can define the second profile. To do so, choose the **Select Profile 2** option from the **Swept Blend** panel and then choose the **Edit Profile** option from the **Mode** panel in the **Modify | Swept Blend** contextual tab; the **Modify | Swept Blend > Edit Profile** contextual tab will be displayed. Sketch the second profile and then choose the **Finish Edit Mode** button from the **Mode** panel; the **Modify | Swept Blend** contextual tab will be displayed again. Now, choose the **Finish Edit Mode** button from the **Mode** panel; the solid swept blend geometry will be created, as shown in Figure 7-54.

Figure 7-53 *The profiles and the 2D path for creating a swept blend geometry*

Figure 7-54 *Family geometry created by using the* **Swept Blend** *tool*

Editing a Family Geometry in the Family Editor

In Autodesk Revit, you can easily edit a family geometry. It can be edited using drag controls or by editing family parameters.

Resizing a Family Geometry by Using Drag Controls

On selecting a family geometry, a number of drag controls will be displayed as arrows. You can use the drag control to drag the desired face. The entire family geometry is automatically updated based on the dragged face. For example, Figure 7-55 shows a cuboid with drag controls displayed on all its faces. When you drag a plane of the cuboid using drag controls, Autodesk Revit immediately updates the geometry, as shown in Figure 7-56.

Figure 7-55 *The geometry with the drag controls*

Figure 7-56 *The family geometry resized using the drag controls*

Editing a Family Geometry

The parameters of a family geometry can be modified in the Family Editor. To do so, select a family geometry created by using the **Extrusion** tool; the **Modify | Extrusion** contextual tab will be displayed. In this tab, choose the **Edit Extrusion** tool from the **Mode** panel; the **Modify | Extrusion > Edit Extrusion** contextual tab will be displayed. From the **Draw** panel of this tab, you can use various sketching tools to alter the sketch of the extrusion profile. You can also change the properties of extrusion like height, material, and visibility from the **Properties** palette. In this palette, you can change the height of extrusion by changing the values of the **Extrusion End** and **Extrusion Start** parameters. Similarly, you can change other parameters. Next, in the

Modify | Extrusion > Edit Extrusion contextual tab, choose the **Finish Edit Mode** button from the **Mode** panel; the editing of the selected extruded mass will be finished.

As discussed earlier, you can also edit other family geometries such as sweept, sweept blend, revolved, and blended geometries.

To a certain extent, family features can also be modified like other building elements. You can use editing tools such as **Mirror**, **Copy**, **Group**, **Array**, and so on along with the family tools.

Creating Cuts in a Family Geometry by Using the Family Editor

You can cut a family geometry by creating a void form in it. This void form is cut or subtracted from the family geometry it intersects. You can create void forms by using the tools displayed in the **Void Forms** drop-down in the **Forms** panel of the **Create** tab. The **Void Forms** drop-down displays five tools: **Void Extrusion**, **Void Blend**, **Void Revolve**, **Void Swept Blend**, and **Void Sweep**. You can choose an appropriate tool to generate the shape and volume of the void form. The method of creating a void form using these tools is similar to that of creating a solid form.

When any of the tools from the **Void Forms** drop-down is invoked, a contextual tab is displayed. For example, if you invoke the **Void Extrusion** tool, the **Modify | Create Void Extrusion** contextual tab will be displayed. You can use the options in this tab to sketch the profile for the extruded void geometry. After sketching the profile of the extruded void geometry, choose the **Finish Edit Mode** button from the **Mode** panel of the **Modify | Create Void Extrusion** contextual tab; the **Modify | Void Extrusion** contextual tab will be displayed. From this tab, you can use various editing options to modify the extruded void geometry. Next, click in the drawing area or press ESC; the void form will automatically cut its shape and volume from the intersecting family geometry.

For example, Figure 7-57 shows the profile of an arcade sketched using the **Void Extrusion** tool. Now, when you choose the **Finish Edit Mode** button from the **Modify | Create Void Extrusion** contextual tab, the cutting geometry, an arcade in this case, is generated and gets automatically cut from the larger family geometry. Figure 7-58 shows the resulting family geometry.

Figure 7-57 Profile for created using the Void Extrusion tool

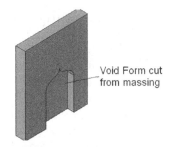

Figure 7-58 The generated void form and the resulting family geometry

Similarly, you can also use the **Void Revolve**, **Void Sweep**, **Void Blend**, and **Void Swept Blend** tools from the **Void Forms** drop-down to create the void form. For example, to create a tunnel through a building block, you can use the **Void Sweep** tool to sketch a semicircular profile and specify its path, as shown in Figure 7-59. The resulting void form will be cut from the cuboid to create an arched opening through the building block, as shown in Figure 7-60.

Figure 7-59 *Sketching the profile for creating a void form*   ***Figure 7-60*** *The generated void form and the resulting family geometry*

You can also use various editing tools such as **Copy**, **Mirror**, **Array**, and so on to create multiple copies of the void form profile for a single family geometry. For example, a commercial building block has a semicircular vertical cut as the void form on one of its sides, you can select the 2D profile of the void form and use the **Copy** tool to create its duplicate.

TUTORIALS

Tutorial 1   Commercial Complex

In this tutorial, you will open the *Commercial Complex* project created in Tutorial 1 of Chapter 6 and add dimensions to it in different structural plan views. Further, you will annotate beams and columns using various annotation tools. Use the following project parameters:

(Expected time: 25 min)

1. File name to be assigned:
           For Imperial   *c07_Commercial-Complex_tut1.rvt*
           For Metric   *M_c07_Commercial-Complex_tut1.rvt*

    The following steps are required to complete this tutorial:

a. Open the project file.
           For Imperial   *c06_Commercial-Complex_tut1.rvt*
           For Metric   *M_c06_Commercial-Complex_tut1.rvt*
b. Dimension grid lines.
c. Add the foundation, column, and slab tags.
d. Add beam annotations.
e. Save the project using the **Save As** tool.
f. Close the project using the **Close** tool.

Opening the Existing Project

In this section, you will open the project file created in the Tutorial 1 of Chapter 6.

1. Choose **Open > Project** from the **File** menu; the **Open** dialog box is displayed.

2. In this dialog box, browse to *C:/revit_2021_structural_projects/c06* location and choose the *c06_Commercial-Complex_tut1.rvt* for Imperial and *M_c06_Commercial-Complex_tut1.rvt* for Metric project file. You can also download this file from *https://www.cadcim.com*. The path of the file is as follows: *Textbooks > Civil/GIS > Revit Structure > Exploring Autodesk Revit 2021 for Structure*.

3. Choose the **Open** button from the **Open** dialog box; the selected project file opens in the drawing window in the **Second Floor** structural plan view.

Dimensioning the Grid Line

In this section, you will add dimensions to the grid lines displayed in the **Entry** structural plan view.

1. Double-click on the **Entry** node in the **Structural Plans** head in the **Project Browser** to open the corresponding structural floor plan view.

2. Choose the **View** tab and then invoke the **Visibility/ Graphics** tool from the **Graphics** panel of this tab; the **Visibility/Graphic Overrides for Structural Plan: Entry** dialog box is displayed.

3. In this dialog box, choose the **Annotation Categories** tab if not selected and then select the **Dimensions** check box displayed if not selected under the **Visibility** column.

4. Choose the **OK** button; the **Visibility/Graphic Overrides for Structural Plan: Entry** dialog box is closed.

5. Choose the **Annotate** tab and then choose the **Aligned** tool from the **Dimension** panel.

6. In the **Properties** palette, ensure that the **Linear Dimension Style : Arrow - 3/32" Arial** option for Imperial or the **Linear Dimension Style : Arrow -2.5mm Arial** option for Metric is selected from the **Type Selector** drop-down list. Next, choose the **Edit Type** button; the **Type Properties** dialog box is displayed.

7. In this dialog box, choose the **Duplicate** button; the **Name** dialog box is displayed.

8. In the **Name** edit box of the dialog box, delete the existing text and enter **Small Dot- 3/32" Arial** for Imperial or enter **Small Dot- 2.5mm Arial** for Metric and then choose the **OK** button; the **Name** dialog box is closed.

9. In the **Type Properties** dialog box, click in the value field of the **Tick Mark** parameter; a drop-down list is displayed. Next, select the desired option from this drop-down list.

    For Imperial   **Filled Dot Small**
    For Metric   **Filled Dot 2mm**

10. Click in the value field of the **Centerline Symbol** parameter; a drop-down list is displayed. Select the **Centerline** option for imperial and for metric select **M_Centerline** from the drop-down list.

11. Choose the **OK** button; the **Type Properties** dialog box is closed. Also, notice that in the drawing area, the dimension symbol appears with the cursor.

12. Move the cursor above grid A and place it over grid 1; the grid 1 gets highlighted.

13. Click and then move the cursor to the right and place it on grid 2. Next, click when grid 2 gets highlighted. Notice that a dimension between grid 1 and grid 2 is displayed, refer to Figure 7-61.

Figure 7-61 *The dimension created between grid 1 and grid 2*

14. Move the cursor over grid 3 and click when it gets highlighted.

15. Using the procedure followed in step 14, provide the dimensions till grid 5.1. After you have clicked over the grid 5.1, move the cursor up and place it above the grid bubbles, as shown in Figure 7-62.

16. Now click at the desired location, refer to Figure 7-62; the dimensions are added. Note that you can place the dimensions based on your requirement.

17. Repeat the procedures followed in steps 12 to 16 and add dimensions for all the horizontal grids from A to I. The dimensions are placed on the right of the structural plan view, refer to Figure 7-63.

Figure 7-62 *Dimensions placed at a location above grid bubbles*

Figure 7-63 *The dimensions placed at a location on the right of grid bubbles*

18. Press ESC twice to exit the tool.

Adding Tags to Foundations, Columns, and the Slab

In this section, you will add tags to foundations, columns, and the slab in the **Entry** structural plan view.

1. Ensure that the **Annotate** tab is chosen and then invoke the **Tag All** tool from the **Tag** panel; the **Tag All Not Tagged** dialog box is displayed.

2. Select the check box corresponding to the **Structural Foundation Tags** category in the **Category** column.

3. Next, select the check box corresponding to the **Structural Column Tags** category with the **Structural Column Tag** as the loaded tag; the selected category is highlighted, as shown in Figure 7-64.

*Figure 7-64   The **Tag All Not Tagged** dialog box with selected categories highlighted*

4. Choose the **Apply** button and then the **OK** button; the **Tag All Not Tagged** dialog box is closed and the selected tag categories are displayed in the **Entry** structural plan view.

5. Next, choose the **Tag by Category** tool from the **Tag** panel and place the cursor over the structural foundation slab; the structural foundation slab is highlighted.

6. Click on the highlighted slab when a preview of the tag appears; the foundation slab tag is added to the foundation slab, as shown in Figure 7-65.

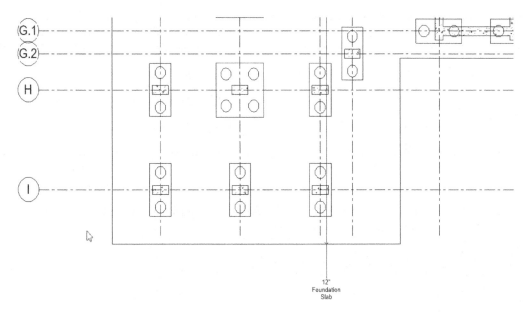

Figure 7-65 *Partial view of the structural plan displaying the added structural column tag*

7.   Press the ESC key twice to exit the selection mode.

Adding the Beam Annotations

In this section, you will tag the beams displayed in the **Second Floor** structural floor plan view.

1.   Double-click on the **Second Floor** node under the **Structural Plans** head in the **Project Browser** to open the corresponding structural floor plan view.

2.   Ensure that the **Annotate** tab is chosen. Choose the **Beam Annotations** tool from the **Tag** panel; the **Beam Annotations** dialog box is displayed.

3.   In the **Placement** area of this dialog box, ensure that the **All beams in current plan view** radio button is selected and then select the **Remove existing beam tags and spot elevations** check box.

4.   In the **Annotation location and type** area of this dialog box, ensure that the **Level beams in plan** tab is chosen.

5.   In this tab, choose the Browse button located at the top middle of the image of the beam; the **Select Annotation Type** dialog box is displayed.

6. In the **Select Element to Place** area of the **Select Annotation Type** dialog box, ensure that the **Structural Framing Tag** radio button is selected. Then, in the **Structural Framing Tag** area, click in the **Type** drop-down list and then select the framing tag option from the list displayed.

        For Imperial   **Structural Framing Tag : Boxed**
        For Metric   **M_Structural Framing Tag : Boxed**

7. Choose the **OK** button; the **Select Annotation Type** dialog box is closed.

8. In the **Level beams in plan** tab of the **Beam Annotations** dialog box, choose the Browse button located at the mid bottom of the image of the beam; the **Select Annotation Type** dialog box is displayed.

9. In the **Select Element to Place** area of the **Select Annotation Type** dialog box, ensure that the **Spot Elevation** radio button is selected.

10. In the **Spot Elevation** area of this dialog box, select the **Beam Elevation (Relative)** option from the **Type** drop-down list and then select the **Entry** option from the **Relative Base** drop-down list.

11. Select the **Top & Bottom Elevations** option from the **Display Elevation** drop-down list in the **Spot Elevation** area.

12. Choose the **OK** button; the **Select Annotation Type** dialog box is closed. Next, choose the **OK** button in the **Beam Annotations** dialog box; the **Beam Annotations** dialog box is closed and the beam annotations are added to all the beams placed in the view, as shown in Figure 7-66.

Figure 7-66 *The beam annotation displayed in the **Second Floor** structural plan view*

Saving the Project

In this section, you will save the project file by using the **Save As** tool.

1. Choose **Save As > Project** from the **File** menu; the **Save As** dialog box is displayed.

2. In this dialog box, browse to the *C:\rst_2021* location and create a folder with name **c07_rst_2021_tut**. Next, open the created folder and enter **c07_Commercial-Complex_tut1** for Imperial and **M_c07_Commercial-Complex_tut1** for Metric unit system in the **File name** edit box.

3. Now, choose the **Save** button; the **Save As** dialog box closes and the project file is saved.

Closing the Project

1. Choose the **Close** option from the **File** menu.

    The file is closed. This completes Tutorial 1 of Chapter 7.

Tutorial 2   Industrial Complex

In this tutorial, you will open the *Industrial Complex project* for Imperial or *M_Industrial Complex project* for Metric created in Tutorial 2 of Chapter 6 and then dimension its different structural plan views. Further, you will annotate the beams and columns using the annotation tools. Use the following project parameters:

(Expected time: 25 min)

The following steps are required to complete this tutorial:

a. Open the project file.
    For Imperial   *c06_Industrial-Complex_tut2.rvt*
    For Metric   *M_c06_Industrial-Complex_tut2.rvt*
b. Dimension the grid lines.
c. Add foundation and column tags.
d. Add beam annotations and floor tags.
e. Save the project by using the **Save As** tool.
f. Close the project by using the **Close** tool.

Opening the Existing Project

In this section, you will open the project file created in Tutorial 2 of Chapter 6.

1. Choose **Open > Project** from the **File** menu; the **Open** dialog box is displayed.

2. In this dialog box, browse to the location *C:/revit_2021_structural_projects/c06* and then choose the *c06_Industrial-Complex_tut2.rvt* for Imperial *M_c06_Industrial-Complex_tut2.rvt* for Metric project file. You can also download this file from *https://www.cadcim.com*. The path of the file is as follows: *Textbooks > Civil/GIS > Revit Structure > Exploring Autodesk Revit 2021 for Structure*.

3. Choose the **Open** button from the **Open** dialog box; the selected project file opens in the drawing window in the **Second Floor** structural plan view.

Dimensioning the Grid Lines

In this section, you will place dimensions to the grid lines displayed in the **Entry** structural plan view.

1. Double-click on the **Entry** node under the **Structural Plans** head in the **Project Browser**; the structural floor plan view at the **Entry** level is displayed.

2. Choose the **Aligned** tool from the **Dimension** panel of the **Annotate** tab; the **Modify | Place Dimensions** contextual tab is displayed.

3. In the **Properties** palette, ensure that the **Linear Dimension Style : Arrow -3/32" Arial** option for Imperial system or **Linear Dimension Style : Arrow -2.5mm Arial** option for Metric system is selected in the **Type Selector** drop-down list and then choose the **Edit Type** button; the **Type Properties** dialog box is displayed.

4. In the **Type Properties** dialog box, choose the **Duplicate** button; the **Name** dialog box is displayed.

5. In the **Name** dialog box, enter **grid-dim-1/8"** for Imperial or **Grid-Dim-3mm** for Metric in the **Name** edit box and then choose the **OK** button; the **Name** dialog box closes.

6. In the **Type Properties** dialog box, click in the value field corresponding to the **Tick Mark** parameter; a down arrow is displayed in the clicked field. Click on the down arrow and then select the **Diagonal 1/8"** option for Imperial or **Diagonal 2mm** option for Metric from the drop-down list displayed.

7. Next, click in the value field corresponding to the **Text Size** parameter and enter **1/8"** for imperial and for metric enter 3 mm to replace the existing value.

8. Choose the **OK** button; the **Type Properties** dialog box is closed.

9. In the drawing area, move the cursor below grid A and place it on grid 9; grid 9 is highlighted.

10. Click on the highlighted grid and move the cursor toward right and place it on grid 8. Next, click when grid 8 is highlighted.

11. Again, move the cursor toward right and place it over grid 7 and click when grid 7 is highlighted. This creates horizontal dimension for grids 7 to 9.

12. Move the cursor down near the grid 8 and then click; the dimensions get placed, as shown in Figure 7-67.

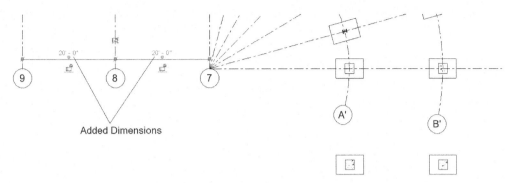

Figure 7-67 *The aligned dimensions added between the grids 7, 8, and 9*

13. Move the cursor and place it near the grid bubble of grid A and then click on the grid A when it is highlighted.

14. Move the cursor in an upward direction and click on grid B and then on grid C. Next, move the cursor and click near the bubble of grid C; aligned dimensions are created between the horizontal grid lines A, B, and C.

15. Choose the **Modify** button from the **Select** panel; the selection is cleared.

16. Invoke the **Angular** tool from the **Dimension** panel of the **Annotate** tab; the **Modify | Place Dimensions** contextual tab is displayed.

17. In the **Properties** palette, select the **Angular Dimension Style : Diagonal - 3/32"Arial** option for Imperial or **Angular Dimension Style : Diagonal -2.5mm Arial** option for Metric from the **Type Selector** drop-down list and then choose the **Edit Type** button from the **Properties** palette; the **Type Properties** dialog box is displayed.

18. In the **Type Properties** dialog box, choose the **Duplicate** button; the **Name** dialog box is displayed.

19. In the **Name** dialog box, enter **Grid-Dim-Ang-1/8"** for Imperial or **Grid-Dim-Ang-3mm** for Metric in the **Name** edit box and then choose the **OK** button; the **Name** dialog box is closed.

20. In the **Type Properties** dialog box, click in the value field of the **Tick Mark** parameter and then select the **Diagonal 1/8"** option for Imperial or **Diagonal 2mm** option for Metric from the drop-down list displayed in the field you clicked.

21. Next, click in the value field of the **Text Size** parameter and enter **1/8"** for Imperial or **3mm** for Metric to replace the existing value.

22. Choose the **OK** button; the **Type Properties** dialog box is closed.

23. Move the cursor near the grid bubble of grid 7 and then place the cursor on grid 7; the grid 7 gets highlighted.

24. Click on the highlighted grid and then move the cursor toward right and click on grid 6; an angular dimension is displayed between grid 7 and grid 6.

25. Move the cursor near the grid bubble 7 and click to place the angular dimension.

   Using the procedure followed in steps 23 to 25, create angular dimensions from grids 6 to 1, as shown in Figure 7-68.

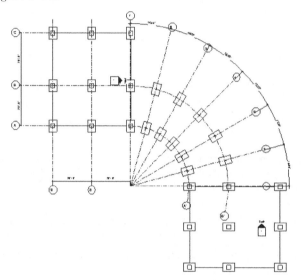

Figure 7-68 *The angular dimensions added from grids 1 to 6*

26. Press the ESC key twice to exit the selection mode.

Adding the Foundation and Column Tags

In this section, you will add tags to the foundations and columns displayed in the **Entry** level view of the structural floor plan

1. Choose the **Tag All** tool from the **Tag** panel of the **Annotate** tab; the **Tag All Not Tagged** dialog box is displayed.

2. Select the check box corresponding to the **Structural Column Tags** category and select the **Structural Column Tag-45 : Structural Column Tag** option from the drop-down list corresponding to the **Structural Column Tags** option. Then, select the check box corresponding to the **Structural Foundation Tags** category.

3. Choose the **Apply** and **OK** buttons; the **Tag All Not Tagged** dialog box is closed and the columns and foundations tags are displayed.

Adding Beam Annotations and Floor Tags

In this section, you will add beam annotations and floor tags to the **Second Floor** structural plan view.

1. Double-click on the **Second Floor** node under the **Structural Plans** head in the **Project Browser**; the structural floor plan view at the **Second Floor** level is displayed.

2. Choose the **Beam Annotations** tool from the **Tag** panel in the **Annotate** tab; the **Beam Annotations** dialog box is displayed.

3. In the **Placement** area of the **Beam Annotations** dialog box, ensure that the **All beams in the current plan view** radio button is selected and then select the **Remove existing beam tags and spot elevations** check box.

4. Choose the **OK** button; the **Beam Annotations** dialog box is closed and the tags are added to all the beams displayed in the view.

5. Next, choose the **Tag By Category** tool from the **Tag** panel; the **Modify | Tag** contextual tab is displayed.

6. In the **Options Bar**, choose the **Tags** button; the **Loaded Tags And Symbols** dialog box is displayed.

7. In this dialog box, choose the **Load Family** button; the **Load Family** dialog box is displayed.

8. In this dialog box, browse to the path **English-Imperial > Annotations > Structural** and choose the **Slab Tag**.*rfa* file for Imperial or **English-Metric > Annotations > Structural** and choose the **M_Slab Tag**.*rfa* file for Metric unit system. Next, choose the **Open** button; the **Load Family** dialog box is closed.

9. In the **Loaded Tags And Symbols** dialog box, choose the **OK** button; the **Loaded Tags And Symbols** dialog box is closed.

10. Place the cursor on the structural floor placed in the left wing of the structural model; the floor gets highlighted and a preview of the tag appears. Click on the highlighted floor; the floor tag is added to the structural floor, refer to Figure 7-69.

11. Next, click on the other two floors one by one and add their corresponding tags, refer to Figure 7-69.

12. Press the **ESC** key twice to exit the selection mode.

Figure 7-69 *The angular dimensions added from grids 1 to 6*

Saving the Project

1. Choose **Save As > Project** from the **File** menu; the **Save As** dialog box is displayed.

2. In this dialog box, browse to *C:\rst_2021\c07_rst_2021_tut* and enter **c07_Industrial-Complex_tut2** for Imperial or **M_c07_Industrial-Complex_tut2** for Metric in the **File name** edit box.

3. Now, choose the **Save** button; the **Save As** dialog box closes and the project file is saved.

Closing the Project

1. Choose the **Close** option from the **File** menu.

Tutorial 3   Trapezoidal Footing

In this tutorial, you will create a family of Trapezoidal footing in Family Editor interface.

(Expected time: 45 min)

The following steps are required to complete this tutorial:

a. Open the existing template.

               For Imperial   *Structural Foundation.rft*
               For Metric   *Metric Structural Foundation.rft*

b. Create the reference plane.
c. Create footing base part using the **Extrusion** tool.
d. Create footing top part using the **Blend** tool.
e. Add parameters to footing.

f.   Assign material to footing.
g.   Save the project by using the **Save As** tool.
h.   Close the project by using the **Close** tool.

Opening the Existing Template

1.   Choose **New > Family** from the **File** menu; the **New Family - Select Template File** dialog box is displayed.

2.   In this dialog box, browse to *C:\ProgramData\Autodesk\RVT 2021\Family Templates\English_I* location and choose the project template *Structural Foundation.rft* for Imperial or *Metric Structural Foundation.rft* for Metric. You can also download this file from *https://www.cadcim.com*. The path of the file is as follows: *Textbooks > Civil/GIS > Revit Structure > Exploring Autodesk Revit 2021 for Structure*.

3.   Choose the **Open** button from the **New Family - Select Template File** dialog box; the selected template with **Ref. Level** plan opens in the drawing window.

Creating Reference Plane

In this section, you will create reference planes.

1.   Choose the **Reference Plane** tool from the **Datum** panel in the **Create** tab; the **Modify|Place Reference Plane** contextual tab is displayed.

2.   Choose the **Pick Lines** tool from the **Draw** panel in the **Modify|Place Reference Plane** contextual tab; Enter the **2' 0"** for Imperial or **600mm** for Metric in the **Offset** edit box in the **Options Bar**.

3.   Hover the cursor over the left side of the vertical reference plane in the drawing window; a new reference plane is highlighted, as shown in Figure 7-70. Next click; the reference plane is created as shown in Figure 7-71.

Figure 7-70 New reference plane highlighted at the left of vertical plane

Figure 7-71 New reference plane created at the left of vertical reference plane

4. Hover the cursor on the right side of the vertical reference plane in the drawing window and click when a new reference plane is highlighted; a reference plane is created at the right side.

5. Repeat the steps 2 and 3 to make reference planes above and below the horizontal reference plane, as shown in Figure 7-72.

6. In the **Modify|Place Reference Plane** contextual tab, enter the **1' 0"** for Imperial and **300mm** for Metric in the **Offset** edit box from the **Options Bar**.

7. Hover the cursor on the left side of the vertical reference plane in drawing window and click when a new reference plane is highlighted, refer to Figure 7-73; a reference plane is created, as shown in Figure 7-74.

Figure 7-72 *Reference plane created on all side of the center reference planes*

Figure 7-73 *New reference plane highlighted at the left of vertical plane*

Figure 7-74 *New reference plane created at the left of vertical reference plane*

8. Hover the cursor on the right side of the vertical reference plane in the drawing window and click when a reference plane is highlighted; the reference plane is created on the right side.

9. Create two horizontal planes one above and one below the horizontal reference plane similar to creating vertical planes in steps 7 and 8, as shown in Figure 7-75.

Figure 7-75 *Reference plane is created at the inner sides of center reference planes*

Creating Footing Base

In this section, you will create footing base part using the **Extrusion** tool.

1. Choose the **Extrusion** tool from the **Forms** panel in the **Create** tab; the **Modify|Create Extrusion** contextual tab is displayed.

2. Choose the **Rectangle** tool from the **Draw** panel in the **Modify|Create Extrusion** contextual tab.

3. Click at the top left intersection of reference planes, as shown in Figure 7-76. Click again at the bottom right intersection of reference plane to complete the rectangle as shown in Figure 7-77.

4. Lock all the boundary lines with their respective planes, as shown in Figure 7-78.

5. Choose the **Finish Edit Mode** tool from the **Mode** panel in the **Modify|Create Extrusion** contextual tab.

6. Choose the **Modify** tool from the **Select** panel in the **Modify|Extrusion** contextual tab.

Figure 7-76 *First point of rectangle at intersection of reference planes*

Figure 7-77 *Second point of rectangle at intersection of reference planes*

Figure 7-78 *Rectangle boundaries locked with reference planes.*

7. Double-click on the **Back** node under the **Elevations (Elevation 1)** head in the **Project Browser**; the structural back elevation view is displayed.

8. Choose the **Reference Plane** tool from the **Datum** panel of the **Create** tab; the **Modify | Place Reference Plane** contextual tab is displayed.

9. Choose the **Pick Lines** tool from the **Draw** panel in the **Modify | Place Reference Plane** contextual tab. Enter the **1' 0"** (**300 mm** for Metric) in the **Offset** edit box in the **Options Bar**. Hover the cursor above the **Ref. Level** and click; a reference plane is created above the **Ref. Level**, as shown in Figure 7-79.

Figure 7-79 *Reference plane is created above*
Ref. Level

10. Hover the cursor over the click to name and click; an edit box appears for naming, as shown in Figure 7-80. Enter **Base Top** and click outside the edit box.

Figure 7-80 *The edit box displayed*

11. Now, hover the cursor over the Base Top reference plane and click; a new reference plane is created. Rename this reference plane as **Footing Top** as explained in step 10 and press the ESC button twice.

Creating Footing Top

In this section, you will create footing top part using the **Blend** tool.

1. Choose the **Set** tool from the **Work Plane** panel in the **Create** tab; the **Work Plane** dialog box is displayed. In this dialog box, select the **Name** radio button if not selected by default. Next, choose the **Reference Plane : Base Top** option from the **Name** drop-down in the **Specify a new Work Plane** area. Choose the **OK** button; the **Get To View** dialog box is displayed. Choose the **Open View** button in this dialog box.

2. Now, choose the **Blend** tool from the **Forms** panel in the **Create** tab; the **Modify|Create Blend Base Boundary** contextual tab is displayed.

3. Choose the **Rectangle** tool from the **Draw** panel in the **Modify|Create Blend Base Boundary** contextual tab.

4. Click at the top left intersection of reference planes, refer to in Figure 7-76. Click again at the bottom right intersection of reference plane, as refer to Figure 7-77.

5. Lock all the boundary lines with there respective planes, refer to in Figure 7-78.

6. Choose the **Edit Top** tool from the **Mode** panel in the **Modify | Create Blend Base Boundary** contextual tab.

7. Choose the **Rectangle** tool from the **Draw** panel in the **Modify | Create Blend Top Boundary** contextual tab.

8. Draw a rectangle and lock its boundary with corresponding reference plane, as shown in Figure 7-81.

Figure 7-81 Locked top boundary of the Blend

9. Choose the **Finish Edit Mode** tool from the **Mode** panel in the **Modify | Create Blend Top Boundary** contextual tab and press the ESC key twice to exit the selection mode.

10. Double-click on the **Back** node under the **Elevations (Elevation 1)** head in the **Project Browser**; the structural back elevation view is displayed.

11. Choose the **Align** tool from the **Modify** panel in the **Modify** tab. Click on the **Reference Plane : Footing Top** and then click on the **Blend : Shape handle**; a lock icon appears, refer to Figure 7-82. Click on this icon.

Figure 7-82 Locked Reference Plane : Footing Top and Blend : Shape Handle

12. Now, click on Reference Plane : Base Top and then click on **Blend : Shape handle**; a lock icon appears. Click on this icon.

Providing Parameters to Footing

In this section, you will provide parameters to footing.

1. Choose the **Aligned** tool from the **Dimension** panel in the **Annotate** tab; the **Modify|Place Dimensions** contextual tab is displayed. Click on the Reference Plane : Footing Top and then click on the Reference Plane : Base Top and then in drawing area; the distance between the two reference planes is annotated.

2. Now, click on the Reference Plane : Base Top, and then Ref. Level, and then in the drawing area; the distance between the two reference planes is annotated, refer to Figure 7-83. Choose the **Modify** tool from the **Select** panel in the **Modify|Place Dimensions** contextual tab.

Figure 7-83 *Distance between reference plane annotated*

3. Hover the cursor on dimension, as shown in Figure 7-84 and click; the **Modify|Dimensions** contextual tab is displayed. Choose the **Create Parameter** button from the **Label Dimension** panel of the **Modify|Dimensions** contextual tab; the **Parameter Properties** dialog box is displayed. In this dialog box, enter **Base Thickness** in the **Name** edit box in the **Parameter Data** area and then choose the **OK** button; the **Parameter Properties** dialog box is closed and parameter is added.

Figure 7-84 *Dimension highlighted on hovering the cursor*

4. Repeat the procedure followed in step 3 and add **Top Thickness** as the parameter to upper dimension, as shown in Figure 7-85.

Figure 7-85 Distance after providing parameter

5. Double-click on the **Ref. Level** node under the **Floor Plans** head in the **Project Browser**; the structural plan view at the **Ref. Level** is displayed, refer to Figure 7-86.

Figure 7-86 Planes for references

Note
Annotations shown in Figure 7-86 are given for the purpose of understanding only and will not appear in the project.

6. Choose the **Aligned** tool from the **Dimension** panel in the **Annotate** tab; the **Modify|Place Dimensions** contextual tab is displayed. Click on reference plane 1 and then on 5 and then in the drawing area; the distance between the reference planes is annotated. Press the **ESC** button twice.

7. Now select this dimension; the **Modify|Dimensions** contextual tab is activated. Choose the **Create Parameter** button; the **Parameter Properties** dialog box is displayed. In this dialog box, enter **B** in the **Name** edit box in the **Parameter Data** area and then choose the **OK** button; the **Parameter Properties** dialog box is closed and parameter is added.

8. Choose the **Aligned** tool from the **Dimension** panel in the **Annotate** tab; the **Modify|Place Dimensions** contextual tab is displayed. Click on reference plane 1, 3 and 5, and then click in the drawing area. Next, choose the **Toggle Dimension Equality** button shown in Figure 7-87 to equalize the distance between reference planes. Press the ESC button twice to terminate the command.

Figure 7-87 Toggle Dimension Equality button

9. Choose the **Aligned** tool from the **Dimension** panel in the **Annotate** tab; the **Modify|Place Dimensions** contextual tab is activated. Click on reference plane 2 and then on 4 and then in drawing area; the distance between the reference planes is annotated. Press the ESC button twice.

10. Now select the dimension between reference planes 2 and 4; the **Modify|Dimensions** contextual tab is activated. Choose the **Create Parameter** button; the **Parameter Properties** dialog box is displayed. In this dialog box, enter **b** in the **Name** edit box in the **Parameter Data** area and then choose the **OK** button; the **Parameter Properties** dialog box is closed and the parameter is added.

11. Choose the **Aligned** tool from the **Dimension** panel in the **Annotate** tab; the **Modify|Place Dimensions** contextual tab is displayed. Click on reference planes 2, 3 and 4, and then on drawing area. Next, choose the **Toggle Dimension Equality** button shown in Figure 7-88 to equalize the distance between reference planes. Press the ESC button twice to terminate the command.

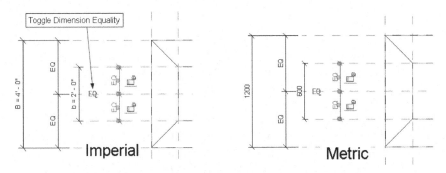

*Figure 7-88 The **Toggle Dimension Equality** button*

12. Choose the **Aligned** tool from the **Dimension** panel in the **Annotate** tab; the **Modify|Place Dimensions** contextual tab is activated. Click on reference plane A and then on E and then on drawing area; the distance between reference planes is annotated. Press the ESC button twice.

13. Now select this dimension; the **Modify|Dimensions** contextual tab is activated. Choose the **Create Parameter** button; the **Parameter Properties** dialog box is displayed. In this dialog box, enter the **L** in the **Name** edit box from the **Parameter Data** area and then choose the **OK** button; the **Parameter Properties** dialog box is closed and parameter is added.

14. Choose the **Aligned** tool from the **Dimension** panel in the **Annotate** tab; the **Modify|Place Dimensions** contextual tab is displayed. Click on the reference planes A, C and E, and then on drawing area. Next, choose the **Toggle Dimension Equality** button in the drawing area, refer to Figure 7-89 to equalize the distance between reference planes. Next, press the ESC button twice.

Figure 7-89 Equalising Dimension

15. Choose the **Aligned** tool from the **Dimension** panel in the **Annotate** tab; the **Modify|Place Dimensions** contextual tab is displayed. Click on reference planes B and D and then in the drawing area; the distance between reference planes is annotated. Press the ESC button twice.

16. Select the dimension between reference planes B and D; the **Modify|Dimensions** contextual tab is displayed. Choose the **Create Parameter** button; the **Parameter Properties** dialog box is displayed. In this dialog box, enter **l** in the **Name** edit box in the **Parameter Data** area and then choose the **OK** button; the **Parameter Properties** dialog box is closed and parameter is added.

17. Choose the **Aligned** tool from the **Dimension** panel in the **Annotate** tab; the **Modify|Place Dimensions** contextual tab is displayed. Click on the reference planes B, C, and then on D and then choose the **Toggle Dimension Equality** button in the drawing area, refer to Figure 7-90, to equalize the distance between reference planes. Next press the ESC button twice.

Figure 7-90 *Distance between reference planes equalized*

Assigning Material

In this section, you will assign material to footing.

1. Double-click on the **View 1** node under the **3D Views** head in the **Project Browser**; the 3D view gets displayed, as shown in Figure 7-91.

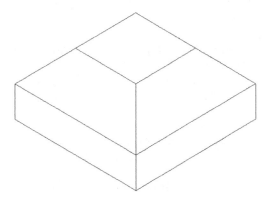

Figure 7-91 *3D view of footing*

2. Select the footing using crossing window; the **Modify|Multi-Select** contextual tab is displayed.

3. Click on the edit box corresponding to **Material** in the **Materials and Finishes** area in the **Properties** palette; a browse button is displayed in this edit box. Click on it; the **Material Browser - Concrete - Cast-in-Place Concrete** edit box is displayed, refer to Figure 7-92.

*Figure 7-92 The **Material Browser - Concrete -**
Cast-in-Place Concrete dialog box*

4. Choose the **OK** button in the **Material Browser - Concrete - Cast-in-Place Concrete** dialog box; the dialog box closes and the material is assigned to footing.

Saving the Project

1. Choose **Save As > Family** from the **File** menu; the **Save As** dialog box is displayed.

2. In this dialog box, browse to *C:\rst_2021\c07_rst_2021_tut* and enter **c07_Trapezoidal Footing_tut3** for Imperial or **M_c07_Trapezoidal Footing_tut3** for Metric in the **File name** edit box.

3. Now, choose the **Save** button; the **Save As** dialog box closes and the project file is saved.

Closing the Project

1. Choose the **Close** option from the **File** menu; the file is closed.

Tutorial 4   L Shape Family

In this tutorial, you will create an L shape Structural Column family of Length 2', Width 1' 6" and Height 10' 0" and place it in a project.   **(Expected time: 45 min)**

The following steps are required to complete this tutorial:

a. Open the structural column family.
b. Create reference planes.
c. Extrude L shape column on the reference planes after assigning the properties.
d. Annotate and create the parameters for the dimensions.

e.   Save the family and load it in a project.

f.   Close the family using the **Close** tool.

Opening a Family

In this section, you will open a new family template.

1.   Choose **New > Family** from the **File** menu; the **New Family - Select Template File** dialog box is displayed.

2.   In this dialog box, choose the **Structural Column.rft** file for Imperial and **Metric Structural Column** for Metric from the **Name** area. Choose the **Open** button, the file is loaded with the **Lower Ref. Level** in the drawing area.

Creating the Reference Planes

In this section, you will learn to create the reference planes.

1.   Click at the lower right corner near the reference planes and then drag the mouse to select all the reference planes in the drawing area. Now, press the DELETE button; a warning message box is displayed informing that the pinned objects cannot be deleted.

2.   Choose the **Reference Plane** tool from the **Datum** panel of the **Create** tab; the **Modify | Place Reference Plane** contextual tab is displayed. Type the value **1' 0"** for Imperial and **300 mm** for Metric in the **Offset** edit box of the **Options Bar** and press ENTER.

3.   Next, place the cursor at the top of the Vertical Reference Plane: Center and click when the **Endpoint** snap is displayed. Bring the cursor vertically downward to the end of the reference plane and click when the **Endpoint and Vertical** snap is displayed. Choose the **Modify** button from the **Select** panel of the **Modify | Place Reference Plane** contextual tab. A new reference plane is created on the right of the Vertical Reference Plane: Center, as shown in Figure 7-93.

4.   Select the last created reference plane; the **Modify | Reference Planes** contextual tab is displayed. Next, choose the **Mirror | Pick Axis** tool from the **Modify** panel of the **Modify | Reference Planes** contextual tab and click on the Vertical Reference Plane: Center; a new reference plane is created, as shown in Figure 7-94. Choose the **Modify** button from the **Select** panel of the **Modify | Place Reference Plane** contextual tab.

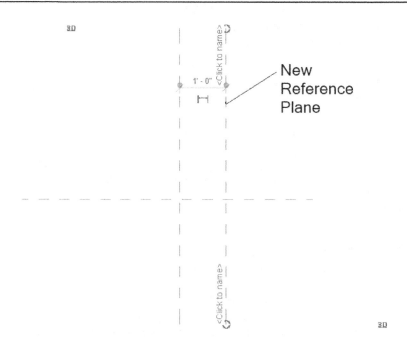

Figure 7-93 *New reference plane created on the right of the Vertical Reference Plane: Center*

Figure 7-94 *New reference plane created on the left of the Vertical Reference Plane: Center*

5. Again, choose the **Reference Plane** tool from the **Datum** panel of the **Create** tab; the **Modify | Place Reference Plane** contextual tab is displayed. Enter the value **0' 9"** in the **Offset** edit box of the **Options Bar**.

6. Next, place the cursor on the left end of the Horizontal Reference Plane: Center and click when the **Endpoint** snap is displayed. Move the cursor horizontally to the right of the reference plane and click when the **Endpoint and Horizontal** snap is displayed; a new reference plane is created at the front of the Horizontal Reference Plane: Center, as shown in Figure 7-95. Choose the **Modify** button from the **Select** panel of the **Modify | Place Reference Plane** contextual tab.

Figure 7-95 *New reference plane created in front of the Horizontal Reference Plane: Center*

7. Select the last created reference plane; the **Modify | Reference Planes** contextual tab is displayed. Choose the **Mirror | Pick Axis** tool from the **Modify** panel of the **Modify | Reference Planes** contextual tab and click anywhere on the Horizontal Reference Plane: Center; a new reference plane is created. Choose the **Modify** button from the **Select** panel of the **Modify | Place Reference Plane** contextual tab; the reference planes created are shown in Figure 7-96.

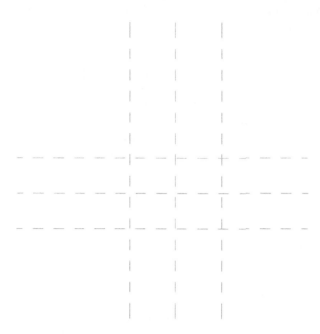

Figure 7-96 *The reference planes created*

Creating the Column using Extrusion Tool

In this section, you will create the L shape column with the help of reference planes.

1. Choose the **Extrusion** tool from the **Forms** panel of the **Create** tab; the **Modify | Create Extrusion** contextual tab is displayed. Select the **Line** tool from the **Draw** panel of the **Modify | Create Extrusion** contextual tab. Also, select the **Chain** check box from the **Options Bar**.

2. Type the value **10' 0"** in the **Extrusion End** edit box in the **Constraints** area of the **Properties** palette. Choose the **Associate Family Parameter** button opposite to the **Material** parameter in the **Materials and Finishes** area of the **Properties** palette; the **Associate Family Parameter** dialog box is displayed, as shown in Figure 7-97. Choose the **Structural Material** option and press the **OK** button; the dialog box is closed.

3. Next, move the cursor at the intersection of the top and left reference planes and click when the **Intersection** snap is displayed. Move the cursor vertically downward to the intersection of the back and the left reference plane and click when the **Intersection and Vertical** snap is displayed.

4. Next, move the cursor horizontal to the right to the intersection of the back and right reference planes and click when the **Intersection and Horizontal** snap is displayed. Then, move the cursor to the intersection of the horizontal center and the right reference planes and click when the **Intersection and Vertical** snap is displayed.

Figure 7-97 The Associate Family Parameter dialog box

5. Move the cursor horizontal to the left at the intersection of both the horizontal and vertical center reference planes and click when the **Intersection and Horizontal** snap is displayed. Next, move the cursor upward to the intersection of the vertical center and front reference planes and click when the **Intersection and Vertical** snap is displayed.

6. Move the cursor horizontal to the left to intersect the front and left reference planes and click when **Intersection and Horizontal** snap is displayed. Next, choose the **Finish Edit Mode** button from the **Mode** panel of the **Modify | Create Extrusion** contextual tab. Then, press the **Modify** button from the **Select** panel of the **Modify | Extrusion** contextual tab; L shape column boundary is created, as shown in Figure 7-98.

7. Now, choose the **Aligned** tool from the **Dimension** panel of the **Annotate** tab; the **Modify | Place Dimensions** contextual tab is displayed. Mark the dimensions and equalize them, as shown in Figure 7-99 and then choose the **Modify** button from the **Select** panel of the **Modify | Place Dimensions** contextual tab.

8. Next, choose the vertical dimension; the **Modify | Dimensions** contextual tab is displayed. Choose the **Create Parameter** button from the **Label Dimension** panel of the **Modify | Dimensions** contextual tab; the **Parameter Properties** dialog box is displayed. In this dialog box, type **Width** in the **Name** edit box of the **Parameter Data** area, as shown in Figure 7-100. Ensure that the **Dimensions** option is selected in the **Group parameter under** drop-down list. Press the **OK** button, the **Parameter Properties** dialog box is closed.

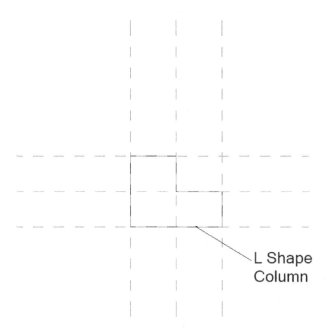

Figure 7-98 L Shape column is created

Figure 7-99 Marked dimensions for the L Shape Column

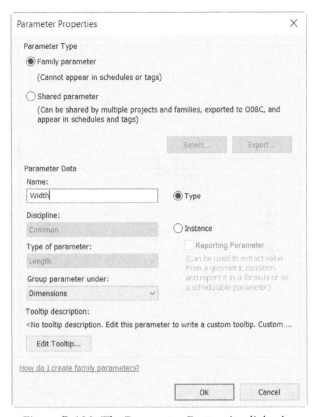

*Figure 7-100 The **Parameter Properties** dialog box*

9. Select the horizontal dimension; the **Modify | Dimensions** contextual tab is displayed. Choose the **Create Parameter** button from the **Label Dimension** panel of the **Modify | Dimensions** contextual tab; the **Parameter Properties** dialog box is displayed. Enter **Length** in the **Name** edit box of the **Parameter data** area. Ensure that the **Dimensions** option is selected in the **Group parameter under** drop-down list. Press the **OK** button, the **Parameter Properties** dialog box is closed.

10. Next, choose the **Modify** button from the **Select** panel of the **Modify | Dimensions** contextual tab; the dimensions are named, as shown in the Figure 7-101.

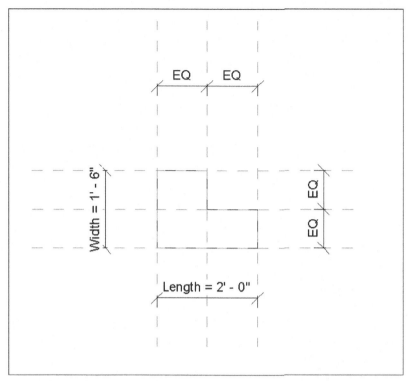

Figure 7-101 *The dimensions of the L Shape Column Family*

Saving the L-shape Family

In this section, you will save the family using the **Save As** tool.

1. Choose the **Save As > Family** option from the **File** menu; the **Save As** dialog box is displayed.

2. In this dialog box, browse to *C:\Program Data\Autodesk\RVT2021\Libraries\US Imperial\Structural Column\Concrete* and then enter **L Shape Column** family in the **File name** edit box.

Note
Program Data is a hidden folder. Unhide the folder to follow the path.

3. Now, choose the **Save** button; the **Save As** dialog box closes and the file is saved.

Loading the Family in a Project

In this section, you will load this family in a project.

1. Choose the **Load into Project and Close** button from the **Family Editor** panel of the **Modify** tab; the project file is opened with the L Shape Column attached to the cursor. Place the L Shape Column to the required locations by clicking on those points. You can place as many columns as required and after placing the columns choose the **Modify** button from the **Select** panel of the **Modify | Place Structural Column** contextual tab.

Note

The family will be loaded in a project only if the project file is already opened in Revit.

Self-Evaluation Test

Answer the following questions and then compare them to those given at the end of this chapter:

1. In Revit, there are two types of dimensions: _____ and _____ .

2. _____ dimensions are displayed while placing elements and components in a view.

3. The _____ tool is used to dimension two orthogonal references or points such as the endpoints of a wall.

4. When a dimension is added in a drawing, the _____ are displayed at the intersection of the dimension line with the witness line.

5. The visibility of tags can be controlled by using the _____ tool.

6. The _____tool is used to dimension the radius of a circular or arc profile.

7. The tags that are loaded in the current view can be viewed by invoking the _____ tool from the **Annotate** tab.

8. Temporary dimensions can be converted into permanent dimensions. (T/F)

9. Text notes are displayed only in the view in which they are created. (T/F)

10. You can annotate the slope of an edge or a face of an element. (T/F)

Review Questions

Answer the following questions:

1. Which of the following tools is used to write notes in a project?

    (a) **Text Notes**   (b) **Text**
    (c) **Notes**   (d) **Linear**

2. The _____ tool is used to dimension the overall length of a curved wall.

3. The _____ tool is used to dimension the shortest distance between two points.

4. The _____ tool is used to tag an element based on its category.

5. The _____ tool can be used to dimension the angle between two non-parallel elements in a project.

6. You can display the coordinates (Northing and Easting) of a point in a structural model by using the _____ tool.

7. You cannot correct the spelling of text notes added in a project. (T/F)

8. Tags are displayed only in the view in which they are created. (T/F)

9. You can lock permanent dimensions displayed in the current view for editing. (T/F)

10. You can tag all the untagged elements displayed in the current view of a project using the **Tag All** tool. (T/F)

EXERCISES

Exercise 1   Academic Institution

In this exercise, you will add dimensions to the grid lines and add tags to columns and foundations at the **Entry** structural floor plan view of the structural model created in the Exercise 1 of Chapter 6. Further, you will add Beam Annotations to the **Roof** structural plan view. Refer to Figures 7-102 and 7-103.   **(Expected time: 1 hr)**

1. Use the **Entry** structural plan view to dimension the grids.
2. Use the **Roof** structural plan view to add beam annotations.
3. File name to be assigned:
   - For Imperial   *c07_Academic-Institution_exer1.rvt.*
   - For Metric   *M_c07_Academic-Institution_exer1.rvt.*

Figure 7-102   *The **Entry** structural plan view displaying the grid dimensions and the tags added to the foundations and columns*

Figure 7-103 *The **Roof** structural plan view displaying the Beam Annotations*

Exercise 2   Factory Shed

In this exercise, you will add dimensions to the grid lines and add foundation, column, and beam tags at different views to the Exercise 2 of Chapter 6. Refer to Figures 7-104 and 7-105.

(Expected time: 30 min)

1. Use the **Plinth** structural plan view to dimension the grids.
2. Name of the new dimension type-
    For Imperial   **dim-grid-1/8"**
    For Metric   **dim-grid-3mm**
3. Tick Mark-
    For Imperial   **Open Dot 1/16"**
    For Metric   **Open Dot 2mm**
4. Use the **Structural Column Tags** and **Structural Foundation Tags** categories.
5. Use the **Roof** structural plain view to add beam annotations.
6. File name to be assigned:
    For Imperial   *c07_Factory-Shed_exer2.rvt.*
    For Metric   *M_c07_Factory-Shed_exer2.rvt.*

*Figure 7-104 The **Plinth** structural plan view displaying the dimensions of the grid lines and the tags*

Figure 7-105 *The* ***Second Floor*** *structural plan view displaying the beam annotations*

Chapter 8

Standard Views, Details, and Schedules

After completing this chapter, you will be able to:
- *Create Elevation Views*
- *Create Section Views*
- *Create Drafting Views*
- *Create Duplicate Views*
- *Generate Graphical Column Schedule*
- *Create Schedule*
- *Generate Material Takeoff Schedule*

In the previous chapters, you learned to create and document a structural model. In this chapter, you will learn to generate standard views and details as well as schedule reports in a structural model.

In Revit, you can generate sections and elevations very easily. The views generated from sections and elevations will help you prepare the detail drafting of a structural model. Also, you can use these views to add various structural elements to a structural model. For example, you can use section views to add reinforcement details to the structural beam, columns, or floors. Similar to the section and elevation views, you can create drafting and detail views for the structural model.

After creating a structural model and generating the required views, the next important task is to generate the reports related to the structural model. These reports help in execution of the construction of the building on site. These reports are in the form of graphical column schedules, general schedules for estimating the quantities of various structural elements, schedules for Material Takeoffs, and others.

ELEVATION VIEWS

Elevation view is the most commonly used orthographic projection for conveying the appearance of a building model from its exterior or interior. In Revit, elevation views are part of the default template file that you can use to create your project. When you open the default template file to create a project, four elevation views are displayed: North, South, East, and West. However, you can create more exterior and interior elevation views of your structural model using various tools available in Revit.

In Revit, you can create two types of elevation views: building and framing. The building elevation views are similar to the sectional views in a model. The building elevations are capable of generating four directional views: North, South, East, and West. These views are located under the **Elevations (Building Elevation)** head in the **Project Browser**. The Framing elevation views are used to place vertical bracing and moment bracing members in a structural model. The framing elevation views are associated to a grid and therefore, it is necessary to have a grid in your view to create a framing elevation view. When you create framing elevation views in a project, the views created are located under the **Elevations (Framing Elevation)** head in the **Project Browser**. In Revit, you can create building and framing elevation views by using the **Elevation** and **Framing Elevation** tools respectively, located in the **View** tab. The methods of creating building elevation views in a structural model are discussed next.

Creating a Building Elevation View

Ribbon:	View > Create > Elevation drop-down > Elevation

 To create a building elevation view of a structural model, open the desired structural plan view from the **Project Browser** and then choose the **Elevation** tool from **View > Create > Elevation** drop-down; the **Modify | Elevation** contextual tab will be displayed and an elevation symbol will appear along with the cursor in the drawing area. Next, set various options related to the elevation views in the **Options Bar** before clicking in the drawing area to insert the elevation symbol, as shown in Figure 8-1.

Modify | Elevation   ☐ Attach to Grid

Figure 8-1 Option related to the elevation view in the Options Bar

In the **Options Bar**, the **Attach to Grid** check box is cleared by default. You can select this check box if you want to create a framing elevation view while using the **Elevation** tool. While creating the building elevation view of a structural model, ensure that the **Attach to Grid** check box is cleared. In the **Reference** panel, the **Reference Other View** check box is also cleared by default. If you select this check box, a reference elevation will be created in the drawing view. Reference elevation refers to an existing elevation or drafting view in the drawing. The reference elevations are placed in a callout view or plan view. On selecting the **Reference Other View** check box in the **Reference** panel, the drop-down list below it becomes active. In this drop-down list, the **<New Drafting View>** option is selected by default. As a result, on adding the building elevation view, an empty drafting view will be created and added under the **Drafting Views (Detail)** head in the **Project Browser**. The default name given to the drafting view is **<Level name>- Elevation 1**. You can edit and rename this view in the **Project Browser**. The other options that can be selected from the drop-down list next to the **Reference other view** check box are: **Elevation: North**, **Elevation: East**, **Elevation: West**, **Elevation: South**. Note that this drop-down list can have more options depending on the presence of some other reference views in a project. You can select any of these options from the drop-down list and add elevation to the current structural view plan.

To add a building elevation view to the current structural plan view, make sure that the **Attach to Grid** and **Reference Other View** check boxes are cleared. Next, move the cursor with the elevation symbol in the drawing area. On moving the cursor near a wall in the drawing area, you will notice that the alignment of the arrow head of the elevation symbol changes and it becomes perpendicular to the wall, as shown in Figure 8-2. Next, click when the elevation arrow head symbol points toward the desired direction; the new elevation view will be created and added to the list of elevations in the **Project Browser**.

Figure 8-2 *The display of a building elevation symbol in a structural plan view*

In the project view, when you select an elevation symbol, its controls are displayed, as shown in Figure 8-3. The controls of the selected elevation symbol include four check boxes along the four directions and a rotation control. Out of these check boxes, only the check box at the placed direction is selected and the other three check boxes are cleared. You can select other check box(es) to create the elevation along that direction. You can use the rotation control to rotate the elevation symbol in the desired direction. To rotate the elevation symbol, move the cursor over the rotation control and then press and drag the left mouse button. On doing so, the elevation symbol will rotate about its center. Release the left mouse button after the rotation of the elevation symbol. Next, set the width of the elevation view using the clip plane control. To view the clip plane control, click on the view arrow of the elevation symbol, refer to Figure 8-3; the clip plane is displayed as a blue line with the drag control dots on its two ends, as shown in Figure 8-4. You can drag the drag control dots to resize the width of the elevation view.

Figure 8-3 *Various controls in the building elevation symbol*

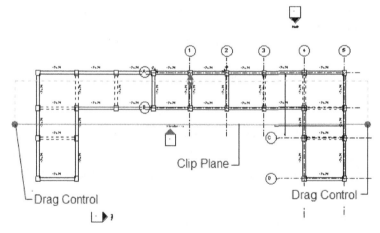

Figure 8-4 *The display of the clip plane*

Note
*If the drag control dots are not displayed with the clip plane, select the check box corresponding to the **Crop View** parameter in the **Properties** palette and then choose **Apply**.*

Tip
*You can also change the elevation view symbol. To do so, select it from the project view and then choose the **Type Properties** tool from the **Properties** panel of the **Modify / Elevation** tab; the **Type Properties** dialog box will be displayed. Click in the **Value** field of the **Elevation Tag** parameter and then choose the Browse button; the **Type Properties** dialog box will be displayed. In this dialog box, select the required elevation tag from the drop-down list corresponding to the **Elevation Mark** parameter.*

After placing the elevation symbols and adjusting clipping planes, you can view the elevations in various ways. The first way is to double-click on the elevation name listed under the **Elevations (Building Elevation)** head in the **Project Browser**. You can also double-click on the arrow head of the elevation symbol. The other way to view the elevation is to move the cursor over the elevation symbol and right-click to display the shortcut menu. Choose the **Find Referring Views** option from the shortcut menu; the **Go To View** dialog box will be displayed, as shown in Figure 8-5. Select the desired view name from the list box in the dialog box and choose the **Open View** button or double-click on the view name in the list box to open the view you require.

Note
*If the clip line is not displayed with the clip plane, then click on the value column of the **Far Clipping** option; the **Far Clipping** dialog box is displayed. Select the **Clip with line** check box and choose the **OK** button; the clip line will be displayed.*

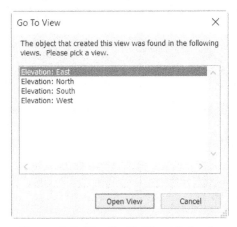

*Figure 8-5 The **Go To View** dialog box*

Note
While working on a structural floor plan, if the building model created extends beyond the clip planes of the four side elevation views, the corresponding elevations will no longer show the complete exterior views. Instead, an elevation view that is cut through the building model will be displayed. You can drag the clip plane controls symbol beyond the extent of the building profile to retain the view as a complete exterior elevation view.

Creating a Framing Elevation View

Ribbon:	View > Create > Elevation drop-down > Framing Elevation

Framing elevation views are used to place the vertical bracing and moment bracing members in a structural model. These views are associated with grid. Framing elevation views in a project are located under the **Elevations (Framing Elevation)** head in the **Project Browser**. You can create a framing elevation view in a structural plan view. To create a framing elevation view, invoke the **Framing Elevation** tool from **Elevation** drop-down in the **Create** panel of the **View** tab; the **Modify | Framing Elevation** contextual tab will be displayed. In the Options Bar, ensure that the **Attach to Grid** check box is selected. The use of the **Reference Other View** check box is the same as in the case of the building elevation view. In the **Properties** palette, you can choose the **Edit Type** button to invoke the **Type Properties** dialog box. The **Type Properties** dialog box can be used to assign various parameters for the tags and label associated with the framing elevation.

After specifying the options and parameters for the framing elevation view, you can add the framing elevation view to your project. To do so, move the cursor and place it over the grid to which you want to associate with the framing elevation view. On doing so, you will notice that a framing elevation symbol appears on the side of the grid where you have moved the cursor, as shown in Figure 8-6. Click on the displayed framing elevation symbol; some check boxes appear next to the symbol. Click on the desired check box to display the symbol on that side. The methods for rotating a symbol and adjusting the clip plane for the framing elevation view are similar to that of the building elevation view. These methods have already been discussed in the **Creating a Building Elevation View** section of this chapter.

Figure 8-6 *The framing elevation symbol displayed*

SECTION VIEWS

Section views are generated by cutting sections through a building model. These views are created to display the wall elevations, floor heights, cross-sectional details of structural elements, and special vertical features of a project. They are also useful in creating and editing reinforcements for various structural elements in a structural model. For example, to emphasize the structural details of the central atrium of an office building model, you may need to show a section through the central atrium. Revit enables you to create the section with relative ease. You can also modify the sectional view to create a section displaying other details. Next, the method of creating and modifying the section view, controlling the visibility of section lines, and creating different types of sectional views are discussed.

Creating a Section View

Ribbon: View > Create > Section

In Revit, you can create a section view in a plan or elevation view by using the **Section** tool. You can use this tool to create different types of section views such as the building section, wall section, and sections of relevant structural elements like beams, columns, slabs, and so on.

To create a section view, invoke the **Section** tool from the **Create** panel of the **View** tab; the **Modify |Section** contextual tab will be displayed, and various options for the section view will be displayed in the Options Bar. Next, you can enter the offset value in the **Offset** edit box of the Options Bar. In the **Properties** palette, you can select any of the three types of section views from the **Type Selector** drop-down list. These types are: **Section : Building Section**, **Section : Wall Section**, and **Detail View : Detail**. By default, the **Section : Building Section** option is selected in the **Type Selector** drop-down list.

To create a section view, move the cursor to the viewing area in the project view; the cursor will change into a cross "**+**" symbol and you will be prompted to draw the section line in the current view. Click at the appropriate location to specify the start point. For creating a section through the entire building, click near the exterior face of the building profile. As you move the cursor, a section line will be displayed with one end fixed at the specified point and the other end attached to the cursor. You can even create a section line at any angle or along the vertical or horizontal axis of the building model, depending upon the project requirement. To create a horizontal section view, move the cursor horizontally across the building model, as shown in Figure 8-7, and click to specify the endpoint. On doing so, the section line along with its controls will be displayed, as shown in Figure 8-8. The section line is represented by a section head and a line. The section head indicates the direction toward which the section will be created. The methods for displaying the created section views are the same as those discussed for the elevation view.

Figure 8-7 The horizontal section line

Figure 8-8 *The section line along with its control*

Modifying the Section View

The location of a section line can be modified by dragging it, as shown in Figure 8-9. On dragging the section line, the corresponding section view will get updated immediately, as shown in Figure 8-10.

Figure 8-9 *Dragging the section line*

Figure 8-10 *The updated section view*

You can modify the parameters of a section view by using the controls available on the section view line. These controls are displayed when you select the section line. The twin-arrow symbol represents the flip tool that can be used to flip the viewing side of the section view. By default, the section head appears on one side. The cyclic control on both ends of the section line is used to change the visibility of the section head and tail at their respective ends. You can click on the symbol to hide or display the control. You can click on the break line symbol which appears in the middle of the section line to break it. You can then resize the two section lines to the required extent of the view. To rejoin the section line, click on the break line control again.

When you create a section view, the view depth is created automatically. The view depth is the extent of the view in the current view. It is represented by a dashed line with the blue arrows as the drag controls. To modify the view depth, drag the arrows to the desired location. The section view shows only those elements that are within the view depth. You can modify the instance properties of a section view by selecting its section line from the drawing and specifying various parameters displayed in the **Properties** palette. In the **Properties** palette for the selected section line, you can modify the values such as **View Name**, **View Scale**, **Crop Region Visible**, and so on by clicking in the corresponding value column and selecting the new value from the drop-down list or by entering a new value in that field. In the **Properties** palette, choose the **Edit Type** button to display the **Type Properties** dialog box and modify the type properties of the section view such as **Callout Tag**, **Reference Label**, and so on.

Creating a Segmented Section

In Revit, you can split a section into segments that are orthogonal to the direction of the section view. This enables you to show different parts of a building model in the same section view.

To create a segmented section line, select the section line; the **Modify| Views** contextual tab will be displayed. In this tab, choose the **Split Segment** tool from the **Section** panel; the cursor will change into a knife symbol. Move it over the section line and click at the point from where you want to split the section line; the section line will break from the specified point. Now, you can move the cursor in the desired direction to split the section line along the head or tail side. Click again to specify the location of the split. The segmented section will be created and the section view will be modified immediately, refer to Figure 8-11.

Figure 8-11 *The updated section view after splitting the section line*

Controlling the Visibility of a Section Line

The section line is visible in the plan, section, and elevation views if the view range intersects the crop region in the current view. The section line created in one view is visible and created simultaneously in all other views. You can also control the visibility of the section line in views. To

hide a section line in a view, select the section line, right-click, and then choose **Hide in View >**
Elements from the shortcut menu displayed. The section line will be hidden in the current view.

CALLOUT VIEWS

A callout view is an enlarged view of a part of a building model which requires more detailing.
Creating callout views is a common practice among engineers as callout views help them look
the project model more precisely and with a higher level of detail. For example, in a structural
model, a callout view can be used to show the details of a connection of a beam and column in
the plan or an elevation view. In a project, you can create a callout view for a plan view, section
view, or elevation view. In these views, the callout tag added to a view will be linked to the callout
view. The view in which the callout tag is added is called the parent view of the callout view. If
the parent view is deleted, the callout will also be deleted. A callout tag, as shown in Figure 8-12,
is an annotation element that represents the location of the callout in the plan, elevation, or
section. The callout tag consists of the following parts: Callout bubble, Callout head, Leader
line, and Reference labels. The callout bubble is the line drawn around that part of the structural
model which you need to enlarge and view in the callout view. The callout head is a symbol that
represents the callout view. When a callout view is placed on a sheet, the callout head displays
a detail number and a sheet number by default. The line that connects the callout head to the
callout bubble is called the leader line. The reference label in a callout tag is used for the callout
views that are referenced.

Various methods for creating callout views, displaying a callout view, modifying callout views
properties, and adding detail lines to a callout view are discussed in the next section.

Figure 8-12 *The display of a callout tag*

Creating a Callout using Rectangular Tool

Ribbon:	View > Create > Callout drop-down > Rectangle

To create a rectangular callout view, choose the **Rectangle** tool from the **Callout** drop-down of
the **Create** panel of **View** tab; the **Properties** palette will display the properties related to the
callout view to be created. In the **Properties** palette, the **Type Selector** drop-down list displays
the type of callout view to be generated. In this drop-down list, you can select any of these two
types: **Detail View : Detail** and **Structural Plan : Structural Plan** (for current view). Select the
Detail View : Detail type if you want to provide detailed information about a specific part in a

building model. Select the **Structural Plan : Structural Plan** (for current view) type if you want to provide more information about a part of the current view. The **Scale** drop-down list in the **Status Bar** can be used to set the view scale. In the **Reference** panel, the **Reference Other View** check box is cleared by default. You can select this check box to create a reference callout. As you select this check box, the drop-down list next to it becomes active. In this drop-down list, you can select an option to specify a view that the callout will refer to. After selecting the desired type and option, move the cursor to the top left corner of the area that you want to enlarge and then drag it toward the lower right corner of the area to create a callout bubble, refer to Figure 8-12. Release the left mouse button when the required area is enclosed in it.

Creating a Callout using the Sketch Tool

Ribbon: View > Create > Callout drop-down > Sketch

In Revit, you can create a customized callout view by using the sketching tools. To do so, invoke the **Sketch** tool from **View > Create > Callout** drop-down; the **Modify | Edit Profile** contextual tab will be displayed. The **Draw** panel of this tab contains various sketching tools such as **Line**, **Rectangle**, **Pick Lines**, and so on. Choose any of the desired tool from this panel to sketch a desired callout view.

Displaying a Callout View

When you create a callout in the existing view, a new callout view is added to the **Project Browser** under the parent category. For example, if you create a callout view in the section view, the callout view will be added under the **Sections** heading in the **Project Browser**. In the **Project Browser**, double-click on the name of the callout view to be displayed; the corresponding callout view will be displayed in the drawing window. Alternatively, highlight the callout bubble and right-click to display the shortcut menu. Next, choose the **Go To View** option from the shortcut menu to display the callout view.

Modifying the Properties of a Callout View

You can modify the appearance of a callout bubble in the parent view. It can be modified by using the bubble controls displayed on selecting a callout view. The extents of a callout view can also be modified by using its drag controls. The rotation control can be used to rotate the callout bubble along with its leader and tag. The leader elbow control can be dragged to any desired location.

The instance properties of a callout view are different for different types of callouts. To modify the instance properties of a view type callout, select it from the drawing; the instance properties of the selected callout will be displayed in the **Properties** palette, as shown in Figure 8-13. The different instance properties displayed in the **Properties** palette are discussed next.

Figure 8-13 *The instance properties of the callout view in the* ***Properties*** *palette*

In the **Properties** palette, you can enter the name to be assigned to a new callout view in the value field of the **View Name** instance parameter under the **Identity Data** head. Similarly, you can enter the title to be given on the sheet in the value field of the **Title on Sheet** parameter.

The **Display Model** parameter under the **Graphics** head is used to set the display type for the view of a building model. By default, this parameter is set to **Normal**. You can set the value of the **Display Model** parameter to **Halftone** to display the model element in the current view as a faded image. You can set the value of this parameter to the **Do not display** option to hide the model element in the current view.

The amount of details to be displayed in a callout view can be controlled by using the **Detail Level** parameter under the **Graphics** head. To display the details, you can select any of the following three options from the drop-down list corresponding to this parameter: **Coarse**, **Medium**, and **Fine**. By default, the **Coarse** option is selected in the drop-down list. As a result, model elements are displayed with fewer details in the current view. You can select the **Fine** option from this drop-down list to display the layers of various materials used in a building model. On selecting the **Fine** option, additional lines are displayed in the callout view. These lines describe composite materials.

The **Edit** button in the value column for the **Visibility/Graphics Overrides** parameter can be used to control the visibility of different models and annotation elements in the callout view. The **View Scale** instance parameter is used to set the scale for a callout view. You can use the drop-down list in the value column to select a scale for the callout view.

Creating Details in a Callout View

Ribbon:	Annotate > Detail > Detail Line

🔲 Detail Line   Revit provides various tools to create details in a callout view. You can sketch lines using the **Detail Line** tool and also add detail components provided in Revit's library to details.

The **Detail Line** tool is used to create lines for a detail view. Detail lines are view-specific and appear only in the view in which they are created. You can use the callout view of a building model and trace detail lines over the image using their varying thickness.

To create detail lines for a detail view, choose the **Detail Line** tool from the **Detail** panel of the **Annotate** tab; the **Modify | Place Detail Lines** contextual tab will be displayed. Select the type of detail lines from the **Line Style** drop-down list in the **Line Style** panel of this tab. You can select the appropriate detail line based on its usage. For example, wide lines can be used to show masonry elements, whereas thin lines can be selected to represent lighter materials such as glass and aluminium.

You can draw these lines by using the sketching tools displayed in the **Draw** panel of the **Modify | Place Detail Lines** contextual tab. To add detail lines, you can trace over the underlay elements. When you trace over the underlay elements, you will notice that the cursor snaps at various elements on the underlay lines. The entire detail can be sketched using a variety of line thicknesses to achieve the desired graphical representation. You can also add dimensions and symbols to the details. However, after completing a detail, you can hide the underlay callout view by selecting the callout view from the drawing and then selecting the **Do not display** option from the drop-down list corresponding to the **Display Model** parameter in the **Properties** palette.

Note
*After adding the detail lines to the callout view, you can add the filled region to the drafted details by invoking the **Filled Region** tool from **Annotate** > **Details** > **Region** drop-down.*

DRAFTING DETAILS

Drafted details are created when you want to access the details that are not referenced to the existing project views. These details are not linked to a building model and therefore they do not get updated with it.

To create a drafted detail, first create a drafting view and then use the drafting tools provided in Revit to sketch the detail. You can also import in-built details from Revit's detail library and use them.

After the drafted detail has been created, this can be used as a reference detail. The method for creating a drafting view and drafting detail are discussed in the next sections.

Creating a Drafting View

Ribbon: View > Create > Drafting View

To create a drafting view, invoke the **Drafting View** tool from the **Create** panel; the **New Drafting View** dialog box will be displayed, as shown in Figure 8-14. In this dialog box, enter a name for the drafting view in the **Name** edit box. Next, select the scale for the detailing from the **Scale** drop-down list. To specify a user-defined scale, select the **Custom** option from the **Scale** drop-down list and then specify a value in the **Scale value 1** edit box. Next, choose the **OK** button; the drafting view will be created and added under the **Drafting Views** subhead in the **Project Browser**.

*Figure 8-14 The **New Drafting View** dialog box*

Note
Drafting views do not use the project views. As a result, when you create drafting views, project views are not displayed in the drawing window.

Drafting a Detail

The method of drafting a detail in a drafting view is similar to the one used in a callout view. In a callout view, lines are traced over an enlarged project view, whereas in a drafting view, the project view is not available and a new detail is drafted as if you are drafting on a blank sheet.

You can draft a detail by using the tools in the **Detail** panel of the **Annotate** tab. The **Detail Lines** tool enables you to draw lines with varying thickness. The **Detail Component** tool is used to add in-built detail components from Revit's detail library. The **Insulation** tool enables you to add a graphical insulation symbol to the drafted detail. You can create graphical patterns to represent various building materials using the **Region** drop-down. The usage of these tools is similar to the tools in a callout view. You can also add dimensions, text notes, and break lines to complete a drafted detail.

DUPLICATE VIEWS

You can create multiple copies of a project view in Revit. These multiple views are called duplicate views. All duplicate views are dependent on the original view from which they are created. Therefore, these views are updated automatically if any changes are made in the original view. Duplicate views are useful when you want to use or place the same view on more than one sheet. These views are also useful in case of huge projects when the overall project view is too large to fit into a single sheet. In such cases, you can crop the parent view to make small segments by using the crop regions, create dependent views from them, and then place the cropped dependent views on the sheet. In Revit, you can create three types of duplicate views. The tools used for creating these duplicate views are: **Duplicate View**, **Duplicate with Detailing**, and **Duplicate as Dependent**. You can use the **Duplicate View** tool to create a view that contains only the model geometry from the current view. The **Duplicate with Detailing** tool can be used to create a view that contains view-specific elements from the current view. You can use the **Duplicate as Dependent** tool to create a view that is dependent on the current view. The method of creating duplicate view as a dependent view is discussed next.

Creating a Duplicate View as a Dependent View

Ribbon:	View > Create > Duplicate View drop-down > Duplicate as Dependent

You can create a dependent view from a plan, elevation, section, or callout view. To create a dependent view, open the view from which you want to create duplicate views and then choose the **Duplicate as Dependent** tool from **View > Create > Duplicate View** drop-down. Alternatively, select the name of the view in the **Project Browser** and right-click; a shortcut menu will be displayed. Choose **Duplicate View > Duplicate as Dependent** from the shortcut menu; the dependent view will display a crop region boundary and will be added in the **Project Browser** as a dependent view under the primary view.

Tip
*Crop regions help exclude unwanted content from a crop view, thereby reducing the view size. In Revit, there are two types of crop regions that allow you to crop views for the model and annotation categories. You can control the visibility of a crop region by using the **Crop View** or **Do Not Crop View** tool from the **View Control Bar**.*

Next, select the crop region boundary to display drag controls. Using the drag controls, resize the primary view and then crop it to include only the required portion of the view in the dependent view. Next, select the name of the dependent view in the **Project Browser** and right-click; a shortcut menu will be displayed. Choose **Rename** from the shortcut menu; an edit box will be displayed. In this edit box, enter a name for the dependent view and choose the **OK** button;

the duplicate view will be renamed. Again, open the primary view and choose the **Show Crop Region** button from the **View Control Bar** to display the crop region boundary. Similarly, create another dependent view as explained above. In this way, you can crop the primary view and create multiple dependent views. To navigate to the primary view from the dependent view, select the crop region boundary of the dependent view and right-click; a shortcut menu will be displayed. Choose **Go to Primary View** from the shortcut menu; the primary view will be displayed on the screen. You can also navigate to the dependent views from the primary view. To do so, choose the **Show Crop Region** button from the **View Control Bar** if the crop regions are not displayed in the primary view. On doing so, the crop regions for all dependent views will be displayed. Select the crop region of the required dependent view and then right-click; a shortcut menu will be displayed. Choose **Go to View** from the shortcut menu; the corresponding dependent view will open. You can display the primary or dependent views by double-clicking on their respective view names in the **Project Browser**.

Note

*The procedure to create duplicate views by using the **Duplicate View** and **Duplicate with Detailing** tools is same.*

GRAPHICAL COLUMN SCHEDULES

In a structural project, the Graphical Column Schedule (GCS) is a useful document which contains information related to the size, connection details, and reinforcement details of columns. The Graphical Column Schedule is a tabular representation of the columns in a project. You can use the information in the Graphical Column Schedule to track the structural columns used in the structural model. The columns displayed in the Graphical Column Schedule are linked to grid intersections. For example, if a column is located at the intersection of grid 1 and grid A, the Graphical Column Schedule will display the location of the column as A-1. If a column is not linked to a grid or grid intersection, Revit will link the column to the nearest grid or grid intersection. In the next section, the creation and use of Graphical Column Schedule in a project are discussed.

Creating Graphical Column Schedule

Ribbon:	View > Create > Schedules drop-down > Graphical Column Schedule

To create a Graphical Column Schedule, choose the **Graphical Column Schedule** tool from **View > Create > Schedules** drop-down; the Graphical Column Schedule will be displayed in the drawing area in a new view, as shown in Figure 8-15. The name of the new view will appear under the **Graphical Column Schedules** head in the **Project Browser**. At the bottom of the Graphical Column Schedule, refer to Figure 8-15, the **Column Locations** row displays the grid intersections available in the project. Also, on the left and right sides of the schedule, the names of the levels along with their respective elevations are displayed. In this schedule, the columns are displayed in cells and are positioned according to their top and bottom constraints. You can select any of the displayed columns in the schedule and change its type and instance properties. On doing so, the change will be applied to the entire project view.

Figure 8-15 *Partial view of the Graphical Column Schedule for a structural model*

USING SCHEDULES IN A PROJECT

Schedule is another format for providing project information. In a building project, there may be different items that can be used a number of times at different locations. Schedules are primarily used to provide information regarding these items in a tabular format. For each item, the schedule tables provide information regarding its size, material, cost, finish, level, and so on. These schedules can then be used by associated agencies for various purposes. These schedule tables can assist the fabricating agency to manufacture all similar items. The quantity surveyors and estimators can calculate the quantity and cost of the grouped items. For example, in a building model, a particular column type may be used a number of times in the same layout plan on different floors. With the help of schedules, you can group columns in different ways based on their parameters such as location in a project, size, section, and so on. The project schedules are created by extracting information from a building model. In a project, all elements are parametric. This means that they have several properties associated with them. When you use these elements, the associated information is automatically added to the building model. This information can then be extracted for creating schedules.

The power of Revit's parametric change engine enables you to modify elements in a building model at any stage of the project development. Changes are reflected immediately in all project views. As elements are bidirectionally associated, the entire project information is updated immediately and the necessary changes in schedules are reflected automatically. Conversely, when you modify an element in a schedule, all its instances are immediately updated in all project views. Revit also enables you to create schedules based on the common group properties of different categories of items. For example, you can create a schedule of all rooms in a project that has the same floor, ceiling, and wall finish. These are termed as Key Schedules.

Generating a Schedule

Ribbon:	View > Create > Schedules drop-down > Schedule/Quantities

You can create a schedule or a quantity report by using the **Schedule/Quantities** tool. To generate a schedule, invoke this tool from the **Create** panel; the **New Schedule** dialog box will be displayed, as shown in Figure 8-16.

*Figure 8-16 The **New Schedule** dialog box*

In the **New Schedule** dialog box, various categories of building elements are listed in the **Category** list box. You can select the required category to create a schedule. For example, you can select the **Structural Framing** option from the **Category** list box to generate a schedule for framing members. The category selected for creating a schedule is displayed in the **Name** edit box. The **Schedule building components** radio button is used to create a schedule of building elements. After selecting a category from the **Category** list box, choose the **OK** button; the **Schedule Properties** dialog box for the selected category will be displayed. Figure 8-17 displays the options in the **Schedule Properties** dialog box for the **Structural Framing** category.

*Figure 8-17 The **Schedule Properties** dialog box*

The **Schedule Properties** dialog box has options to set various element properties, their formats, and appearance in a schedule. It contains five tabs: **Fields**, **Filter**, **Sorting/Grouping**, **Formatting**, and **Appearance**. The options in the **Fields** tab can be used to select the fields that would appear in a schedule. Select the required fields from the **Available fields** list box and choose the **Add parameter(s)** button to add fields to the **Scheduled fields (in order)** area. Choose the **Remove parameter(s)** button to remove the selected scheduled fields. You can use the **Move parameter up** and **Move parameter down** buttons to move and arrange fields in the desired order. By choosing the **New Parameter** button, the **Parameter Properties** dialog box is displayed from which you can add your own custom field. You can choose the **Add calculated parameter** button; the **Calculated Value** dialog box will be displayed. You can create a field that will be a percentage of another field, or specify a formula to define the field from the **Calculated Value** dialog box. You can choose the **Combine Parameters** button to combine the parameters for the schedule. The **Include elements in link** check box can be selected to include elements from the linked Revit files to the schedules and drawing files of model elements such as columns, walls, beams, and so on.

The options in the **Fields** tab enable you to restrict the display of elements based on certain conditions. You can use maximum four filters for a schedule based on the parameters and values. For example, in a structural framing schedule, if you want to display the beams constrained to **Level 1**, add the **Level** option available in the **Available fields** list box to the **Scheduled fields (in order)** list box. Next, in the **Filter** tab, select the **Level** option from the **Filter by** drop-down list and then select the **Level 1** option from the drop-down list next to it. This way you can create filters for schedules in a project. This helps in organizing data in schedules.

The options in the **Sorting/Grouping** tab can be used to sort and group rows in a schedule. The parameter for sorting a schedule can be selected from the **Sort by** drop-down list. You can sort it in the ascending or descending order by selecting a radio button. Next, to arrange door types in the ascending order of their width, select the **Width** option from the **Sort by** drop-down list and then select the **Ascending** radio button. The **Grand totals** check box can be selected to display the sum total of all elements.

In the **Formatting** tab, you can set the parameters related to the appearance of headings. You can select a heading from the **Fields** list and enter a new heading name in the **Heading** edit box. The orientation of a heading and its alignment can be specified by selecting desired options from the **Heading orientation** and **Alignment** drop-down list, respectively. The **Field Format** button is used to format the appearance of fields with numerical values. For such fields select the required option from the drop-down list below the **Show conditional format on sheets** check box. By default, the **No calculation** option is selected from this drop-down list. You can select the **Hidden field** check box to hide a field in a schedule. On doing so, you can sort out or filter a schedule by using the selected field without actually displaying it in the schedule.

The options in the **Appearance** tab can be used to change the appearance of a schedule view. You can use various parameters such as **Header text**, **Body text**, and so on to modify the appearance of a schedule. In a wide schedule, you can also set alternate rows in contrasting colors. To do so, select the **Stripe Rows** check box located in the **Appearance** tab. Now, select the **First Row Strip Color** option from the **Stripe Row** drop-down and choose the desired color from the **Color** dialog box displayed on choosing the color icon. Similarly, select the **Second Row Strip Color** option to assign a different color to the alternate rows. Next, choose the **OK** button; the alternate rows will be displayed in contrasting colors, as shown in Figure 8-18. Note that the **Show Stripe Rows on Sheets** check box is selected to display the alternate colored rows on the sheets.

When you choose the **OK** button from the **Schedule Properties** dialog box, Revit scans the building model for the category of elements and displays the schedule based on the parameters specified. Figure 8-18 shows an example of a structural foundation schedule with the scheduled fields.

You can modify the properties of a schedule even after creating it. To do so, click on the schedule name in the **Project Browser**. Next, in the **Properties** palette, choose the **Edit** button in the value column corresponding to the **Fields**, **Filter**, **Sorting/Grouping**, **Formatting**, and **Appearance** instance parameters to access their respective tabs in the **Schedule Properties** dialog box.

For example, the schedule shown in Figure 8-18 can be edited to create a simplified schedule in which the foundation with a particular type mark can be grouped together. You can access the options in the **Sorting/Grouping** tab, select the **Grand totals** check box, and clear the **Itemize every instance** check box to summarize the schedule. On doing so, the modified schedule will be displayed, as shown in Figure 8-19.

\<Structural Foundation Schedule\>				
A	B	C	D	E
Family and Type	Area	Foundation Thickne	Volume	Width
Foundation Slab: 12" Foundation Slab				
Foundation Slab: 1	3541 SF	1' - 0"	3541.05 CF	53' - 6"
Pile Cap-2 Pile: 31"x61"x35"				
Pile Cap-2 Pile: 31"	16 SF	2' - 11"	29.81 CF	5' - 10"
Pile Cap-2 Pile: 31"	16 SF	2' - 11"	29.81 CF	5' - 10"
Pile Cap-2 Pile: 31"	16 SF	2' - 11"	29.81 CF	5' - 10"
Pile Cap-2 Pile: 31"	16 SF	2' - 11"	29.81 CF	5' - 10"
Pile Cap-2 Pile: 31"	16 SF	2' - 11"	29.81 CF	5' - 10"
Pile Cap-2 Pile: 31"	16 SF	2' - 11"	29.81 CF	5' - 10"
Pile Cap-2 Pile: 31"	16 SF	2' - 11"	29.81 CF	5' - 10"
Pile Cap-2 Pile: 31"	16 SF	2' - 11"	29.81 CF	5' - 10"
Pile Cap-2 Pile: 31"	16 SF	2' - 11"	29.81 CF	5' - 10"
Pile Cap-2 Pile: 31"	16 SF	2' - 11"	29.81 CF	5' - 10"
Pile Cap-2 Pile: 31"	16 SF	2' - 11"	29.81 CF	5' - 10"
Pile Cap-2 Pile: 31"	16 SF	2' - 11"	29.81 CF	5' - 10"
Pile Cap-2 Pile: 31"	16 SF	2' - 11"	29.81 CF	5' - 10"
Pile Cap-2 Pile: 31"	16 SF	2' - 11"	29.81 CF	5' - 10"
Pile Cap-2 Pile: 31"	16 SF	2' - 11"	29.81 CF	5' - 10"
Pile Cap-2 Pile: 31"	16 SF	2' - 11"	29.81 CF	5' - 10"

Figure 8-18 *Schedule displaying the properties of a structural foundation*

Structural Foundation Schedule					
Family and T	Area	Mark	Foundation T	Volume	Width
1					
Footing-R	39 SF	1		36.00 CF	4' - 0"
2					
Wall Foun		2	1' - 0"		3' - 0"
14					

Figure 8-19 *Schedule displaying the grouped properties of a structural foundation*

After calculating the required material quantity, you can use the cost per unit to calculate the total estimated cost for that item. For example, to calculate the total cost of walls for a project, first create a wall schedule showing the area of each wall type. Next, enter the value of the cost per square feet for each wall type directly in the created schedule. Revit automatically assigns the cost to all instances of the same wall type. You can then use the **Add Parameter** button in the **Schedule Properties** dialog box to add a new column for **Total Cost** for each type of wall. Use the **Calculated Value** button and assign the formula **Cost*Area/1'$^\wedge$2** to calculate the total cost of each type of wall (the factor 1'$^\wedge$2 is used to suppress the units). In the **Formatting** tab, select the **Calculate total** check box for the **Total Cost** column and generate the total cost of the walls in the building project. This procedure can be adopted for each category of elements such as windows, doors, floor, roof, furniture, and so on and then the gross total cost of all building elements can be calculated.

Editing a Schedule

You can use a schedule to modify elements in it. To do so, select a schedule from the **Project Browser** and then click any of the cells displayed in it; the **Modify Schedule/Quantities** contextual tab will be displayed. You can use the tools displayed in this tab to delete, hide, unhide, highlight, group, and ungroup the properties of the elements displayed in a schedule.

GENERATING THE MATERIAL TAKEOFF SCHEDULE

| **Ribbon:** | View > Create > Schedules drop-down > Material Takeoff |

Material takeoff schedules display the information of the material used to create structural elements in a model. This schedule helps the quantity surveyor in estimating the materials used to fabricate the structural elements in the site.

The method of generating the material takeoff schedule is the same as that of generating the quantity schedule. To generate a material takeoff schedule, choose the **Material Takeoff** tool from **View > Create > Schedules** drop-down; the **New Material Takeoff** dialog box will be displayed as shown in Figure 8-20.

Figure 8-20 The New Material Takeoff dialog box

In this dialog box, select a category of structural elements from the **Category** list box for which you want to create the takeoff schedule. On selecting a category from the **Category** list box, you will notice that the default name for the takeoff schedule is displayed in the **Name** edit box. You can enter text in this edit box to specify the name of the takeoff schedule to be created. Next, you can select an option from the **Phase** drop-down list to specify the phasing stage of the structural model for which the takeoff schedule will be created. In this drop-down list, you can select the **Existing** option for the working phase or you can select the **New Construction** option for a new phase. To include all categories present in the project in the **Category** list box, select the respective check boxes from the **Filter list** drop-down in the **New Material Takeoff** dialog box. Now select the category from the **Category** list box and then choose the **OK** button; the **Material Takeoff Properties** dialog box will be displayed. The options in this dialog box are similar to those in the **Schedule Properties** dialog box as discussed in the previous section. After using various options in this dialog box, choose the **OK** button; the material takeoff schedule will be displayed on the screen. You will also notice that a node is added for the takeoff schedule under the **Schedules/Quantities** head in the **Project Browser**. Figure 8-21 displays a material takeoff schedule for framing members used in a structural model.

<Structural Foundation Material Takeoff>					
A	B	C	D	E	F
Family and Type	Elevation at Bottom	Material: Area	Material: Name	Material: Volume	Count
Footing-Rectangular: 72" x 48" x 18"					
Footing-Rectangula		2696 SF	Concrete, Cast-in-Pl	868.00 CF	28
Foundation Slab: 6" Foundation Slab					
Foundation Slab: 6"	-6' - 6"	4032 SF	Concrete, Cast-in-Pl	2016.00 CF	2
Grand total: 30		6728 SF		2884.00 CF	30

Figure 8-21 *Schedule displaying the grouped properties of a Structural Foundation*

TUTORIALS

Tutorial 1   Commercial Complex

In this tutorial, you will create a section view, an elevation view, and a quantity schedule for the project created in Tutorial 1 of Chapter 7.   **(Expected time: 1 hr 15 min)**

The following steps are required to complete this tutorial:

a. Open the *c07_Commercial-Complex_tut1.rvt* project file.
b. Hide annotations and dimensions.
c. Create section views.
d. Create the framing elevation view.
e. Generate Graphical Column Schedule.
f. Create quantity schedule for columns.
g. Save the project.
h. Close the project.

Opening the Project File

In this section, you will open the project file created in Tutorial 1 of Chapter 7.

1. To open the project file, choose **Open > Project** from the **File** menu; the **Open** dialog box is displayed.

2. In this dialog box, browse to *C:\rst_2021\c07_rst_2021_tut* folder location and then choose the *c07_Commercial-Complex_tut1.rvt* for Imperial, and for Metric choose *M_c07_Commercial-Complex_tut1.rvt* project file. You can also download this file from *https://www.cadcim.com*. The path of the file is as follows: *Textbooks > Civil/GIS > Revit Structure > Exploring Autodesk Revit 2021 for Structure*.

3. Next, choose the **Open** button from the **Open** dialog box; the selected project file opens in the drawing window.

Hiding Annotations and Dimensions

In this section, you will hide annotations and dimensions in the **Second Floor** structural plan view so that sections can be placed easily.

1. Double-click on the **Second Floor** node under the **Structural Plans** head in the **Project Browser**; the structural floor plan view at the **Second Floor** level is displayed.

2. Choose the **View** tab and then choose the **Visibility/ Graphics** tool from the **Graphics** panel; the **Visibility/Graphic Overrides for Structural Plan: Second Floor** dialog box is displayed.

3. Choose the **Annotation Categories** tab from this dialog box. In this tab, ensure that the **Structure** option is selected in the **Filter list** drop-down list. Next, in the **Visibility** column, clear the check boxes corresponding to the following categories: **Dimensions**, **Structural Column Tags**, **Structural Foundation Tags**, **Structural Framing Tags**, **Spot Coordinates**, and **Spot Elevations**.

4. Choose the **OK** button; the **Visibility/Graphic Overrides for Structural Plan: Second Floor** dialog box is closed.

Creating Section Views

In this section, you will create sectional views for the project by using the **Section** tool.

1. Choose the **Section** tool from the **Create** panel of the **View** tab; the **Modify | Section** contextual tab is displayed.

2. In the **Properties** palette, ensure that the **Section : Building Section** option is selected in the **Type Selector** drop-down list.

3. Move the cursor between the grid bubbles of grid D and grid E, and then click to specify the start point of the grid line.

4. Move the cursor horizontally across the building model till you have crossed the vertical grid 5.1. Click at the desired point, as shown in Figure 8-22, to specify the endpoint of the section line. The section view is created and the name **Section 1** is displayed in the **Sections (Building Section)** head in the **Project Browser**.

Figure 8-22 Creating a section line for the section view

5. In the **Properties** palette, scroll the palette, if required and then click in the value field of the **View Name** parameter under the **Identity Data** area, and enter **Section-X** to replace the existing value.

6. Next, click in the value field corresponding to the **Title on Sheet** parameter under the **Identity Data** area and enter **Sectional View-Longitudinal** in it.

7. In the **Properties** palette, click in the value field corresponding to the **Detail Level** parameter under the **Graphics** area and select the **Fine** option from the drop-down list displayed.

8. Next, click in the value field of the **Far Clip Offset** parameter under the **Extents** area and enter **20'(6096** mm) in it. Choose the **Apply** button in the **Properties** palette.

9. Now, choose the **Split Segment** tool from the **Section** panel of the **Modify | Views** contextual tab; a pencil mark appears in place of the cursor.

10. Place the cursor over the section line; the section line gets highlighted. Next, click over the section line at its intersection with grid 4. As you move down the cursor toward the right, the split section line also moves. Place the cursor along with the split cursor line at grid F and click; the section line is displayed, as shown in Figure 8-23.

The section view is created and the name **Section-X** is displayed under the **Sections (Building Section)** head in the **Project Browser**.

Figure 8-23 *Section line for longitudinal section after splitting the segment*

11. Repeat steps 1 to 9 to create a transverse section view of the building model. Name the view as **Section-Y** and the title for the sheet as **Sectional View-Transverse** and set the **Far Clip Offset** parameter to **45'(13716** mm). For the location of the section line, refer to Figure 8-24.

Figure 8-24 *Section line for transverse section after splitting the segment*

12. Click on the '+' symbol on the left of the **Sections (Building Section)** head in the **Project Browser** to display the section names created. The **Section X** and **Section Y** is created under the **Sections(Building Section)** head.

13. Press ESC to exit the current selection.

14. Double-click on the name **Section-X** to display the corresponding section view on the drawing window, as shown in Figure 8-25.

15. Similarly, double-click on the name **Section-Y** to display the corresponding section view in the drawing window, as shown in Figure 8-26.

Figure 8-25 *Section view for* **Section-X**

Figure 8-26 *Section view for* **Section-Y**

 Note
*You can drag the drag points of the **Crop Region** to customize the view of your section.*

Creating Framing Elevation Views

In this section, you will create the elevation views for the project using the **Framing Elevation** tool and the **Building Elevation** tool.

1. Double-click on the **Second Floor** node under the **Structural Plans** head of the **Project Browser**.

2. Invoke the **Framing Elevation** tool from **View > Create > Elevation** drop-down.

3. Place the cursor over grid C; it is highlighted and an elevation symbol is displayed. Note that the elevation symbol will flip above and below the grid line as you move the cursor.

4. Move the cursor slightly below grid C such that the elevation symbol is displayed below the highlighted grid line.

5. Move the cursor toward right and place it at the location, as shown in Figure 8-27, and click; the elevation tag is added. Also, an elevation view is created and added under the **Elevations (Framing Elevation)** head in the **Project Browser**.

6. Press ESC and then select the arrow head of the elevation tag just added; the **Modify | Views** contextual tab is displayed. In the **Properties** palette, click in the value field corresponding

to the **View Name** parameter under **Identity Data** head and enter **Elevation-GRC** in it. Choose the **Apply** button.

7. Press ESC twice to exit the current selection.

8. Repeat steps 2 to 6 and create an elevation at grid 3.1, refer to Figure 8-28. Then, name it as **Elevation GR-3.1**.

Figure 8-27 *Placing the elevation tag at grid C*   **Figure 8-28** *Placing the elevation tag at grid 3.1*

9. Double-click on **Elevation-GRC** under the **Elevations (Framing Elevation)** node in the **Project Browser** to display the elevation view, as shown in Figure 8-29.

10. Double-click on **Elevation-GR3.1** to display its corresponding view, as shown in Figure 8-30.

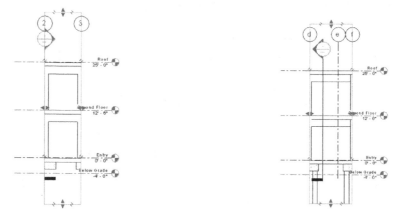

Figure 8-29 *The **Elevation-GRC** sectional view*   **Figure 8-30** *The **Elevation-GR3.1** sectional view*

Generating the Graphical Column Schedule

In this section, you will create the graphical schedule for column and the quantity schedule for columns using the **Graphical Column Schedule** tool.

1. Invoke the **Graphical Column Schedule** tool from **View > Create > Schedule** drop-down; the graphical column schedule is displayed in the drawing window.

2. In the **Properties** palette, select the check box corresponding to the **Group Similar Locations** parameter under the **Graphics** area; the columns at the similar grid line are grouped and displayed in the schedule.

3. Now, click in the **View Scale** parameter under the **Graphics** area and then select the **1/4" = 1'-0" (1:25)** option from the drop-down list displayed. Next, choose the **Apply** button; the viewing scale of the Graphical Column Schedule is changed, as shown in Figure 8-31.

Figure 8-31   The Graphical Column Schedule view

 Note
*As you create the schedule, the name of the schedule is displayed as **Graphical Column Schedule 1** under the **Graphical Column Schedule** head in the **Project Browser**.*

Generating a Quantity Schedule for Columns

In this section, you will create a schedule for displaying the quantity columns and their associated properties used in the project.

1. Invoke the **Schedule/Quantities** tool from **View > Create > Schedules** drop-down; the **New Schedule** dialog box is displayed.

2. In this dialog box, select the **Structural Columns** option from the **Category** list box and then choose the **OK** button; the **Schedule Properties** dialog box is displayed.

3. In the **Available fields** list box, select the **Count** option. Now, press and hold the CTRL key and select the following options from the list box: **Base Level**, **Family and Type**, **Length**, and **Volume**.

4. Next, release the CTRL key and choose the **Add parameter(s)** button; the selected options are added to the **Scheduled fields (in order)** list box.

5. Click on the **Family and Type** option in the **Scheduled fields (in order)** list box and choose the **Move parameter up** button till the option comes at the top in the list.

6. Repeat step 5 to reorder all the options in the **Scheduled fields (in order)** list box, as shown in Figure 8-32.

Figure 8-32 The Schedule Properties dialog box

7. In the **Schedule Properties** dialog box, choose the **Sorting/Grouping** tab and then select the **Family and Type** option from the **Sort by** drop-down list. Ensure that the **Ascending** radio button is selected.

8. Select the **Header** and **Footer** check boxes and then ensure that the **Title, count, and totals** options are selected in the drop-down lists next to them.

9. Select the **Grand totals** check box and ensure that the **Itemize every instance** check box is selected.

10. Choose the **Formatting** tab and then in the **Fields** list box, select **Count**. Next, select the **Calculate totals** option from drop-down list below the **Show conditional format on sheets** check box.

11. Repeat step 10 and select the **Calculate totals** check box for the **Length** and **Volume** options in the **Fields** list box.

12. Choose the **OK** button; the **Structural Column Schedule** is displayed, as shown in Figure 8-33.

Note
*When you create the schedule, its name is displayed as **Structural Column Schedule** under the **Schedules/Quantities (all)** head in the **Project Browser**.*

Saving the Project
In this section, you will save the project file using the **Save As** tool.

1. To save the project, choose the **Save As > Project** option from the **File** menu; the **Save As** dialog box is displayed.

2. In this dialog box, browse to *C:\rst_2021* and create a folder with the name *c08_rst_2021_tut*. Now, open the created folder and then enter **c08_Commercial-Complex_tut1** in the **File name** edit box.

3. Choose the **Save** button; the **Save As** dialog box is closed and the project file is saved.

Closing the Project
1. To close the project, choose the **Close** option from the **File** menu.

The file is closed. This completes Tutorial 1 of Chapter 8.

<Structural Column Schedule>				
A	B	C	D	E
Family and Type	Count	Length	Base Level	Volume
Concrete-Rectangular-Column: 12 x 24				
Concrete-Rectangular	1	11' - 6"	Entry	23.00 CF
Concrete-Rectangular	1	11' - 6"	Entry	23.00 CF
Concrete-Rectangular	1	11' - 6"	Entry	23.00 CF
Concrete-Rectangular	1	11' - 6"	Entry	23.00 CF
Concrete-Rectangular	1	11' - 6"	Entry	23.00 CF
Concrete-Rectangular	1	11' - 6"	Entry	23.00 CF
Concrete-Rectangular	1	11' - 6"	Entry	23.00 CF
Concrete-Rectangular	1	11' - 6"	Entry	23.00 CF
Concrete-Rectangular	1	11' - 6"	Entry	23.00 CF
Concrete-Rectangular	1	12' - 6"	Entry	12.50 CF
Concrete-Rectangular	1	12' - 6"	Entry	23.00 CF
Concrete-Rectangular	1	12' - 6"	Entry	23.00 CF
Concrete-Rectangular	1	12' - 6"	Entry	23.00 CF
Concrete-Rectangular	1	11' - 6"	Entry	23.00 CF
Concrete-Rectangular	1	11' - 6"	Entry	23.00 CF
Concrete-Rectangular	1	11' - 6"	Entry	23.00 CF
Concrete-Rectangular	1	11' - 6"	Entry	23.00 CF
Concrete-Rectangular	1	11' - 6"	Entry	23.00 CF
Concrete-Rectangular	1	11' - 6"	Entry	23.00 CF
Concrete-Rectangular	1	11' - 6"	Entry	23.00 CF
Concrete-Rectangular	1	11' - 6"	Entry	23.00 CF
Concrete-Rectangular	1	12' - 6"	Entry	25.00 CF
Concrete-Rectangular	1	12' - 6"	Entry	25.00 CF
Concrete-Rectangular	1	12' - 6"	Entry	25.00 CF
Concrete-Rectangular	1	12' - 6"	Entry	25.00 CF
Concrete-Rectangular	1	11' - 6"	Entry	23.00 CF
Concrete-Rectangular	1	11' - 6"	Second Floor	23.00 CF
Concrete-Rectangular	1	11' - 6"	Second Floor	23.00 CF
Concrete-Rectangular	1	11' - 6"	Second Floor	23.00 CF
Concrete-Rectangular	1	11' - 6"	Second Floor	23.00 CF
Concrete-Rectangular	1	11' - 6"	Second Floor	23.00 CF
Concrete-Rectangular	1	11' - 6"	Second Floor	23.00 CF
Concrete-Rectangular	1	11' - 6"	Second Floor	23.00 CF
Concrete-Rectangular	1	11' - 6"	Second Floor	23.00 CF
Concrete-Rectangular	1	12' - 6"	Second Floor	23.00 CF
Concrete-Rectangular	1	12' - 6"	Second Floor	23.00 CF
Concrete-Rectangular	1	12' - 6"	Second Floor	23.00 CF
Concrete-Rectangular	1	12' - 6"	Second Floor	23.00 CF
Concrete-Rectangular	1	11' - 6"	Second Floor	23.00 CF
Concrete-Rectangular	1	11' - 6"	Second Floor	23.00 CF
Concrete-Rectangular	1	11' - 6"	Second Floor	23.00 CF
Concrete-Rectangular	1	11' - 6"	Second Floor	23.00 CF
Concrete-Rectangular	1	11' - 6"	Second Floor	23.00 CF
Concrete-Rectangular	1	11' - 6"	Second Floor	23.00 CF
Concrete-Rectangular	1	11' - 6"	Second Floor	23.00 CF
Concrete-Rectangular	1	11' - 6"	Second Floor	23.00 CF
Concrete-Rectangular	1	12' - 6"	Second Floor	25.00 CF
Concrete-Rectangular	1	12' - 6"	Second Floor	25.00 CF
Concrete-Rectangular	1	12' - 6"	Second Floor	25.00 CF
Concrete-Rectangular	1	12' - 6"	Second Floor	25.00 CF
Concrete-Rectangular	1	11' - 6"	Second Floor	23.00 CF
Concrete-Rectangular Volume: 12 x 24	60	708' - 0"		1385.50 CF
Grand total: 60	60	708' - 0"		1385.50 CF

Figure 8-33 The schedule view for columns

Tutorial 2   Industrial Complex

In this tutorial, you will create a section view, an elevation view, and a quantity schedule for the project created in Tutorial 2 of Chapter 7.   **(Expected time: 1hr 15min)**

The following steps are required to complete this tutorial:

a. Open the *c07_Industrial-Complex_tut2.rvt* project file.
b. Generate section view.
c. Generate quantity schedule for beams.
d. Generate material takeoff schedule for foundations.
e. Create Callout View.
f. Save the project.

Opening the Project File
In this section, you will open the project file created in Tutorial 2 of Chapter 7.

1. To open the project file, choose **Open > Project** from the **File** menu; the **Open** dialog box is displayed.

2. In this dialog box, browse to the location *C:\rst_2021\c07_rst_2021_tut* and then choose the *c07_Industrial-Complex_tut2.rvt for Imperial and for Metric open M_c07_Industrial-Complex_tut2.rvt* project file. You can also download this file from *https://www.cadcim.com*. The path of the file is as follows: *Textbooks > Civil/GIS > Revit Structure > Exploring Autodesk Revit 2021 for Structure*.

3. Next, choose the **Open** button from the **Open** dialog box; the selected project file opens in the drawing window with the **Second Floor** structural plan view.

Generating Section Views
In this section, you will generate a sectional view for the project using the **Section** tool.

1. Double-click on the **Foundation Level** node under the **Structural Plans** head in the **Project Browser**; the **Foundation Level** structural plan opens.

2. Choose the **Section** tool from the **Create** panel in the **View** tab; the **Modify | Section** contextual tab is displayed.

3. In the **Properties** palette, ensure that the **Section : Building Section** option is selected in the **Type Selector** drop-down list.

4. Move the cursor between the grid bubbles of grid B and grid C and then click to specify the start point of the section line.

5. Move the cursor horizontally across the building model until it has crossed the building model. Click at the desired point, as shown in Figure 8-34, to specify the endpoint of the section line. The section view is created and the name **Section 1** is displayed in the **Section (Building Section)** head in the **Project Browser**.

6. In the **Properties** palette, scroll the palette, if required, and click in the value field of the **View Name** parameter under the **Identity Data** head and enter **Section-X** to replace the existing value.

7   Choose the **Apply** button in the **Properties** palette.

8. Next, choose the **Split Segment** tool from the **Section** panel of the **Modify | Views** contextual tab; a pencil mark replaces the cursor.

9. Place the cursor on the section line; the section line gets highlighted. Next, click on the section line at some suitable point between grid 5 and grid 6. As you move the cursor downward in the right direction, the split section line also moves. Place the cursor along with the split cursor line at some suitable location below grid 1 and then click; the section line appears, as shown in Figure 8-35.

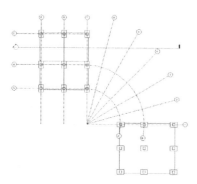

Figure 8-34 The section line created

Figure 8-35 The modified segmented section line

10. Click on the '+' symbol on the left of the **Sections (Building Section)** head in the **Project Browser** to display the section names created.

11. Double-click on the name **Section-X** to display the corresponding section view in the drawing window, as shown in Figure 8-36.

*Figure 8-36 The section view displayed for the **Section-X** section line*

Generating the Quantity Schedule for Beams

In this section, you will generate schedule for displaying the quantity of beams and their associated properties used in the project.

1. Invoke the **Schedule/Quantities** tool from **View > Create > Schedules** drop-down; the **New Schedule** dialog box is displayed.

2. In this dialog box, select the **Structural Framing** option from the **Category** list box and then choose the **OK** button; the **Schedule Properties** dialog box is displayed.

3. Select the **Count** option from the **Available fields** list box. Then, press and hold the CTRL key and select the following options from the list box: **Cut Length**, **Family and Type**, **Length**, **Structural Usage**, and **Volume**.

4. Release the CTRL key and choose the **Add parameter(s)** button; the selected options get added to the **Scheduled fields (in order)** list box.

5. Click on the **Family and Type** option in the **Scheduled fields (in order)** list box and click on the **Move Parameter up** button till the option is placed at the top in the list.

6. Reorder all the options in the **Scheduled fields (in order)** list box, as shown in Figure 8-37.

Figure 8-37 The Schedule Properties dialog box for scheduling the beams

7. Choose the **Sorting/Grouping** tab in the **Schedule Properties** dialog box and then select the **Family and Type** option from the **Sort by** drop-down list. Ensure that the **Ascending** radio button is selected.

8. Select the **Header** check box below the **Sort by** drop-down list.

9. Select the **Grand totals** check box and clear the **Itemize every instance** check box.

10. Choose the **Formatting** tab. In the **Fields** list box, select the **Count** option and then select the **Calculate totals** option from the drop-down list below the **Show conditional format on sheets** check box.

11. Repeat step 10 and select the **Calculate totals** check boxes for the following options in the **Fields** list box: **Cut Length**, **Length**, and **Volume**.

12. Choose the **OK** button; the schedule is displayed, as shown in Figure 8-38.

<Structural Framing Schedule>					
A	B	C	D	E	F
Family and Type	Structural Usage	Cut Length	Count	Length	Volume
Concrete-Rectangular Beam: 12 x 24					
Concrete-Rectangul	Girder	936' - 0"	48	1032' - 0"	1872.00 CF
W Shapes: W14X30					
W Shapes: W14X3	Girder	226' - 1 3/4"	18	245' - 3 3/4"	13.66 CF
Grand total: 66		1162' - 1 3/4"	66	1277' - 3 3/4"	1885.66 CF

Figure 8-38 Partial view of the quantity schedule for structural framing member

Generating the Material Takeoff Schedule

In this section, you will generate the Material Takeoff Schedule for the foundation elements used in the project.

1. Invoke the **Material Takeoff** tool from **View > Create > Schedules** drop-down; the **New Material Takeoff** dialog box is displayed.

2. In the **Category** list box, select the **Structural Foundations** option. Next, choose the **OK** button; the **Material Takeoff Properties** dialog box is displayed.

3. In the **Available fields** list box, select the **Count** option. Then, press and hold the CTRL key and select the following options in the list box: **Elevation at Bottom**, **Family and Type**, **Material: Area**, **Material: Name**, and **Material: Volume**.

4. Release the CTRL key and choose the **Add parameter(s)** button; the selected options are added to the **Scheduled fields (in order)** list box.

5. Click on the **Family and Type** option in the **Scheduled fields (in order)** list box and choose the **Move parameter up** button till the option is placed at the top in the list.

6. Repeat step 5 to reorder all options in the **Scheduled fields (in order)** list box, refer to Figure 8-39.

7. In the **Material Takeoff Properties** dialog box, choose the **Sorting/Grouping** tab and then select the **Family and Type** option from the **Sort by** drop-down list. Ensure that the **Ascending** radio button is selected.

8. Select the **Header** check box below the **Sort by** drop-down list.

9. Select the **Grand totals** check box and ensure that the **Itemize every instance** check box is cleared.

10. Choose the **Formatting** tab, and then in the **Fields** list box, select the **Count** option. Next, select the **Calculate totals** option from the drop-down list below the **Show conditional format on sheets** check box in the **Field formatting** area.

Figure 8-39 The **Material Takeoff Properties** *dialog box*

11. Repeat step 10 and select the **Calculate totals** check box corresponding to following options in the **Fields** list box: **Material: Area** and **Material: Volume**.

12. Choose the **OK** button; the Material Takeoff Schedule is displayed, as shown in Figure 8-40.

<Structural Foundation Material Takeoff>					
A	B	C	D	E	F
Family and Type	Elevation at Bottom	Material: Area	Material: Name	Material: Volume	Count
Footing-Rectangular: 72" x 48" x 18"					
Footing-Rectangula		2696 SF	Concrete, Cast-in-Pl	868.00 CF	28
Foundation Slab: 6" Foundation Slab					
Foundation Slab: 6"	-6' - 6"	4032 SF	Concrete, Cast-in-Pl	2016.00 CF	2
Grand total: 30		6728 SF		2884.00 CF	30

Figure 8-40 The Material Takeoff Schedule for the foundations

Creating a Callout View

In this section, you will create a callout view.

1. Double-click on the **Second Floor** node under the **Structural Plans** head of the **Project Browser**; the **Second Floor** structural plan is displayed.

2. To create a callout view, invoke the **Rectangle** tool from the **Callout** drop-down list of the **Create** panel in the **View** tab; the **Modify| Callout** contextual tab is displayed.

3. Select the **Detail** option from the **Type Selector** drop-down list. Also, select the **1/2" = 1'-0"** option from the **View Scale** drop-down list.

4. Now to create a rectangular callout, click at the first and opposite corner, as shown in Figure 8-41. Now, press the ESC key.

Figure 8-41 *The reference points for creating the callout*

5. After creating the rectangular callout, select it; the **Modify | Views** contextual tab is displayed.

6. In the **Properties** palette of the selected callout, click in the value fields corresponding to the **Display Model** and **Detail Level** parameters and select the **Halftone** and **Fine** options from the drop-down lists in the **Graphics** area, respectively.

7. In the **Properties** palette, click in the value field of the **View Name** parameter under the **Identity Data** area and enter the text **Beam-Column Detail** to replace the existing value. Choose the **Apply** button.

8. Double-click on the **Beam-Column Detail** node under the **Structural Plans** head in the **Project Browser** to display the callout view, as shown in Figure 8-42.

*Figure 8-42 The **Beam-Column Detail** callout view*

Note
*You can sketch details in the callout view displayed by using various annotation tools available in the **Annotate** tab.*

Saving the Project
In this section of the tutorial, you will save the project file using the **Save As** tool.

1.   To save the project file, choose **Save As > Project** from the **File** menu; the **Save As** dialog box is displayed.

2.   In this dialog box, browse to *C:\rst_2021\c08_rst_2021_tut* and enter **c08_Industrial-Complex_tut2** in the **File name** edit box.

3.   Choose the **Save** button; the **Save As** dialog box closes and the project file is saved.

Closing the Project
1.   To close the project, choose the **Close** option from the **File** menu.

     The file is closed. This completes Tutorial 2 of Chapter 8.

Self-Evaluation Test

Answer the following questions and then compare them to those given at the end of this chapter:

1. In Revit, you can create two types of elevations: _____ and _____ .

2. When you invoke the **Building Elevation** tool, the _____ check box in the Options Bar can be selected to create an elevation view associated to a grid.

3. A _____ view is used to show an enlarged view of a part of a building model that requires more detailing.

4. The _____ tool can be used to display the graphical arrangement of columns in a project.

5. You can create a duplicate dependent view by using the _____ tool.

6. You can use the _____ tool from the **Annotate** tab to add detail components to the drafting views.

7. You can use the _____ tool from the **Annotate** tab to create lines of varying thickness.

8. In Revit, you can create a section view from an elevation view. (T/F)

9. The Framing Elevation views can only be associated to grids. (T/F)

10. In Revit, you can create multiple copies of a project view. (T/F)

Review Questions

Answer the following questions:

1. Which of the following options can be used to create details in a callout view?

    (a) **Detail Line**   (b) **Filled Region**
    (c) **Detail Component**   (d) All

2. In Revit, you can create a segmented section using the _____ tool.

3. A section view of the **Building Section** type is displayed under the _____ head in the **Project Browser**.

4. You can select the _____ type from the **Properties** palette for the **Section** tool to create a detail section view.

5. _____ schedules display the information of the material that are used to create the structural elements in a model.

6. In the **Schedule Properties** dialog box, the _____ check box is selected to include elements from the linked Revit files into schedules.

7. _____ details cannot be referred to the existing project views.

8. The instance and type properties of the columns displayed in a Graphical Column Schedule cannot be modified within it. (T/F)

9. You cannot create a dependent view from a callout view. (T/F)

10. In a callout view, you can control the display of elements present in other levels. (T/F)

EXERCISES

Exercise 1   Academic Institution

In this exercise, you will create the section and framing elevation views and a callout view for the *Academic Institution* project created in Exercise 1 of Chapter 7. For the locations of section line, elevation tag, and callout, refer to Figure 8-43. Also, you will add a callout.

(Expected time: 30 min)

1. Use the **Roof** structural plan view to create the section, elevation, and callout views.
2. File to be referred: *c07_Academic-Institution_exer1.rvt*.
3. File name to be assigned: *c08_Academic-Institution_exer1.rvt*.

Figure 8-43 *The **Roof** level structural plan view displaying the section line, elevation tag, and callout*

Exercise 2   Factory Shed

In this exercise, you will create Quantity Schedule for beams and foundations to the *Factory Shed* project created in Exercise 2 of Chapter 7. Refer to Figures 8-44 and 8-45.

(Expected time: 30 min)

1. File to be referred: *c07_Factory-Shed_exer2.rvt.*
2. File name to be assigned: *c08_Factory-Shed_exer2.rvt.*

Structural Foundation Schedule								
Family and T	Structural Us	Area	Count	Elevation at	Height Offset	Perimeter	Volume	Width
Footing-Rectangular: 72" x 48" x 18"								
Footing-R		1014 SF	26	-13' - 0"		0' - 0"	936.00 CF	104' - 0"
Wall Foundation: Bearing Footing - 36" x 12"								
Wall Foun	Bearing	0 SF	30	0' - 0"		0' - 0"	798.00 CF	90' - 0"
Grand total: 56		1014 SF	56	-13' - 0"		0' - 0"	1734.00 CF	194' - 0"

Figure 8-44 The structural foundation schedule

Structural Framing Schedule				
Family and T	Reference L	Structural Us	Count	Volume
Concrete-Rectangular Beam: 12 x 24				
Concrete-			80	1796.00 CF
Grand total: 80			80	1796.00 CF

Figure 8-45 The structural framing schedule

Answers to Self-Evaluation Test

1. Framing, Building, **2. Attached to Grid**, **3.** Callout, **4. Graphical Column Schedule**,
5. Duplicate as Dependent, **6. Detail Component**, **7. Detail Line**, **8.** T, **9.** T, **10.** T

Chapter 9

3D Views, Sheets, Analysis, and Reinforcements

Learning Objectives

After completing this chapter, you will be able to:
- *Create 3D views*
- *Generate shadows*
- *Create sheets*
- *Use analytical models*
- *Add reinforcements*
- *Link building models and share coordinates*
- *Create massing geometry*

In this chapter, you will learn how to generate three-dimensional views and 3D section views, add sheets, generate shadows, work with analytical models, and prepare the analytical model for analysis. You will also learn about adding reinforcements to concrete structural elements in a project.

THREE-DIMENSIONAL (3D) VIEWS

In Autodesk Revit, you can create and display two types of three-dimensional (3D) views, Orthographic 3D View, and Perspective View.

Orthographic 3D View: An orthographic 3D view is a 3D view where all components are of same size regardless of how far they are from the camera. This is a default 3D view. Once this view has been displayed, you can then use various tools to modify its properties.

Perspective View: A perspective view is a real eye view. It can be created by placing a camera at eye elevation and specifying its target position.

Creating Orthographic 3D Views

Ribbon:	View > Create > 3D View drop-down > Default 3D View

An orthographic 3D view is the view in which all elements are displayed in their actual size, irrespective of their distance from the source. In Autodesk Revit, the default 3D view is an orthographic view. To view the orthographic 3D view of a building model, invoke the **Default 3D View** tool from the **Create** panel; the current view will change into the default 3D view. If you are creating the orthographic 3D view for the first time in a project, the camera is automatically placed at a default position (southeast corner) and the corresponding view is displayed in the drawing window. The default view is named as **{3D}** and is added under the **3D Views** head in the **Project Browser**. Figure 9-1 shows an example of the 3D view of the structural model of a building displayed using the **Default 3D View** tool.

Figure 9-1 A three-dimensional view of the structural model of a building

Creating Perspective Views

Ribbon: View > Create > 3D View drop-down > Camera

Perspective views provide a realistic view of the exterior or interior space of a building model. Whenever you see an exterior or an interior view of a building with naked eyes, it appears as the perspective view with the wall edges of the building converging at imaginary points. You can easily create the perspective views of a building model by defining the camera location and the target point. In most building projects, you will find it easier to use a floor plan view to define these points (camera location and camera target). You can then modify the view parameters to achieve the desired result.

To create a perspective view, first open the structural floor plan, elevation, or section view of the building model. Next, in the opened view, invoke the **Camera** tool from the **3D View** drop-down of the **Create** panel; the Options Bar will be displayed with various related options for the camera to be placed in the view. In the Options Bar, the **Perspective** check box is selected by default. As a result, the camera will create a perspective 3D view. If you clear the **Perspective** check box, the camera will generate an orthographic 3D view. In the Options Bar, you can set the elevation of the eye point by selecting a level in the **From** drop-down list and entering a value in the **Offset** edit box. The value that you enter from the **Offset** edit box will determine the distance of the eye point from the level selected from the **From** drop-down list. For example, if the current project plan view is **Level 2** and you want to generate a camera view from the eye point located at **5'0"** for Imperial or **1524mm** for Metric above level 1, then select **Level 1** from the **From** drop-down list and enter the value **5'0"** for Imperial or **1524mm** for Metric in the **Offset** edit box in the Options Bar. This process should be followed before selecting the eye point.

Next, click on the desired location in the drawing area to specify the camera location. After specifying the camera location in the drawing area, you need to specify the target point. To do so, move the cursor away from the camera location; you will notice that three rays are generated from the location point, as shown in Figure 9-2.

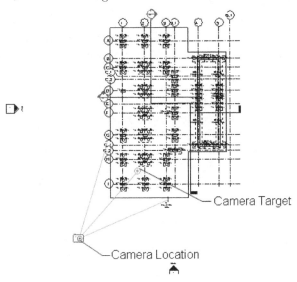

Figure 9-2 Three rays generated from the camera location

Note
*You can reset the position of the camera's target point to the center of the crop region. In case the camera target is displayed during modification of the camera field view, you can choose the **Reset Target** tool to center the camera target point.*

These rays depict the field of view for the selected camera point. You can use the **Offset** and **From** options in Options Bar to specify the level and the offset elevation of the target point. Next, move the cursor and specify the location of the target point. The target point must be placed inside or beyond the building model for the camera to capture the model. Once you have selected the target point, Autodesk Revit will automatically generate the 3D perspective view of the building model and display it in the drawing window. Next, you can use drag controls to increase the extent of the camera view. After extending the view, press ESC to exit the **Camera** tool. Figure 9-3 shows the camera view of a building model.

Figure 9-3 Camera view generated from the camera placed

The view generated will be added to the **3D Views** node of the **Project Browser** and will be named as **3D View 1**, **3D View 2**, and so on. However, you can rename them by using the **Rename** option from the shortcut menu, which is displayed on right-clicking on the newly created 3D view in the **Project Browser**.

You can also create orthographic views by using the **Camera** tool. To do so, clear the **Perspective** check box in the Options Bar; the **Scale** drop-down list will be activated. You can select the scale of the view from this drop-down list. Move the cursor in the drawing window; a camera will be attached to it. Also, you will be prompted to specify the location of the eye point or the point from where you want to view the model. Click to specify its location and then click again to specify the target point, an orthographic 3D view will be generated.

Modifying Perspective View Properties

After creating the perspective view, you can modify its properties to achieve the desired effect. To do so, select the perspective view and modify the instance properties in the **Properties** palette, as shown in Figure 9-4.

The instance properties of the 3D view will be displayed in the **Properties** palette. Some of the commonly used instance properties are discussed next.

In the **Properties** palette, the **View Name** instance parameter under the **Identity Data** head is used to rename a view. The **Detail Level** instance parameter is used to set the level of details required in a view.

The **Edit** button in the value column of the **Visibility/ Graphics Overrides** instance parameter is used to set the visibility of models and annotations. On choosing this button, the **Visibility/Graphic Overrides for 3D View** dialog box will be displayed. In this dialog box, you can set the visibility parameters of the model. Next, to modify the elevation of the eye point, enter the new value in the value column of the **Eye Elevation** instance parameter in the **Properties** palette. Similarly, you can enter a new value for the **Target Elevation** instance parameter in its corresponding value column. As soon as you choose the **Apply** button, the perspective view is modified in the drawing window.

*Figure 9-4 The **Properties** palette for the camera view*

Tip
*To modify the camera and target locations, open the view in which the camera was placed. Right-click on the name of the 3D view in the **Project Browser** and then choose the **Show Camera** option from the shortcut menu displayed. On doing so, the location of the camera and target points will be displayed in the drawing window. Next, drag the camera and target points to a new location; Autodesk Revit will immediately regenerate the 3D view for the new location.*

Creating 3D Section Views

In BIM, sometimes it is difficult to interpret the typical two dimensional views as they do not completely display the design intent of a model. However, the 3D section view gives the better inside view of a model. You can create 3D section views by using the **Selection Box** tool. This tool works in all views and allows you to isolate the element(s) in the 3D view. This is different from isolating an element using Temporary Hide/Isolate mode as in this isolation process, you can isolate the elements as well as create the section views.

To create a 3D section view of a model, open 3D view. In the **Properties** palette, choose the **Section Box** check box under the **Extends** head, refer to Figure 9-5. The section box will be created around the model. Select the section box, the control points will be activated. These control points will determine the range of section view to be displayed. The selection box helps to enhance your documentation or to view the model. You can use these control points to resize the selection box and to display different section views of the element, refer to Figure 9-6.

Figure 9-5 *Partial view of the **Properties** palette with **Section Box** selected*

Figure 9-6 *The selection box created around the selected element*

GENERATING SHADOWS

One of the powerful features provided in Autodesk Revit is its ability to generate shadows based on location of the Sun with respect to the building. Shadows can be generated in a plan, elevation, section, or 3D view. To use this feature, open the desired view and click on the inclined arrow symbol (**Graphic Display Options**) in the **Graphics** panel of the **View** tab; the **Graphic Display Options** dialog box will be displayed, as shown in Figure 9-7. In this dialog box, you can specify the settings to enhance the visual output of the project view. You can use the **Style** drop-down list to select an option to specify pre-defined visual settings in the project view. In the **Style** drop-down list, if you select the **Shaded** or **Realistic** option, the **Show Edges** check box will be activated. On selecting this check box, the edges of the model will be displayed in the pre-defined visual settings. You can enhance the display of your project by using the **Smooth lines with anti-aliasing** check box. On selecting

Figure 9-7 The Graphic Display Options dialog box

this check box, the lines and edges in the view will be displayed more smoothly. In the **Model Display** area, you can drag the **Transparency** slider to set the transparency of the entire project view. Also, you can use the **Silhouettes** drop-down list to select an option to create silhouette in the model.

The options in the **Shadows** area of the **Graphic Display Options** dialog box are used to control the display of the shadow in the project view. In this area, select the **Cast Shadows** check box to cast shadow of the model. You can select the **Show Ambient Shadows** check box to display the shadow created by ambient light. By default, this check box is cleared.

The options in the **Sketchy Lines** area of the **Graphic Display Options** dialog box are used to control the appearance of sketchy lines in the current view. In this area, select the **Enable Sketchy Lines** check box to turn on sketchy lines for the current view. You can set the degree of the variability of the sketched lines using the **Jitter** slider.

In the **Lighting** area of the **Graphic Display Options** dialog box, choose the button on the right of the **Sun Setting** text; the **Sun Settings** dialog box will be displayed. By default, the **Lighting** radio button is selected in this dialog box. Select the **Still** radio button in the **Solar Study** area and then set the time and date for the solar study in the **Date** and **Time** edit boxes. To specify the location for the solar study, choose the button on the right of the **Location** edit box; the **Location Weather and Site** dialog box will be displayed. In the **Location** tab of the dialog box, select the **Default City List** option from the **Define Location by** drop-down list. On doing so, the options to set the locations will be displayed below this drop-down list. Specify the latitude and longitude in the **Latitude** and **Longitude** edit boxes for a precise solar study or select a city from the **City** drop-down list. Next, choose the **OK** button to close the **Location Weather and Site** dialog box. In the **Sun Settings** dialog box, clear the **Ground Plane at Level** check box to view the shadow pattern on the terrain. If you want the shadows to fall at a particular level or at the entry level, select the **Ground Plane at Level** check box and then select a level from the drop-down list displayed below it. Next, choose the **OK** button to return to the **Graphic Display Options** dialog box.

If you want to create a solar study based on the azimuth and altitude of the Sun from the horizontal surface, select the **Lighting** radio button in the **Sun Settings** dialog box and specify the azimuth and altitude for the solar study. After specifying the settings for the solar study, choose the **OK** button.

Next, select the **Realistic** option from the **Style** drop-down list in the **Model Display** area of the **Graphic Display Options** dialog box. Next, expand the **Realistic** area; the options for setting the exposure of the view will be enabled. The **Automatic** radio button is selected by default in this area. As a result, the exposure control of the project view will be set automatically. If you select the **Manual** radio button from this area; the **Value** slider will be activated. You can use this slider to set the exposure control to your desired value. You can also specify the color settings of the project view in the **Realistic** area. To do so, choose the **Color Correction** button; the **Color Correction** dialog box will be displayed. You can use this dialog box to specify the intensity of the shadows, white point settings, highlights, and color saturation in a project view. After specifying the desired settings, choose the **OK** button; the **Color Correction** dialog box will be closed.

Next, you can select a background for your current view by clicking in the drop-down list in the **Background** area. When you choose the **Sky** option, you can specify the color of the background by choosing the button on the right of the **Ground Color** option; the **Color** dialog box will be displayed. Select the color of your choice and choose the **OK** button to return to the **Graphic Display Options** dialog box. Choose the **Gradient** option from the drop-down list in the **Background** area. You will notice that now you can assign color to sky, horizon, and ground. Choose the button on the right of the **Sky Color**, **Horizon Color**, and **Ground Color** option. You can also select the **Image** option from the drop-down located on the right of the **Background** option to set an image in the background of your current view. When you choose this option, the **Customize Image** button appears in the **Background** area. When you chose this button, the **Background Image** dialog box will be displayed. You can browse an image from your computer by clicking on the **Image** button in this dialog box. After choosing the desired image, click on **OK** button to return to the **Graphic Display Options** dialog box.

Next, in the **Graphic Display Options** dialog box, choose the **Save as View Template** button; the **New View Template** dialog box will be displayed. In this dialog box, enter a name for the settings in the **Name** edit box and choose the **OK** button; the **View Templates** dialog box will be displayed. In the **View Properties** area of this dialog box, you can specify options to edit the view properties of the current setting. In this dialog box, choose the **Apply Properties** and the **OK** buttons to close it. You will notice that the shadows are displayed in the model. The shadows displayed will be based on the specified date, time, and location.

Note
1. In the Graphic Display Options dialog box, the Background area will be displayed only for 3D views.

2. If the shadow does not appear, choose the Shadow On button from the View Control Bar.

Solar Study

Solar study helps you to visualize and then analyze the position of the Sun and the solar effects on buildings and sites in the real world at a specified time, date, duration, and location. You can analyze the effects of the Sun on the same building at different locations, such as Boston or Melbourne, by changing the location of the building from Boston to Melbourne. The solar studies help you analyze the amount and impact of the natural Sunlight and shadows on a building and a site at a particular time in a day and at a particular location. It also helps you study the amount of lighting inside a building at different times of a day and year, at a particular location.

To create a still solar study, open the structural floor plan view. In the **Properties** palette of the opened view, set the value of the **Orientation** parameter to **True North** and choose the **Apply** button. Next, choose the **Rotate True North** tool from **Manage > Project Location > Position** drop-down; a rotation symbol will be displayed in the drawing area. In the Options Bar, specify the rotation angle in the **Angle from Project to True North** edit box. This angle will be the angle difference of the building from the project **North** direction to the **True North** direction. You can rotate the building to the **East** or **West** of the **True North** direction. In Autodesk Revit, you can choose the **Place** button from the Options Bar and change the point of rotation of the view to a different location in the view.

Next, after setting the True North of the project, open the 3D view of the building and adjust the view of the building as required. Choose the **View** tab and then choose the inclined arrow symbol in the **Graphics** panel; the **Graphic Display Options** dialog box will be displayed. In the **Lighting** area of this dialog box, choose the button on the right of the **Sun Setting** text; the **Sun Settings** dialog box will be displayed. In the **Solar Study** area of this dialog box, select the **Still** radio button, and in the **Settings** area, set the time and date for the solar study in the **Date** and **Time** edit boxes. To specify the location for the solar study, choose the button on the right of the **Location** edit box in the **Settings** area; the **Location Weather and Site** dialog box will be displayed. In the **Location** tab of this dialog box, select the **Default City List** option from the **Define Location by** drop-down list; the options to set the locations will be displayed below this drop-down list. Specify the latitude and longitude in the **Latitude** and **Longitude** edit boxes for a precise solar study or select a city from the **City** drop-down list. Next, choose the **OK** button to close the **Location Weather and Site** dialog box. In the **Sun Settings** dialog box, ensure that the **Ground Plane at Level** check box is cleared so that you can view the shadow pattern on the terrain. If you want the shadows to fall at a particular level or at the entry level, select the **Ground Plane at Level** check box and then select a level from the drop-down list displayed below it. Next, choose the **OK** button to return to the **Graphic Display Options** dialog box.

If you want to create a solar study based on the azimuth and altitude of the Sun from the horizontal surface, select the **Lighting** radio button in the **Sun Settings** dialog box and specify the azimuth and altitude for the solar study. After you have specified the settings for the solar study, choose the **OK** button to close the **Sun Settings** dialog box.

Next, in the **Shadows** area of the **Graphic Display Options** dialog box, you can select the **Cast Shadows** and **Show Ambient Shadows** check boxes to enable the ray trace shadows and ambient shadows in the view.

In the **Lighting** area of the **Graphic Display Options** dialog box, you can set the intensities of Sun, Ambient Light, and Shadows by using the **Sun**, **Ambient Light**, and **Shadows** sliders, respectively. You can use the **Shadows** slider to make the shadow light or dark. Next, choose the **OK** button to notice the shadows based on the specified date, time, and location. The shadow patterns generated in a still solar study for a structural model at a specified location at different times during a day are illustrated in Figures 9-8 to 9-11.

Note

Shadows cannot be generated for the following visual styles: **Wireframe** *and* **Consistent Colors***.*

Figure 9-8 *After the sunrise around 6 AM*

Figure 9-9 *In the morning at 9:30 AM*

Figure 9-10 *In the afternoon at 1.25 PM*

Figure 9-11 *In the evening at 4.30 PM*

In Autodesk Revit, you can see the path of the Sun for creating solar study. The Sun path is a visual representation of the range of the movement of the Sun across the sky at the geographic location specified for a project. To display the Sun path, choose the **Sun Path Off** button from the **View Control Bar** and then select the **Sun Path On** option from the flyout displayed, as shown in Figure 9-12. On doing so, the **Sun Path- Sun Not Displaye**d window will be displayed. In this window, you can choose any of the two options: **Use the**

Figure 9-12 *Choosing the Sun Path On option from the flyout*

specified project location, date, and time instead and **Continue with current settings**. If you choose the **Use the specified project location, date, and time instead** option from this window, the Sun settings for the Sun path will change to the **<In-session, Still>** setting. If you choose the **Continue with current settings** option from the window, the Sun settings for the Sun path will use the **<In-session, Lighting>** setting. Next, as you choose an option from the **Sun Path- Sun Not Displayed** window, the path of the Sun along with its components are displayed in the drawing area, as shown in Figure 9-13.

Figure 9-13 *The Sun path along with its components*

SHEETS

Ribbon: View > Sheet Composition > Sheet

In Autodesk Revit, a sheet or a drawing sheet is a document set that is used for the final working drawings in a site. A drawing sheet contains sheet views that consist of multiple drawing views or schedules added in a project. Sheets are defined by a border and a title block. To create a drawing sheet, you first need to add a sheet view to the project and then add the required project views to the added sheet views.

Adding a Drawing Sheet to a Project

To create a drawing sheet for a project, first you need to decide its title block. In Revit, title blocks are loaded as families. A title block is used to convey project information and drawing sheet title. Project information includes client name, project name, project title, project number, date of issue of drawing, drawing sheet number, scale, and so on. The project information can be added to a project by using the **Project Information** tool, which has been discussed in Chapter 3. The type of title block will decide the size of the sheet. In Revit, there are some predefined title blocks that can be used in a project. To load these title blocks so that they can be used in the sheet, choose the **Load Family** tool from the **Load from Library** panel in the **Insert** tab; the **Load Family** dialog box will be displayed, as shown in Figure 9-14. In this dialog box, browse to **English-Imperial > Titleblocks** for Imperial system or **English-Metric > Titleblocks** for Metric system. In this location, you can select the required title block for the project.

Figure 9-14 *The **Load Family** dialog box*

 Note
The sizes of title blocks available in the library are based on ANSI standards for sheet size. These title blocks are available both in vertical (portrait) and horizontal (landscape) alignments.

After selecting a file for the title block from the **Load Family** dialog box, choose the **Open** button; the selected title block(s) will be loaded into the project file. Next, you need to add a drawing sheet to the project. To do so, choose the **Sheet** tool from the **Sheet Composition** panel of the **View** tab; the **New Sheet** dialog box will be displayed. This dialog box has two areas: **Select titleblocks** and **Select placeholder sheets**. Select the required title block for the drawing sheet from the list of title blocks. To load the title block that is not loaded, choose the **Load** button; the selected title block will be loaded into the project and added in the **Select titleblocks** area. On choosing the **OK** button, Autodesk Revit will create a sheet view and display the borders and the title block in the drawing window, as shown in Figure 9-15. As you add sheets to the project, their names and numbers will be displayed in the **Sheets** head in the **Project Browser**.

Adding Views to a Drawing Sheet
After adding a drawing sheet to a project, you need to add project views to it. To do so, choose the **Place View** tool from the **Sheet Composition** panel of the **View** tab; the **Views** dialog box will be displayed, as shown in Figure 9-16.

Figure 9-15 *Sheet view displayed in the drawing window*

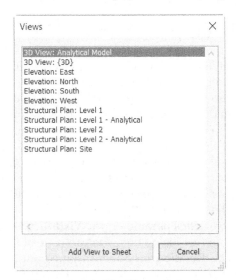

Figure 9-16 *The **Views** dialog box*

This dialog box displays the list of project views available in a project. Select the project view that you want to add to the sheet and choose the **Add View to Sheet** button; the selected view will appear as a viewport represented by a rectangle attached to the cursor. Move the cursor to the drawing area in the sheet and click at the preferred location to add the selected view. Next, in the **Properties** palette, change the **View Scale** parameter by selecting a suitable scale from the drop-down list in its value field and choose **Apply**. The view added will adjust to the specified scale and appear in the sheet, as shown in Figure 9-17.

Figure 9-17 *The specified view added to the sheet*

The viewport of the inserted view will display a label line at the bottom left corner. A label line shows the view name, view scale, and view number. You can modify the properties associated with the viewport in the **Properties** palette. You can also activate the project view and then pan it to adjust the view area that you need to display in the viewport. Various options to modify the properties of the views in the viewport and to pan the view areas are discussed in the next section.

Modifying View Properties

To modify the properties of the project views added in a sheet, select the viewport associated with it; the **Properties** palette for the view will be displayed with various instance parameters associated to it. You can modify these values based on your project requirement. When you enter a new value for the **View Name** parameter, the corresponding levels and views are also renamed accordingly. You can modify the scale of a view by selecting a scale from the drop-down list in the value column of the **View Scale** parameter. When you modify the view scale of a view, the corresponding view in the viewport is scaled automatically. You can move the view to another location, if required. You can select the **Coarse**, **Medium**, or **Fine** option from the drop-down list corresponding to the value column of the **Detail Level** instance parameter to define the level of details to be displayed in a view. You can control the visibility of different categories of elements in each viewport. To do so, choose the **Edit** button displayed in the value field corresponding to the **Visibility/ Graphics Overrides** parameter; the **Visibility/Graphics Overrides for Sheet** dialog box will be displayed. In this dialog box, you can control the visibility of various model and annotation elements. The **Rotation on Sheet** instance parameter in the Options Bar is used to rotate the view clockwise or counter-clockwise. The view range of the view can be set by using the **Edit** button corresponding to the **View Range** parameter. You can also modify the appearance of the label line. To do so, choose the **Edit Type** button in the **Properties** palette; the **Type Properties** dialog box will be displayed, as shown in Figure 9-18. In this dialog box, the visibility of the title and extension lines can be controlled by using their respective type parameters. Some other parameters of the label line such as line weight, color, and line pattern can also be modified by using this dialog box.

*Figure 9-18 The **Type Properties** dialog box*

Panning Views

After adding views and modifying view properties, you may need to pan the viewport in a suitable location in the sheet. To do so, first you need to activate the view in the viewport and then pan or move the views to a desired location in the sheet. To activate the view, select the viewport corresponding to it in the sheet and then right-click to display the shortcut menu. Next, choose the **Activate View** option from the shortcut menu; the view in the selected viewport will be activated. Again, right-click and choose the **Pan Active View** option from the shortcut menu displayed; the cursor will change into a symbol with four arrows. Left-click in the viewport, press and hold the left mouse button, and drag it to move entities in the viewport. Once you have panned and placed the entities at an appropriate location in the sheet, right-click and then choose **Deactivate View** from the shortcut menu to revert to the sheet.

Modifying a Building Model in Sheets

In sheets, sometimes you may need to make quick modifications in the elements of building model. To do so, you need to activate a view and make the desired modifications in it. To activate a view from a drawing sheet, select a viewport. Next, choose the **Activate View** button from the **Viewport** drop-down of the **Sheet Composition** panel in the **View** tab; the view will be activated. Alternatively, you can activate the selected viewport by choosing the **Activate View** button in the **Viewport** panel of the **Modify| Viewports** contextual tab. In the activated view, you can work on the building model as in any other project views. The elements in the building model can be edited using the editing tools. When the building model is edited, the parametric change engine of Autodesk Revit modifies other project views immediately. As a result, all project views update automatically. For example, modifications made to the location of a column in an activated viewport of the drawing sheet are automatically reflected in the corresponding floor plan, sections, and other associated views. After making necessary modifications in the model, ensure that the viewport is selected and then choose the **Deactivate View** tool from **View > Sheet Composition > Viewports** drop-down list to return to the drawing sheet view. Note that new views can also be added to the project when the viewport is activated. You can also create a new plan, elevation, section, callout, detail view, and so on, while working on the activated view. The activated view can then be deactivated. Also, the newly created views can be added to the drawing sheet.

Adding Schedules to a Drawing Sheet

You can easily add schedules created in a project to a drawing sheet. To do so, drag the schedules created (required schedules) from the **Project Browser** and drop them into the drawing sheet; the preview image of the schedule will be attached to the cursor. Move the cursor and click at the desired location to place the schedule. The selected schedule will appear with blue triangles for each column and a break line on the right side, as shown in Figure 9-19. You can modify the appearance and properties of a schedule. The blue triangles representing the controls for the column width can be dragged to modify the width of each column in the schedule. The break line on the right border represents the split control. It is used to split the schedule table into multiple sections. When the split control is used, the schedule splits into two sections. These sections are placed adjacent to each other. In this way, the schedule can be split into a number of sections that fit into the drawing sheet.

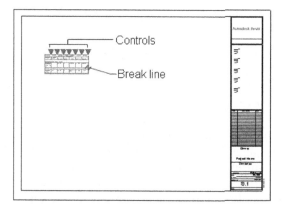

Figure 9-19 *The selected schedule with its controls*

The sections of a schedule can be moved by using the move control available at the center of the schedule section. They can also be resized by dragging the blue dot of the schedule's end. When the schedule section is resized, the additional or reduced rows are automatically adjusted between the sections. However, the last section cannot be resized, as it contains the remaining rows. The split sections of a schedule can be rejoined. As they are sequential, a section can be joined only to its previous or next section. To join a split section, drag a section by using the move control over the previous or the next section; the two schedule sections will merge into a single schedule section.

ANALYTICAL MODELS

Autodesk Revit is a multi-material (steel, precast, cast-in-place concrete, masonry, wood, and so on) modeling software for structural design, analysis, and documentation. A physical model is made up of beams, walls, columns, slabs, and footings. An analytical model is a simplified representation of the physical model in which all members are connected to each other continuously. An analytical model contains loads, load case and load combinations specific to the project being analyzed. An analytical model also includes material properties and release conditions for structural analysis.

A single structural model integrates the physical model (for layout, coordination and documentation) with an independent editable analytical model. This integration enables you to link the structural model bidirectionally to leading analysis applications such as ADAPT-Builder concrete design, RISA, Fastrak Building Designer, Autodesk Robot Structural Analysis, and other application partners. To know more about various software packages that partner with Autodesk Revit, visit *www.autodesk.com*.

Figures 9-20 and 9-21 show the 3D views of a structural model as a physical model and an analytical model, respectively. In Figure 9-21, each element in the project consists of a set of structural member analytical models. In a project, the following structural elements have structural member analytical models: Structural Columns, Structural Framing elements (such as beams and braces), Structural Floors, and Structural Walls.

Figure 9-20 *The physical model view of a project*   *Figure 9-21* *The analytical model view of a project*

In Autodesk Revit, you can control the visibility of the analytical model in a project. You can hide the analytical model in the current view. To display the analytical model in a project view, choose the **Analytical Model** node under the **3D Views** head from the **Project Browser**. If the model is not displayed, you need to choose the **Show Analytical Model** button from the **View Control bar**, refer to Figure 9-22.

Figure 9-22 *The **Show Analytical Model** button*

In a project, the analytical model contains various instance parameters that can be modified from its corresponding **Properties** palette. Further, you can specify various settings for analytical checks in an analytical model by using the options in the **Analytical Model Settings** tab of the **Structural Settings** dialog box. These options are discussed later in this chapter. The instance parameters and the settings for the analytical model are discussed next.

Note
*To remove the association of an analytical model, select it and then choose the **Disable Analytical** button from the **Analytical Model** panel of the contextual tab.*

Instance Parameters for an Analytical Model

In this section, you will learn about the instance parameters of a structural element that are required to be specified for performing an analysis. The instance parameters of structural elements such as beams, columns, floor, and walls have already been discussed in the earlier chapters. The parameters that are required for analysis are called structural analytical instance parameters. These parameters are explained under different heads: Parameters for Analytical projection planes, Parameters for physical material properties, and Parameters for release conditions for beams and columns, and Parameters for rigid links of beams and columns. These headings are discussed next.

Analytical Projection Planes and its Parameters

In Autodesk Revit, major enhancements have been made in the project planes for analytical models. For an analytical model, the projection planes can be specified by using various parameters available under the **Analytical Alignment** head in the **Properties** palette. When you add a structural element in a project, by default, its analytical model will have analytical project planes associated with it. These analytical projection planes are different based on the types of structural element added. For example, the default analytical projection plane for a column differs from that of a slab. The default projection planes for different structural types are described next.

Default Analytical Projection Planes for Columns

The default analytical projection planes for columns are placed at their top and base. These planes define the limits of the structural column analytical model and are at an offset distance from the specified level.

Default Analytical Projection Planes for Structural Walls

The default analytical projection planes for walls are placed at their central plane.

Default Analytical Projection Planes for Beams

The default analytical projection plane for a beam is parallel to its x-axis. This plane is defined at a desired level or relative to the beam section geometry.

Default Analytical Projection Planes for Structural Floors

The analytical projection plane for a structural floor is parallel to the plan level on the first placement. The subsequent structural floor placements reference the last used projection plane.

Default Analytical Projection Planes for Foundation Slabs

The top face of the foundation slab is its default analytical projection plane.

Apart from setting the default location of the project planes for each structural element type, you can set different projection planes for different structural element types. The locations of these projection planes are relative either to the levels of the or to the structural element itself. In the next sections, you will learn about various planes that need to be set for different structural element types.

Analytical Projection Planes for Columns

In Autodesk Revit, a column will have projection planes at its top and base. To modify the projection planes of a column, select its analytical model from the view; the instance properties of the selected column will be displayed in the **Properties** palette. To change the projection plane of the base of the column, click in the **Value** field corresponding to the **Base Alignment Method** parameter under the **Analytical Alignment** head and select the **Projection** option from the drop-down list displayed. Next, to align the projection plane of the column base to x, y, or z axis, select the desired options for the following parameters: **Base x-Direction Projection**, **Base y-Direction Projection**, **Base Extension Method**, and **Base z-Direction Projection**. By default, the **Location line** option will be specified for these parameters. As a result, the projections of these parameters will be based on the location line assigned for the physical model of the concerned analytical model.

To change the projection plane of the top of the column, click in the **Value** field corresponding to the **Top Alignment Method** parameter and select the **Projection** option from the drop-down list displayed. Next, to align the projection plane of the column base to x, y, and z axes, select the desired options for the following parameters: **Top x Projection**, **Top y Projection**, **Top Extension Method**, and **Top z Projection**.

Note
*In the **Properties** palette of the analytical column, the default value specified for the **Base Alignment Method**, **Top Alignment Method**, **Top Extension Method**, and **Base Extension Method** is **Auto-Detect**. On keeping this value intact for these parameters, you will allow the endpoints at the top and base of the column to adjust automatically with its neighboring structural elements in terms of its continuity and consistency of the joints.*

Analytical Projection Planes for Beams

In Autodesk Revit, a beam will have projection planes at its start point and endpoint. To modify the projection planes of a beam, select its analytical model from the view; the instance properties of the selected beam will be displayed in the **Properties** palette.

To change the projection plane of the start point of the beam, click in the value field corresponding to the **Start Alignment Method** parameter under the **Analytical Alignment** head and select the **Projection** option from the drop-down list displayed. Next, to align the projection plane of the start point of the beam to y and z axes, select the desired options for the following parameters: **Start y Projection** and **Start z Projection**. To align the projection plane of the endpoint of the beam to y and z axes, select the desired options for the following parameters: **End y Projection** and **End z Projection**.

Note
*In the **Properties** palette of the analytical beam, the default value specified for the **Start Alignment Method** and **End Alignment Method** is **Auto-detect**. If you retain the default value of these parameters, you will allow the endpoint of the beam to adjust automatically with its neighboring structural elements in terms of its join continuity and consistency.*

Analytical Projection Planes for Structural Floors

Structural floors can have any of the following options as the analytical projection plane: Top of the floor, center of the floor, bottom of the floor, level, and reference plane. To specify the analytical projection plane for the structural floor, you need to use the **Properties** palette. In the **Properties** palette, click in the value field of the **Alignment Method** parameter and select the **Projection** option from the drop-down list displayed. Next, to align the projection plane of the floor, click on the drop-down list corresponding to the **Projection** parameter and select an option from the drop-down list displayed.

Analytical Projection Planes for Structural Wall

Structural walls have projection planes at their top and bottom. The top of a structural wall can have any of the following options as the analytical projection plane: level, top of the wall, and reference plane. The bottom of a wall can have any of the following options as its analytical projection plane: level, bottom of the wall, and reference plane. To specify the analytical projection plane for the top and bottom of the wall, you need to use the **Properties** palette. In the **Properties** palette for the analytical model of the structural wall, click on the drop-down list corresponding to the **Alignment Method** parameter and select the **Projection** option from the drop-down list displayed. Next, to specify the face of the wall that will be used for locating the projection plane, click on the value field corresponding to the **Projection** parameter and select an option from the drop-down list displayed. Next, to align the projection plane of the top and base of the wall, select the desired options for the following parameters: **Top Extension Method**, **z Projection**, **Base Extension Method**, **Top y Projection** and **Base y Projection**.

Parameters for Physical Material Properties

All materials have specific structural properties such as density, Poisson's ratio, Young's modulus, and so on. These properties are known as the physical properties of materials. These properties are further used in structural analysis.

To assign a material to an element, you need to invoke the **Material Browser** dialog box. To invoke the **Material Browser** dialog box for a beam or a column, select any of them from the drawing area and then click in the value field corresponding to the **Structural Material** instance parameter. Next, choose the button displayed in the value field corresponding to the **Structural Material** parameter; the **Material Browser** dialog box will be displayed. For structural floors and structural walls, you can invoke the **Material Browser** dialog box from the **Edit Assembly** dialog box that has been discussed in Chapter 4 and Chapter 5.

In the **Project Material: All** area of the **Material Browser** dialog box, click on the desired material; the properties of the selected material will be displayed, refer to Figure 9-23. In the **Material Editor** dialog box, you can edit various properties of the desired material such as **Graphics**, **Appearance**, **Physical**, **Identity** and **Thermal**.

Figure 9-23 *The options in the* ***Material Browser*** *dialog box*

The **Graphics** properties of the desired material will be used to assign the shade, surface, and section patterns to it. To edit the **Graphics** properties, choose the **Graphics** tab; the **Graphic** section will be displayed along with various properties. The **Appearance** property of the material is used to assign the texture or pattern to the material for its display after rendering. The **Physical** property of the material is used to assign various intrinsic properties of a material such as its strength, mechanical behavior, and thermal characteristics. In the **Material Browser** dialog box, choose the **Physical** tab to view and edit physical properties of the selected material. The **Thermal** property of the material is used to assign various thermal characteristics of the material such as its thermal conductivity, specific heat, porosity, and so on. You can edit the **Thermal** property of the material. To do so, click on the **Thermal** tab; the **Information** and **Basic Thermal** sections with various editable parameters such as **Name**, **Description**, **Source**, **Specific heat**, **Compressibility** and more will be displayed. You can edit the properties under this section as per your requirement. After editing the properties of the desired material, choose **Apply** and then the **OK** button to save changes and close the dialog box.

Note
All the physical and thermal properties of materials are a part of the assets defined in the ***Asset Browser*** *dialog box.*

Parameters for Release Conditions

Release conditions are applied for linear elements such as beams and columns. These conditions do not apply to structural walls or structural floors. In Autodesk Revit, the release conditions that can be applied for beams and columns are Fixed, Pinned, Bending Moment, and User-defined. To specify the desired release conditions, select the analytical column and specify the release conditions at its top and bottom by clicking in the value fields corresponding to the **Top Release** and **Base Release** parameters and selecting the desired release option from the drop-down lists displayed. Similarly, for beams, you can specify release conditions at their start and end by clicking in the value fields corresponding to the **Start Release** and **End Release** parameters and selecting the desired release option from the drop-down lists displayed. A release condition is defined by six components: Fx - axial force (X direction), Fy - shear force (Y direction), Fz - shear force (Z direction), Mx - torsion force (X direction), My - bending moment (Y direction), and Mz - bending moment (Z direction).

The Pinned release condition is defined when all Moments are released, the Fixed release condition is defined with no releases, whereas the Bending Moment Release Condition is defined when My and Mz are released (torsion (Mx) not released).

Settings for an Analytical Model

The Analytical Model is useful for a project from the analysis point of view. Generally, before you take this model to an analysis software or at the time of modeling, its consistency and continuity has to be checked. To make the analytical model consistent, you can specify tolerance for the elements and perform checks at various stages of modeling. To do so, choose the **Structural Settings** tool in **Structural Settings** drop-down from the **Settings** panel of the **Manage** tab; the **Structural Settings** dialog box will be displayed. In this dialog box, choose the **Analytical Model Settings** tab to display options for specifying various analytical settings, as shown in Figure 9-24.

Alternatively, to invoke the **Structural Settings** dialog box with the **Analytical Model Settings** tab chosen, choose the **Analytical Model Settings** button located in the **Analytical Model Tools** panel of the **Analyze** tab, refer to Figure 9-25. The **Analytical Model Settings** tab consists of five areas: **Automatic Checks**, **Tolerances**, **Member Supports Check**, **Analytical / Physical Model Consistency Check**, and **Analytical Model Visibility**. These areas are discussed next.

Figure 9-24 The options in the **Analytical Model Settings** tab of the **Structural Settings** dialog box

Figure 9-25 Choosing the **Analytical Model Settings** button

Automatic Checks Area

This area consists of two check boxes: **Member Supports** and **Analytical / Physical Model Consistency**. On selecting the **Member Supports** check box, the automatic support checking facility for all structural members will be enabled. Now, if you add a structural member in a project, the **Warning** message box will be displayed.

Note

*The selection of the **Member Supports** check box in the **Automatic Checks** area is useful when most of the modeling tasks for a project are completed and you want to know whether further changes in the elements of the model can affect the stability of the model.*

Next, in the **Automatic Checks** area, you can select the **Analytical / Physical Model Consistency** check box to display warning message at an early stage of the structural modeling if there is any inconsistency in the structural model. This warning message informs about the structural instability of a model and it helps you introspect the design prior to submitting them for complete analysis. Warning message is displayed at the time you add structural members to a project.

However, there are certain rules that must be followed while adding elements to your project. These rules will help you to avoid instability in the structural model so that the model can be easily taken to the analytical software for analysis. The rules that are applicable for structural columns, structural walls, beams, and floors are as follows:

Tip

*It is not recommended to select the **Member Supports** check box in the early stage of structural modeling because the number of unsupported elements in the early stage of the project is more and therefore the modeling process may become time consuming.*

Structural column should have a point support at least on one of its ends. The valid support can include any of the following: another column (above or below), isolated or continuous foundations, beams, walls, or structural floors.

Structural wall should be supported by one line support or two-point supports. A valid support can be any of the following: Foundations (continuous or isolated), beams, or structural walls.

Beam should either have two-point supports one each located at the either ends or one point support located at one end with the release condition set to fixed. A valid support to the beam can include intersecting columns, foundations (continuous or isolated) adjoining beams, or walls.

A structural floor should have any of the following supports: at least two-point supports, one line support and a point support that is non-collinear, or two non-collinear line supports. Valid supports include: columns, continuous or isolated foundations, beams, or walls.

Tolerance Area

In this area, you can specify distances in the edit boxes to meet specifications for the analytical model to be consistent. In the **Support distance** edit box, you can enter a value to specify the distances between the supports. In the **Analytical-to-physical model distance** edit box, you can enter a value to specify the distance between an analytical and a physical model. In the **Analytical auto detect - Horizontal** edit box, you can enter a value to specify the distance between the analytical and physical models for horizontal elements. In the **Analytical auto detect - Vertical** edit box, you can enter a value to specify the distance between the analytical and physical models for vertical elements. In the **Analytical Link auto detect** edit box, you can enter a value to specify distance by which an automatic analytical link will be created in 3D space. These analytical links provide the rigidity to the analytical model without adding physical geometry.

Member Supports Check Area

In this area, the **Circular references** check box is selected by default. As a result, circular support conditions in members are checked and identified.

Analytical / Physical Model Consistency Check Area

In this area, all check boxes are selected by default. This enables consistency checks for various specifications related to an analytical model with a physical model.

Analytical Model Visibility

In this area, the **Differentiate ends of linear analytical models** check box remains selected by default. As a result, the color displayed on the ends of the analytical model will be different. If this check box is clear, the color will be uniform throughout for all analytical models.

Applying Loads in Analytical Model

Before you take the analytical model to another software for analysis, it is important to apply various loads to the structural model. These loads can then be classified into various load cases and combined for analysis and design.

In a structural model, you can apply point, line, and area loads. Each of these loads contains instance and type parameters that can be modified before or after placing them in the structural model. You can apply these loads either by sketching or by using host components, such as floors and beams. You can edit load force and moment parameters before or after placing them in the structural model. You can also create load cases and combinations that help you classify loads on the basis of their nature and then combine them based on the design code of practices for analysis.

In the forthcoming sections, you will learn the methods of viewing, adding, and editing load cases, combining load cases, and placing loads in a model.

Load Cases

Ribbon:	Analyze > Analytical Model > Load Cases

 Load cases are different types of loads that can be applied to a structural model. Load types can be dead, live, wind, seismic, and others, depending on the nature of the load applied to a structural model.

In Autodesk Revit, you need to apply a load case in the analytical model. To view, add, and edit load case in a structural model, choose the **Load Cases** tool from the **Analytical Model** panel of the **Analyze** tab; the **Structural Settings** dialog box chosen will be displayed with the **Load Cases** tab. In this tab, various load cases and options to add load cases and natures will be displayed, as shown in Figure 9-26.

*Figure 9-26 The options in the **Load Cases** tab of the **Structural Settings** dialog box*

There are two areas in the **Load Cases** tab: **Load Cases** and **Load Natures**. The options in these areas are discussed next.

Load Cases Area

This area displays a table that contains four columns: **Name**, **Case Number**, **Nature**, and **Category**; and eight rows, each row specifying a load case. For example, row 1 specifies a dead load case, refer to Figure 9-26. In this row, the name of the case in the value field of the **Name** column is specified as **DL1**. You can change the name by clicking in the value field and entering a text. In this table, load case number, nature of load, and load category are specified in the value field of their respective columns. You can change existing values from the value fields by entering a value or selecting them from the drop-down list, wherever required.

The value displayed in the value field of the **Case Number** column for a particular load case is unique and read-only. It represents load case with a numeric value. This value is important for tracing load case at the time of analysis.

The value displayed in the value field of the **Nature** column for a particular load case specifies the nature of the load case. To change the value displayed in the value field, click in the value field and select any of the following options displayed in the drop-down list: **Dead, Live, Wind, Snow, Roof Live, Accidental, Temperature,** and **Seismic**. You can add more options in this drop-down list by choosing the **Add** button in the **Load Cases** area of the **Load Cases** tab. This will be discussed in the next section. In the value field of the **Category** column for a particular load case, you can specify the category of the load case. To do so, click in the value field and select an option from the drop-down list displayed. The options displayed in the drop-down list are: **Accidental Loads**, **Dead Loads**, **Live Loads**, **Roof Live Loads**, **Seismic Loads**, **Snow Loads**, **Temperature Loads**, and **Wind Loads**.

In the table of the **Load Cases** area, you can add a duplicate load case. To do so, select the row corresponding to the load case for which you want to create a duplicate load case and then choose the **Duplicate** button; a copy of the selected load case will be added in a row below the selected row corresponding to a load case. To delete a load case from the table, select the row corresponding to the load case and then choose the **Delete** button; the **Delete Load Case** message box will be displayed. If you choose the **Yes** button, the load case along with its load elements will be deleted from the table as well as from the project. On choosing the **No** button, the load case and its elements will not be deleted either from the table or from the project.

Load Natures Area
This area displays a table that contains the **Name** column and eight rows. Each row displays the nature of the load that can be assigned to a load case. The following load natures are displayed in the table: **Dead**, **Live**, **Wind**, **Snow**, **Roof Live**, **Accidental**, **Temperature**, and **Seismic**. To add a load nature or a row to the table, choose the **Add** button; a row will be added below the last row in the table and it will also have a default name. You can change the name by clicking in its value field and entering a new name.

Placing Loads
In a structural model, you can place any of the three types of load: Point, Line, and Area. You can either place these loads by sketching them in the view or by associating them with a host element such as a floor or a beam.

While placing a load in a structural model, Revit uses any of the following coordinate systems for loads: Project coordinate system, current work plane, and work plane of the host element. The project coordinate system refers to the coordinate system of a project. The current work plane is the plane for placing objects. When the current work plane is used to place loads, loads are placed perpendicular to the current work plane. The host work plane is the plane in which the element hosting a load resides. In the next section, you will learn how the three types of load are placed in the structural model.

Placing Point Load
You can place a point load in a structural model by sketching or by associating it with a host element. These methods are discussed next.

Sketching a Point Load: To sketch a point load in a model, open the structural plan level - analytical view with a framing plan model. Next, choose the **Loads** tool from the **Analytical Model** panel of the **Analyze** tab; the **Modify | Place Loads** contextual will be displayed. In this tab, ensure that the **Point Load** tool is chosen. Next, select an option from the **Placement Plane** drop-down list in the Options Bar to specify the level or plane in which the load will be placed. If the level selected is different or not the current level, a **Warning** message box will be displayed immediately after placing loads, informing that the load placed will not be displayed in the current view. After selecting an option from the Options Bar, you can use the **Properties** palette to specify the instance and type parameters of the point load. In the **Properties** palette, click in the value field corresponding to the **Load Case** parameter and select an option from the drop-down list displayed; the selected option will specify the load case to which this load belongs.

Next, click in the value field corresponding to the **Orient to** parameter and select any of the following options: **Project** and **Workplane**. The selection of any of the options will determine the orientation of the coordinated system. If you select the **Project** option, the coordinate system followed for specifying loads will be oriented on the basis of the project coordinate system. Similarly, if you select the **Workplane** option from the drop-down list, the coordinate system for placing the loads will be oriented based on the coordinate system of the current work plane.

In the **Fx**, **Fy**, **Fz**, **Mx**, **My**, and **Mz** parameters, enter a suitable value in their corresponding value fields to specify the magnitude and directions of the concentrated forces and moments associated with the load definition.

After specifying the instance parameters of the point load, you can edit its type parameters. To do so, choose the **Edit Type** button; the **Type Properties** dialog box will be displayed. In this dialog box, you can use the **Force scale** and **Moment scale** parameters to change the view scale of the forces and moments displayed in the model. To change the scale of these parameters, enter the required values in their respective **Value** fields. In the **Type Properties** dialog box, you can also change the type of arrow heads used for displaying loads (forces and moments) in the model. To do so, you can use the following parameters: **Force arrowhead**, **Moment arrowhead**, and **Moment arrowhead (alternate)**. To change values for these parameters, click in their respective **Value** fields and select an option from the drop-down list displayed. After specifying the type parameters in the **Type Properties** dialog box, choose the **Apply** button and then the **OK** button to apply the changes and close the **Type Properties** dialog box.

You will notice that a circle is attached to the cursor in the plan view, as shown in Figure 9-27. This circle represents the load to be placed. Next, move the cursor and place it at the required position. To add more point loads, keep on clicking on the desired position to place them. Note that while adding point loads you can keep the same parameters or change them by using the **Properties** palette and after placing the loads, press ESC twice.

Placing Hosted Point Load: A hosted point load is a concentrated load that is associated with a beam, brace, or column. You can place the hosted point load in an analytical view (structural plan or 3D view). The physical geometry of a model does not accept the load. The hosted point loads are placed at the endpoints of beams, columns, and braces. To place the hosted point load, open an analytical view and then choose the **Loads** tool from the **Loads** panel of the **Analyze** tab. In the **Properties** palette, specify the desired parameters; you will notice that a placing symbol appears with the cursor in the drawing window. Place the cursor on one of the ends of a beam, column, or brace. Click when the desired member is highlighted; the load will be added and associated to the member.

Figure 9-27 Circle attached to the cursor in the plan view

Placing Line Load
Like point loads, you can sketch a line load or associate it with a structural member. The methods for placing the line loads are discussed next.

Sketching Line Load: To sketch a line load, open the structural plan level - analytical view with a framing plan model. Next, choose the **Loads** tool from the **Analytical Model** panel of the **Analyze** tab; the **Modify | Place Loads** contextual tab will be displayed. In this tab, choose the **Line Load** tool from the **Loads** panel. In the Options Bar, select an option from the **Placement Plane** drop-down list to specify the level of placement of the line load. In the Options Bar, select the **Chain** check box. If this check box is selected, you can add a continuous line load in the model. To add a line load with a break, clear the **Chain** check box.

Next, you can use the **Properties** palette to assign the instance and type parameters to the line load. The use of the **Load Case** and **Orient to** parameters is the same as that used for placing point loads. In the **Properties** palette, the check box displayed in the value field of the **Uniform Load** parameter is selected by default. As a result, the line load will be uniform from start to end. Notice that values for the **Fx 1**, **Mx 1**, **Fy 1**, **My 1**, **Fz 1**, and **Mz 1** parameters can be entered only when the **Uniform Load** check box is selected in the **Properties** palette. The **Fx 2**, **Mx 2**, **Fy 2**, **My 2**, **Fz 2**, and **Mz 2** parameters are disabled for entering values. These parameters will be enabled for entering values when the check box corresponding to the **Uniform Load** will be cleared. Next, you can enter two values of a line load in a particular direction. For example, if the values entered for the **Fz 1** parameter is **-15 kip/ft (-219 kN/m)** and for the **Fz 2** parameter is **-20 kip/ft (-292 kN/m)**, then the line load will start with a load of **-15 kip/ft (-219 kN/m)** and end with a load of **-20 kip/ft (-292 kN/m)**.

You can modify the type properties of the line load. To do so, choose the **Edit Type** button from the **Properties** palette; the **Type Properties** dialog box will be displayed. To change the view scale for the linear force or moment added in the structural model, you can use the **Linear force scale** parameter. To change the distance between the arrows displayed in the loads, you can use the **Distance between arrows** parameter. The usage of other parameters in the **Type Properties** dialog box is the same as that for point loads. After specifying type properties, choose the **OK** button; the **Type Properties** dialog box will be closed. Now, in the project view, move the cursor and click at a desired point to mark the start point of the line load. Move the cursor in the direction of the line load, refer to Figure 9-28; you will notice a magenta-colored line emerging from the start point. At certain points in this line, you will notice symbols of arrows. The number of arrows in this line depends on the value specified for the **Distance between arrows** parameter in the **Type Properties** dialog box. Click again to mark the endpoint of the line load. Next, you can continue adding more line loads or press ESC twice to exit the **Line** load tool.

Figure 9-28 The line load placed in a structural member

Placing Hosted Line Load: A hosted line load is a linear load that is associated with a beam, brace, or column. You can place the hosted line loads in an analytical view (structural plan or 3D view). The physical geometry of a model does not accept load. The hosted line loads are placed throughout the length of the beams, columns, or braces. To place a hosted line load, open an analytical view and choose the **Loads** tool from the **Analytical Model** panel of the **Analyze** tab. Next, choose the **Hosted Line Load** tool from the **Loads** panel. In the **Properties** palette, enter the desired parameters. In the drawing window, notice that a placing symbol appears with the cursor. Place the cursor on a beam, column, or brace. Click when the desired member is highlighted; the load will be added throughout the length of the highlighted member and will be associated to it.

Placing Area Load

You can sketch an area load or associate it with a structural member. Area loads are applied to a structural model to represent a thrust or pressure force on the members. The methods for placing area loads in a structural model are discussed next.

Sketch an Area Load: To sketch an Area load, open the structural plan level - analytical view with a framing plan model. Next, choose the **Loads** tool from the **Analytical Model** panel of the **Analyze** tab; the **Modify | Place Loads** contextual tab will be displayed. In this tab, choose the **Area Load** tool from the **Loads** panel; the **Modify | Create Area Load Boundary** contextual tab will be displayed. In this tab, you can use various sketching tools from the **Draw** panel. By default, the **Line** tool is chosen. You can use other tools depending on the requirement of the boundary. After choosing an appropriate tool from the **Draw** panel in the **Options Bar**, you can enter a suitable offset distance for the sketched boundary in the **Offset** edit box. In the **Options Bar**, the **Chain** check box is selected for the **Line** tool. As a result, you can draw a continuous chain of the boundary of the area load using the **Line** tool.

After sketching the boundary line in the **Modify | Create Area Load Boundary** contextual tab, you can use the **Reference Point** tool to create sloped area loads by specifying load values for up to 3 vertices of an area load. These vertices refer to the forces F1 (Fx 1, and Fy 1, and Fz 1), F2 (Fx 2, Fy 2, and Fz 2), and F3 (Fx 3, Fy 3, and Fz 3) parameters found in the properties of the area load in the **Properties** palette. These parameters will not be enabled until the reference points have been selected with the **Reference Point** tool. In the **Properties** palette, you can assign various instance parameters related to the load magnitudes and plane orientation. In the project view, sketch the closed boundary using the sketching tools in the **Draw** panel to represent the extent of the area load. After sketching the closed boundary, choose the **Finish Edit Mode** button from the **Mode** panel to finish the sketching of the area load. Figure 9-29 shows the area load placed in the structural model.

Placing Hosted Area Load: A hosted area load is a pressure load that is associated with a structural floor or a structural wall. You can place an area load in a structural floor or a structural wall. You can place hosted area loads in an analytical view (structural plan or 3D view). The physical geometry of the model does not accept the load. To place an area load, open an analytical view suitable for placing loads and then choose the **Loads** tool from the **Analytical Model** panel; the **Modify | Place Loads** contextual tab will be displayed. In this tab, invoke the **Hosted Area Load** tool from the **Loads** panel. Next, in the **Properties** palette, you can specify the orientation plane, magnitude and direction of forces, and load case. In the **Properties** palette, you can choose the **Edit Type** button to invoke the **Type Properties** dialog box. In this dialog box, you can specify the type parameter for the area load such as the **Area force scale**, **Force arrowhead**, and **Distance between arrows** in their respective **Value** fields. Now, choose the **OK** button; the **Type Properties** dialog box will close. Now, place the cursor at any of the edges of the structural floor or wall and then click when the edge gets highlighted. On doing so, the area load will be added around the perimeter of the structural floor or wall. Figure 9-30 displays a hosted area load placed in a structural floor.

Figure 9-29 *The area load placed in the structural model*

Figure 9-30 *The hosted area load placed in a structural floor*

Note
In Revit 2021, the area hosted load can be placed on the curve walls as well.

Setting Boundary Conditions

Ribbon:	Analyze > Boundary Conditions > Boundary Conditions

 In an analytical model, boundary conditions are model elements that define the support conditions of a structural element (beams, columns, or floors). These elements are used to add the assumed support conditions to structural elements so that they can be communicated easily to the analysis software to which a model will be exported for analysis.

To specify a boundary condition for a structural model, open an analytical structural plan view and then choose the **Boundary Conditions** tool from the **Analytical Model** panel of the **Analyze** tab; the **Modify | Place Boundary Conditions** contextual tab will be displayed, as shown in Figure 9-31. The **Boundary Conditions** panel of this tab is used to add different types of boundary conditions. Various tools for setting the boundary conditions are discussed next.

*Figure 9-31 Various options in the **Modify / Place Boundary Condition**s tab*

Area Tool

Ribbon: Modify | Place Boundary Conditions > Boundary Conditions > Area

The **Area** tool is used to add boundary conditions along the perimeter of a structural floor, a foundation slab, or a structural wall. You can invoke the **Area** tool from the **Boundary Conditions** panel. After invoking the **Area** tool, you can select an option from the **State** drop-down list in the Options Bar to specify support conditions. The options available in the **State** drop-down list are **Pinned** and **User**. By default, the **Pinned** option is selected in the **State** drop-down list. As a result, when you add the area boundary condition to a structural floor, slab or wall, a pinned support condition is created throughout the perimeter of the structural floor, slab, or wall. You can select the **User** option from the **State** drop-down list, if you want to add a specific boundary condition that is specific to a site. On selecting the **User** option, the following parameters will become active in the **Properties** palette: **X Translation**, **Y Translation**, and **Z Translation**. You can click in the value field of any of these parameters and select any of the following options from the drop-down list displayed: **Fixed**, **Release**, or **Spring**. The option that you select from the drop-down list will specify the support conditions of the structural element in their respective axes. For example, if the **Spring** option has been selected for the **X Translation** parameter, it means that the support in the element along its X axis will be a Spring support. After selecting a state of the support from the Options Bar and specifying various options in the **Properties** palette (if required), click on any of the edges of the floor, slab, or wall; the area boundary condition will be applied throughout the perimeter of the selected structural element, as shown in Figure 9-32.

Figure 9-32 The area boundary condition applied to a structural floor

Point Tool

Ribbon:	Modify | Place Boundary Conditions > Boundary Conditions > Point

You can use the **Point** tool from the **Boundary Conditions** panel to create boundary condition at the end of a beam, column, or brace. To use the **Point** tool, invoke it from the **Boundary Conditions** panel and then select an option from the **State** drop-down list in the Options Bar. The options available in the **State** drop-down list are **Pinned**, **Fixed**, **Roller**, and **User**. By default, the **Fixed** option is selected in the **State** drop-down list. As a result, when you add boundary condition to the end of a beam, column, or brace, a fixed support condition is created at that end. You can select any of the remaining options from the **State** drop-down list based on your design requirement. On selecting the **User** option from the **State** drop-down list in the Options Bar, the following parameters in the **Properties** palette will become active: **X Translation**, **Y Translation**, **Z Translation**, **X Rotation**, **Y Rotation**, and **Z Rotation**. You can click in the value field of any of these parameters and select any of the following options from the drop-down list displayed: **Fixed**, **Release**, or **Spring**. The option that you select will specify the support conditions of the structural element in their respective axes. For example, if the **Release** option is selected for the **X Rotation** parameter, it means that the support at the end of the element for its rotational movement along the X axis will be released. After selecting a state of the support from the Options Bar, and specifying various options in the **Properties** palette (if required), click on any of the endpoints of a beam, column, or brace; the area boundary condition will be applied at that point of the structural element.

Line Tool

Ribbon:	Modify | Place Boundary Conditions > Boundary Conditions > Line

You can use the **Line** tool from the **Boundary Conditions** panel to create a linear boundary throughout the length of a beam, a column, an edge of a slab, an edge of a wall, or an edge of a floor. To use the **Line** tool, invoke it from the **Boundary Conditions** panel and then select an option from the **State** drop-down list in the Options Bar. The options available in the **State** drop-down list are **Pinned**, **Fixed**, and **User**. By default, the **Fixed** option is selected in the **State** drop-down list. As a result, when you add the boundary condition to the end of a beam, column, or brace, a fixed support condition will be created at that end. You can select any of the remaining options from the **State** drop-down list based on your design requirement. On selecting the **User** option from the **State** drop-down list in the Options Bar, the following parameters in the **Properties** palette will become active: **X Translation**, **Y Translation**, **Z Translation**, and **X Rotation**. The option that you select will be the support conditions of the structural element in their respective axes.

After selecting a state of the support from the Options Bar and specifying various options in the **Properties** palette (if required), click on a beam, column, brace, edge of a wall, edge of a floor, or edge of a wall; the line boundary condition will be applied to the entire length of the selected element or at the edge of the element (wall, slab, or floor).

After specifying the boundary condition, you can set the family symbol for various support conditions and adjust the spacing for each boundary condition representation. Note that you can also apply these settings before adding the boundary conditions to the elements in the project. To set a family symbol and adjust spacing for each boundary condition representation, click on the arrow on the right of the **Boundary Conditions** in the **Analyze** tab, as shown in Figure 9-33. On doing so, the **Structural Settings** dialog box with the options in the **Boundary Conditions Settings** tab will be displayed, as shown in Figure 9-34. In the **Family Symbol** area of this tab, you can specify different family symbols for different states of support. These family symbols are pre-loaded in structural templates and can also be duplicated and edited to meet the display standards or requirements.

Figure 9-33 *Choosing the **Boundary Condition Settings** tool from the **Boundary Conditions** panel*

Figure 9-34 *The options in the **Boundary Conditions Settings** tab of the **Structural Settings** dialog box*

In the **Family Symbol** area, you can select any of the four drop-down lists, **Fixed**, **Pinned**, **Roller**, and **User Defined** to specify the symbol of the type of support assigned in the boundary condition. The options that you can select for the four drop-down lists are: **Boundary Condition-Fixed**, **Boundary Condition-Pinned**, **Boundary Condition-Roller**, and **Boundary Condition-Variable**. In the **Family Symbol** area, you can enter a distance in the **Area and Line Symbol Spacing** edit box to specify the distance between the symbols that are used for area or line boundary condition. After specifying various options in the **Boundary Conditions** tab, choose the **OK** button; the **Structural Settings** dialog box will close and the settings will be applied to the boundary condition in the structural model.

Analytical Model Tools

The Analytical Model tools are used to refine an analytical model before you export it to another software for analysis and design purpose. The refinement of a structural model includes doing analytical adjustment between members, checking for the consistency of an analytical model, resetting the analytical model to its previous state, and checking the support conditions of the model. Various tools involved in this refinement are available in the **Analytical Model Tools** panel of the **Analyze** tab. The tools available for refinement are **Adjust**, **Reset**, **Supports**, and **Consistency**. These tools are discussed next.

Adjust Tool

Ribbon:	Analyze > Analytical Model Tools > Adjust

 The **Adjust** tool is used to adjust the alignment of an analytical model with reference to the elements it is joined to. The application of this tool has been explained through an example given next. Figure 9-35 shows a 3D view of a structural model.

In this model, you will use the **Adjust** tool to align the analytical model of the beam with that of the structural wall. To do so, choose the **Adjust** tool from the **Analytical Model Tools** panel; the physical model of the structural elements in the project view will be grayed out and various node points of the analytical model will be displayed, as shown in Figure 9-36.

Figure 9-35 *The structural model showing various structural elements*

Figure 9-36 *Various node points in the analytical model*

Also, as you invoke the **Adjust** tool, the **Edit Analytical Model** panel will be displayed as a floating panel in the project view, as shown in Figure 9-37.

Figure 9-37 *The options in the **Edit Analytical Model** panel*

The analytical node points in the analytical model can be directly manipulated at both the ends. As you click on a node, a 3D control to move the node point in the local coordinate system will be displayed. In this example, you need to align the analytical model of the beam with that of the wall. To do so, click on the node point located at the left end of the beam; the node point will get highlighted and a 3D control will be displayed on it, as shown in Figure 9-38. Now, click and hold the left mouse button on the highlighted node and drag the highlighted node to the left node of the structural wall; the left node of the beam will get joined with the left node of the structural wall, as shown in Figure 9-39. Next, to align the right end of the beam with the right end of the structural wall, same procedure can be followed. After both ends are aligned, the structural model will appear, as shown in Figure 9-40. Now, in the **Edit Analytical Model** panel, choose the **Finish** button to finish the editing of the analytical model.

Figure 9-38 *The highlighted node point of the beam*   *Figure 9-39* *Node of the beam joined with the node of the wall*

Figure 9-40 *The analytical model of the beam aligned with the analytical model of the structural wall*

 Note
*From the **Edit Analytical Model** panel, you can choose the **Wall Adjustments** tool to adjust the analytical wall element in relation to other analytical wall models present in the project.*

Reset Tool

Ribbon:	Analyze > Analytical Model Tools > Reset

 After adjusting the members of an analytical model, you can bring the structural member analytical model back to its previous state. To do so, choose the **Reset** tool from the **Analytical Model Tools** panel and then select the analytical model member that was selected while using the **Adjust** tool; the selected analytical model member will regain its previous state.

Supports Tool

Ribbon:	Analyze > Analytical Model Tools > Supports

This tool is used to check the support stability of an analytical model before it is exported to another software for analysis. To check the support stability, choose the **Supports** tool from the **Analytical Model Tools** panel of the **Analyze** tab; a **Warning** message box informing you about the stability of the supports in the model will be displayed, as shown in Figure 9-41. You can review the warning message by choosing the **Expanding warning dialog** button displayed on the right of the **Warning** message box. On doing so, the **Autodesk Revit 2021** window will open, as shown in Figure 9-42. You can use this window to review the warning displayed in the **Warning** message box.

*Figure 9-41 The **Warning** message box*

*Figure 9-42 The **Autodesk Revit 2021** window*

Consistency Checks Tool

Ribbon:	Analyze > Analytical Model Tools > Consistency

This tool is used to verify the consistency of the analytical and physical models of a project. To check the consistency of an analytical or physical models, choose the **Consistency** tool from the **Analytical Model Tools** panel of the **Analyze** tab; the **Warning** message box will be displayed. This message box will inform you about any possible inconsistency in the model. You can review the warning message by using the **Autodesk**

Revit 2021 window which can be invoked by choosing the **Expanding warning dialog** button displayed on the right in the **Warning** message box.

 Note
*The options in the **Analytical Model Settings** tab of the **Structural Settings** dialog box can be used to set the criterion for consistency check. These options have already been discussed under the **Settings for the Analytical Model** section in this chapter.*

ADDING REINFORCEMENTS

Reinforcements are added to concrete structural members based on the design requirement. In Revit, you can add reinforcements to concrete structural members such as floors, beams, columns, and slabs by using various tools. These tools are discussed next.

Place Rebar Parallel to Work Plane Tool

For a concrete column, beam, structural floor, or foundation, you can place rebars parallel to the current work plane. To do so, select a concrete structural member in the current workplane and then choose the **Rebar** tool from the **Reinforcement** panel of the **Structure** tab; the **Revit** message box will be displayed with the information that the hooks will be included in the Rebar Shape definitions. Now, choose the **OK** button; the **Modify | Place Rebar** contextual tab with the **Rebar Shape Browser** will be displayed. In the **Placement Orientation** panel of this tab, choose the **Parallel to Work Plane** tool; the Options Bar displaying various options to place the rebars will be displayed. In the Options Bar, you can select a rebar shape from the **Select Rebar Shape type** drop-down list. Alternatively, you can select the rebar shape from the **Rebar Shape Browser** displayed in the drawing area. In case the **Rebar Shape Browser** is not displayed by default, you can choose the **Launch/Close Rebar Shape Browser** button in the Options Bar. In the **Placement Plane** panel, you can select an option to specify the workplane used for placing rebars. After selecting the shape of the rebar and specifying the placement plane, you can modify the instance parameters of the rebars from the **Properties** palette. Some of the instance parameters that you can specify are described in the table given next.

Instance Parameter	Description
Schedule Mark	Specifies a mark in the rebars, which will help in identifying them while scheduling.
Style	It is a read-only parameter. This parameter is used to specify the style for controlling the bend radius of the rebars.
Shape	Specifies a number for the rebar shape.
Hook at Start	Specifies the type of rebar hook at the start of the rebar of the selected style. Click in its value field and select a type from the drop-down list displayed.
Hook at End	Specifies the type of rebar hook at the end of the rebar of the selected style. Click in its value field and select a type from the drop-down list displayed.

Reinforcement Volume	It is a read-only parameter and displays the calculated estimate for the reinforcement volume.
Bar Length	It is a read-only parameter and displays the length of individual rebar.
Spacing	This parameter is displayed only after you place the rebars to the hosted elements. This parameter will be active if the **Layout Rule** parameter is set to **Maximum Spacing** layout rule. This parameter specifies the spacing for the rebar placed in the major direction of the hosted element.
Layout Rule	This parameter is displayed only after you place the rebars to the hosted elements. It specifies the type of rebar layout. You can click in its value field and select any of the options: **Maximum Spacing**, **Fixed Number**, **Single**, **Number with Spacing**, and **Minimum Clear Space**.
Quantity	This parameter is displayed only after you place the rebars to hosted elements. It specifies the number of rebar instances placed. It is only active if the **Layout Rule** parameter is set to **Fixed Number**.
A, B, C,... (default)	Specifies the variable length of a rebar shape. The quantities of these parameters are defined by the content of the shape.

After specifying the instance parameters of the rebars from the **Properties** palette, you can modify their type properties. To do so, choose the **Edit Type** button from the **Properties** palette; the **Type Properties** dialog box will be displayed. Some of the type parameters in the **Type Properties** dialog box are described in the table next.

Type Parameter	Description
Material	Specifies the material assigned to rebars.
Bar Diameter	Specifies the diameter of non-hook bends for a selected type of bar. The change in this parameter does not affect the shape of the rebar.
Stirrup/Tie Bend Diameter	Specifies the diameter of the bend rebar. This bend can be either a standard bend or a stirrup/tie bend.

Hook Lengths	Specifies hook length based on a specific type of rebar. Choose the **Edit** button in its value field to display the **Rebar Hook Lengths** dialog box. You can use this dialog box to specify hook lengths for different hook types.

After specifying the type properties of the rebars from the **Type Properties** dialog box, place the cursor inside the placement area of the selected member; a preview of the selected rebar along with a dotted line representing the cover distance will be displayed, refer to Figure 9-43. Next, click when the preview is displayed; rebars will be placed parallel to the current work plane. Figure 9-44 shows the rebars of the **Rebar Shape : T6** type placed in a concrete rectangular beam by using the **Fixed Number** layout rule.

Figure 9-43 *The rebar added to a beam cross-section*

Figure 9-44 *The 3D view of a structural model displaying the added rebars*

Place Rebar Perpendicular to Cover Tool

You can place rebars that are perpendicular to the nearest cover reference in a member. To do so, open the desired view of the member. Next, select it and then choose the **Rebar** tool from the **Reinforcement** panel of the contextual tab; the **Modify | Place Rebar** contextual tab will be displayed. In this tab, choose the **Perpendicular to Cover** tool from the **Placement Orientation** panel and then select a rebar shape from the **Select Rebar Shape type** drop-down list. Now, place the cursor near the edge of the member; the dashed lines will be displayed at an offset from the edges of the member. These dashed lines represent the cover of the member. Also, as you move the cursor, the preview of the rebar will be displayed. Click to add the rebar.

Cover Tool

The **Cover** tool is used to edit the cover settings in the entire length of the host of a rebar. The host of a rebar can be a beam, column, slab, or floor. The cover settings define the offset distance of the bars from the faces of the rebar host. To edit the cover settings, invoke the **Cover** tool from the **Reinforcement** panel of the **Structure** tab; the Options Bar displays two tools: **Pick**

Elements and **Pick Faces**. You can choose the **Pick Elements** tool to specify the cover distance for the entire length of the host element. Alternatively, you can choose the **Pick Faces** tool to specify the cover distance for the desired face of the host element. After choosing any of the tools and selecting an element or the face of an element, you can select an option from the **Cover Settings** drop-down list to specify the cover distance of the selected element or face. On selecting an option from the **Cover Settings** drop-down list, the cover distance for the placed rebars changes.

Area Tool

Ribbon:	Structure > Reinforcement > Area

You can use the **Area** tool to place reinforcement in the entire area of a floor or a slab. To add area reinforcement to a floor or a slab, invoke the **Area** tool from the **Reinforcement** panel of the **Structure** tab; you will be prompted to select a structural floor or a structural wall. Click on the desired structural wall or structural floor; the **Modify | Create Reinforcement Boundary** contextual tab will be displayed. In the **Draw** panel of this tab, ensure that the **Rebar Line** tool is chosen, and then choose any of the sketching tools from the list box. After choosing a sketching tool, sketch the boundary of the reinforcement area, wherever required. Next, you can choose the **Major Direction** tool from the **Draw** panel of the **Modify | Create Reinforcement Boundary** contextual tab and define the major direction of the area reinforcement either by sketching a line in the required area or by picking a line from the drawing area. Now, in the **Properties** palette, you can specify various instance parameters for the area reinforcement. Various instance parameters of the area reinforcement that can be specified are the layout rule, diameter of the major and minor rebars to be placed in the top and bottom of the slab or wall, hook type for major and minor directions, hook orientations, and others. You can also specify the type parameters of the area reinforcement. After specifying various instance parameters, choose the **Finish Edit Mode** button in the **Mode** panel, the area reinforcement will be added in the sketched area. Figure 9-45 shows the area reinforcement added to a structural floor. Figure 9-46 shows a section view displaying the distribution of rebars in an area reinforcement.

Figure 9-45 *The area reinforcement added to a structural floor*

Figure 9-46 *Section view showing the placement of the rebars in a structural floor*

Path Tool

Ribbon:　　　Structure > Reinforcement > Path

You can use the **Path** tool to sketch lines in a slab or wall. These lines indicate the path of evenly reinforcing bars that are created perpendicular to the sketch lines. To create this path, choose the **Path** tool from the **Reinforcement** panel of the **Structure** tab and then select a wall or floor from the drawing; the **Modify | Create Reinforcement Path** contextual tab will be displayed. You can use the options in this tab to draw the sketch of the reinforcement path.

FREE FORM REBAR

Ribbon:　　　Structure > Reinforcement > Rebar > Free Form Rebar

The **Free Form Rebar** tool increases the versatility of 3-D rebar detailing and modeling. This tool helps in defining the accurate reinforcement for irregular shapes of concrete structures having complex geometry such as curved beams, curved piers, and so on. This tool models rebars in 3-D views and aligns rebars according to the shape of the element.

Using the **Free Form Rebar** tool, you can create a single rebar or a set of rebars with specified spacing between them. To create reinforcement in a curved beam, select and isolate the beam in the **Default 3-D** view; the **Modify|Structural Framing** contextual tab will appear. Now, choose the **Rebar** tool from the **Reinforcement** panel and then, choose the **Free Form Rebar** tool from the **Placement Methods** panel of the **Modify|Place Free Form Rebar** contextual tab. To create closed rebars such as stirrups in the beam, choose the **Aligned** tool from the **Distribution Type** panel; the cursor changes into a selection cursor with a message **Select a Host Surface**. Select all four faces of the beam as host surfaces, as shown in Figure 9-47. Next, choose the **Path** tool for the direction of stirrups and click on the edge of the top face of the beam, as shown in Figure 9-48. Click on the **Finish** mode; a stirrup will be created in the middle of the beam.

Figure 9-47 *All four faces of the beam selected as the host surfaces*

Figure 9-48 *Selecting edge of the top face of the beam*

To apply hooks, select the stirrup and choose the **Bend** option from the drop-downs corresponding to the **Workshop Instructions** option of the **Properties** palette. Similarly, choose the **Stirrup/Tie** option and the **Stirrup/Tie 135** option from the drop-down corresponding to the **Style** and **Hook At Start** options, respectively, as shown in Figure 9-49. Similarily, choose the **Stirrup/Tie 135** option from the drop-down corresponding to the **Hook At End** option; hooks are created in the stirrup. For providing spacing in the stirrups, click on the drop-down corresponding to the **Layout** option from the **Rebar Set** panel of the **Modify|Structural Rebar** contextual tab and choose the desired method. Press the **Esc** button; stirrup set with desired spacing is created, as shown in Figure 9-50.

To create main bars, select the beam and then select the **Rebar** option from the **Reinforcement** panel of the **Modify|Structural Framing** contextual tab. Next, choose the **Surface** tool from the **Distribution Type** panel of the **Modify|Place Free Form Rebar** contextual tab; the cursor changes into a selection cursor with a message **Select a Host Surface**. Select the top surface of the beam as the host surface, choose the **Start Surface** option from the **Next** panel, and select the start surface of the beam, as shown in Figure 9-51.

Figure 9-49 *Options for applying hooks in the **Properties** palette of stirrup*

Figure 9-50 *Stirrup set with desired spacing in the beam*

Similarily, choose the **End Surface** option from the **Next** panel and select the end surface of the beam, as shown in Figure 9-52. Click on **Finish** in the **Mode** panel of the **Modify|Place Form Rebar** contextual tab; top main bar will be created. Select the created rebar and choose the desired method to provide spacing from the **Layout** drop-down of the **Rebar Set** panel of the **Modify|Structural Rebar** contextual tab and press the **ESC** button. Repeat the same procedure to apply main bars and provide spacing in the bottom face of the beam by selecting the bottom face as the host surface and press the **ESC** button.

Figure 9-51 Start Surface of beam for main bar

Figure 9-52 End Surface of beam for main bar

Fabric Area Tool

Ribbon: Structure > Reinforcement > Fabric Area

Fabric Area

You can use the **Fabric Area** tool to place fabric sheet in the entire area of floor, walls, and foundation slab. To add fabric area reinforcement, invoke the **Fabric Area** tool from the **Reinforcement** panel of the **Structure** tab; you will be prompted to select a structural floor or a structural wall. Click on the desired structural wall or structural floor; the **Modify | Create Fabric Boundary** tab will be displayed. In the **Draw** panel of this tab, ensure that the **Boundary Line** tool is chosen, and then choose any of the sketching tools from the list box. After choosing a sketching tool, sketch the boundary of the area wherever required. Next, you can choose the **Major Direction** tool from the **Draw** panel of the **Modify | Create Fabric Boundary** contextual tab and define the major direction of the fabric area either by sketching a line in the required area or by picking a line from the drawing area. Now, in the Properties palette, you can specify various instance parameters such as Location, Lap Splice Position, Major Lap Splice Length, and Additional Cover Offset for the fabric area reinforcement. You can also specify the type of fabric sheet reinforcement in the defined area by choosing an option from the drop-down list corresponding to **Fabric Sheet** under the **Construction** area in the **Properties** palette. After specifying various instance parameters, choose the **Finish Edit Mode** button in the **Mode** panel; the fabric area reinforcement will be added in the sketched area.

Fabric Sheet Tool

Ribbon: Structure > Reinforcement > Fabric Sheet

Fabric Sheet

You can use the **Fabric Sheet** tool to place fabric sheet in the floor, walls, and foundation slab. To add fabric sheet reinforcement, invoke the **Fabric Sheet** tool from the **Reinforcement** panel; the **Modify | Place Fabric Sheet** contextual tab will be displayed and you will be prompted to place a fabric sheet in the structural floor or a structural wall. Click on the desired place in the structural wall or structural floor to place the fabric sheet. To switch the position of the fabric sheet, press the space bar on your key board before placing the fabric sheet. Now, in the **Properties** palette, you can specify various instance parameters such as **Location**, **Additional Cover Offset**, and **Cut by Host Cover** for fabric sheet reinforcement. You can also the type of fabric sheet reinforcement by selecting an option from the **Fabric Sheet** drop-down list in the **Properties** palette. After specifying various instance parameters, choose the **Modify** tool in the **Select** panel to finish the command.

Rebar Coupler Tool

| Ribbon: | Structure > Reinforcement > Rebar Coupler |

Rebar Coupler

You can use the **Rebar Coupler** tool to place coupler between two reinforcement bars or at the end of the bar. To add a coupler between reinforcement bars, invoke the **Place between Two Bars** tool from the **Placement Option** panel of the **Modify | Insert Rebar Coupler** contextual tab; you will be prompted to select the rebars to place the coupler. Before selecting rebars, select appropriate size of coupler from the **Coupler** drop-down list in the **Properties** palette. In the **Properties** palette, you can specify various instance parameters for the coupler, such as, the **Partition**, **Schedule Mark**, and so on. After specifying the instance parameters for the coupler, you can edit its type parameters. To do so, choose the **Edit Type** button; the **Type Properties** dialog box will be displayed. In this dialog box, you can specify different parameters, such as, **Bar Size 1**, **Bar Size 2**, **Material**, **External Diameter**, and so on. After selecting appropriate size of coupler, select the bars; the coupler as per the size and other parameters specified will be added between the bars, refer to Figure 9-53. To place the coupler at the end of the bar, invoke the **Place on Bar End** tool from the **Placement Option** panel of the **Modify | Insert Rebar Coupler** contextual tab; you will be prompted to select the rebar to place the coupler. After selecting appropriate size of the coupler, select the end of the bar; the coupler will be placed at the end of bar, refer to Figure 9-54

Figure 9-53 *Coupler between bars*

Figure 9-54 *Coupler at the end of bars*

Note
If the size of the coupler does not match the size of the bars, a warning message will be displayed. You can add couplers only at the same axis of the bars.

LINKING BUILDING MODELS AND SHARING COORDINATES

Large projects may require to develop independent building models and later combine these models into a comprehensive project. For example, in a large educational campus project, you need to independently develop the building models of the administrative building, academic complex, faculty residences, student accommodation, and so on, and later add them into a single host project file. You can do so by using the linking and sharing coordinate tools of Autodesk Revit that enable you to link models and share their coordinates within a single host project file. These tools also enable you to work on building models in other project files. When you link projects, you need to share the coordinates of the host model with the linked model so that the linked files retain their positions. To do so, invoke the **Acquire Coordinates** tool from **Manage > Project Location > Coordinates** drop-down and then select the linked project in your drawing; the origin of the shared coordinates for the linked project becomes the origin for the shared coordinates of the host project. Revit provides flexibility and easy management of the linked models by enhancing the linking of the models and organizing the linked files in the **Project Browser**. You can easily access the linked files, the nested link files, and the Link Manager from the **Project Browser**. The nested Revit links are also listed under the **Revit Links** head with the host link in the **Project Browser**.

Linking or Importing Models

To link or import one project to the other, open the host project file and choose the **Insert** tab; various options in this tab will be displayed, as shown in Figure 9-55. You can choose the options in the **Import** or **Link** panel of the **Insert** tab, depending upon the file format to be imported or linked. Before you import or link a file, make sure that the file contains the data and geometry that is compatible with Revit. To link *.dwg, .dwf, .skp, .dgn,* and other files, choose the **Import CAD** tool from the **Import** panel of the **Insert** tab; the **Import CAD Formats** dialog box will be displayed, as shown in Figure 9-56. In this dialog box, select the file type from the **Files of type** drop-down list. Next, browse to the required location and select the file.

*Figure 9-55 Various options in the **Insert** tab*

*Figure 9-56 The **Import CAD Formats** dialog box*

Linking or Importing CAD Files

In Revit, you can link or import the CAD files to the current project. If a CAD file is linked to a project, all changes made in it will simultaneously be updated in the project. However, if you import a file in a project, it will remain unchanged, irrespective of the changes made in the file imported to the project.

To link a CAD file to a project, choose the **Link CAD** tool from the **Link** panel of the **Insert** tab of the ribbon; the **Link CAD Formats** dialog box will be displayed. Select the desired CAD file and then choose **Open**; the selected CAD file will be displayed and linked to the Revit project file. Similarly, you can import a CAD file to a project. To do so, choose the **Import CAD** tool from the **Import** panel of the **Insert** tab; the **Import CAD Formats** dialog box will be displayed. Select the desired CAD file and choose **Open**; the selected file will be imported to the Revit file.

While importing or linking a CAD file to your project, you can control its availability either in all views or only in the current view. If you select the **Current view only** check box in the **Import CAD Formats** or **Link CAD Formats** dialog box, you can import or link the drawing in the CAD format only in the active view of the project in Revit. However, if you clear this check box, you can import the drawing in the CAD format in all views of Revit. In this case, the lines and geometries of the drawing will be imported without the text.

The **Layers/Levels** drop-down list in the **Import CAD Formats** or **Link CAD Formats** dialog box allows you to specify the layers to be imported from the linked file. On selecting **All** from the **Layers/Levels** drop-down list, all layers will be imported or linked. The **Visible** options in this list allow you to import or link the visible layers in the view. The **Specify** option allows you to import the specified layers and levels in the project.

Linking or Importing PDF Files

In Revit 2021, you can also link or import PDF files to current project. If a PDF file is linked to a project, all changes made in it will simultaneously be updated in the project. However, if you import a file in a project, the project will remain unchanged irrespective of the changes made in the file imported to the project.

To link a PDF file to a project, choose the **Link PDF** tool from the **Link** panel of the **Insert** tab of the ribbon; the **Link CAD Formats** dialog box will be displayed. Select the desired PDF file and then choose **Open**; the selected PDF file will be displayed in the **Import PDF** dialog box. You can choose the desired resolution of the PDF file by clicking on the drop-down located on the right of **Resolution** option. To import a PDF file, choose the **Import PDF** tool from the **Import** panel of the **Insert** tab; the **Import PDF** dialog box will be displayed. Select the desired PDF file and choose **Open**; the selected file will be imported to the Revit file.

INTRODUCTION TO MASSING

In the earlier chapters, you learned how to use different building elements and components to create a building model. These building elements are parametrically associated and enable you to generate a building model based on specific design requirements such as wall types, door width, window height, and so on. Each of the elements must be assigned specific properties to achieve the desired element parameters, thereby making a building model accurate. Needless to say, this is a fairly time-consuming procedure. Autodesk Revit provides you with an alternative and much easier method to create a building model, known as massing.

UNDERSTANDING MASSING CONCEPTS

At the conceptualization stage of a project, you may want to study it in terms of its building volumes and shapes. You may also want to convey the basic idea of the structure of a building in a three-dimensional form without putting in a lot of detailing. This can be achieved by using various tools for creating massing geometries.

The tools for creating massing geometry not only enable you to conceive and create a variety of building shapes and volumes with relative ease but also conveys the potential design in terms of building masses and geometric shapes. You can create and edit geometric shapes and amalgamate them to form a building structure. This process can be compared to the creation of building a model using foam blocks. You have the freedom of choice to add or cut geometric shapes and join different blocks or masses to form an assembly. Figure 9-57 shows a group of volumes that can be created to represent the building volume and mass.

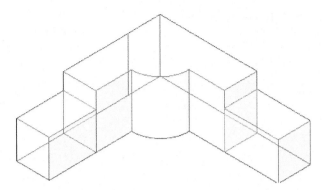

Figure 9-57 Building blocks created using the massing geometry

Autodesk Revit also enables you to convert the building mass into building elements. Building blocks can be transformed into an assembly of individual building elements such as walls, roof, and floor. The transformation, carried out by using the tools provided for replacing massing faces with predefined wall, roof, and floor types, allows you to convert the same building mass into a building model. You can then develop it into a detailed building model by incorporating individual building elements with specified parameters.

Autodesk Revit provides a much-needed continuity in the design development of a building project by using the same building model from its conceptualization to completion. It also enables you to control the visibility of geometry between the building volumes (massing) and building elements (shell) during the initial stages of project development. Other project information such as its total area can also be extracted from the building massing.

It is, however, important to understand the limitations of the massing tool. This tool is only meant for conceptual design development using simple geometric shapes. You can place the predefined massing family elements provided in additional libraries. Autodesk Revit attempts to translate the massing geometry into building elements or shell. So, it is recommended not to use massing geometry for the development of a detailed geometry such as columns, cavity walls, footing, and so on.

CREATING THE MASSING GEOMETRY

In Autodesk Revit, you can create the massing geometry in any of these three environments: Family Editor, Conceptual Design, and Project.

To create the massing geometry in the Family Editor environment, choose **New > Family** from **File** menu; the **New Family - Select Template File** dialog box will be displayed. In this dialog box, choose the *Generic Model.rft* file (commonly used) from the **English_I** folder for Imperial or choose the *Metric Generic Model Adaptive.rft* file from the **English** folder and then choose the **Open** button; a new file will open in the Family Editor environment. In this new file, you can create the massing geometry using various tools available in the ribbon.

The Conceptual Design environment is a new environment in Revit. This environment is a type of Family Editor that provides the advanced modeling tools and techniques for creating massing families. To start creating a mass in this environment, choose **New > Conceptual Mass** from **File** menu; the **New Conceptual Mass - Select Template File** dialog box will be displayed. In this dialog box, select the **Mass** template file from the **Conceptual Mass** folder and then choose **Open**; a new file will open in the Conceptual Design environment. In the new file, you can create the massing geometry using various tools available in the ribbon, as shown in Figure 9-58.

Figure 9-58 Different tools in the ribbon of the conceptual design environment

The Project environment is the most common environment used in a project design. To start creating a mass in this environment, open a new file or an existing file by choosing **New > Project** or **Open > Project** from **File** menu. After opening a new file or an existing file, choose the **Massing & Site** tab. In this tab, the massing tools can be accessed from the **Conceptual Mass** panel. The **Conceptual Mass** panel contains the following tools for massing: **In-Place Mass**, **Show Mass**, and **Place Mass**.

The options in the **Model by Face** panel are used to convert the conceptual mass created into real building elements like walls, floors, roofs, and curtain systems. As such, these tools are also called the Building Maker tools.

When you create shapes in massing, Autodesk Revit creates its corresponding building elements. It is, therefore, imperative to consider the associativity of the massing and shell elements. The massing elements may need to be transformed into individual building elements simultaneously. Therefore, the massing geometry must be created accordingly.
For example, when you create a complex geometric massing shape and convert faces into building elements, you may find that some planes do not acquire the desired building element characteristics. The inclined planes and the curved surfaces are converted into in-place roofs.

To create massing geometry in different environments (**Family Editor**, **Conceptual Design** and **Project**), choose the **Extrusion**, **Blend**, **Revolve**, **Sweep**, or **Swept Blend** tool from the **Forms** panel of the **Create** tab. Similarly, to create a void form, choose the **Void Extrusion**, **Void Blend**, **Void Revolve**, **Void Sweep**, or **Void Swept Blend** tool from the **Void Forms** drop-down in the **Forms** panel.

Tip
In Autodesk Revit, the massing tools enable you to create a variety of shapes and volumes. You can use a combination of these tools on the basis of geometry to be created. The massing geometry thus created can be used to generate the rendered views of conceptual building volumes. The massing tools are very effective in communicating the design intent to the project team before actually implementing the detailed project plans.

TUTORIALS

Tutorial 1   Commercial Complex

In this tutorial, you will create a camera view in the **Entry** structural plan view of the *Commercial Complex* project for Imperial or *M_Commercial Complex* project for Metric created in Tutorial 1 of Chapter 8. Also, you will generate shadows, create a sheet, and add hosted area loads to the structural elements in the project.   **(Expected time: 45 min)**

The following steps are required to complete this tutorial:

a.   Open the existing project file.

               For Imperial   *c08_Commercial-Complex_tut1.rvt*
               For Metric   *M_c08_Commercial-Complex_tut1.rvt*

b.   Create a camera view.
c.   Generate shadows.
d.   Create a sheet and add project view to it.
e.   Add hosted area loads.
f.   Save the project by using the **Save As** tool.
g.   Close the project by using the **Close** tool.

Opening the Existing Project

In this section, you will open the project file created in Tutorial 1 of Chapter 8.

1.   Choose **Open > Project** from the **File** menu; the **Open** dialog box is displayed.

2.   In this dialog box, browse to *C:\rst_2021\c08_rst_2021_tut* location and choose the project file *c08_Commercial-Complex_tut1.rvt* for Imperial or *M_c08_Commercial-Complex_tut1.rvt* for Metric. You can also download this file from *https://www.cadcim.com*. The path of the file is as follows: *Textbooks > Civil/GIS > Revit Structure > Exploring Autodesk Revit 2021 for Structure*.

3.   Choose the **Open** button from the **Open** dialog box; the selected project file with a schedule opens in the drawing window.

Creating a Camera View

In this section, you will create a camera view for the *Commercial Complex* project. The camera view will be created at a height of **5'6"** for Imperial or **1676** mm for Metric from the **Entry** level of the project.

1.   Double-click on the **Entry** node under the **Structural Plans** head in the **Project Browser**.

2.   Invoke the **Camera** tool from **View > Create > 3D View** drop-down; the options for inserting the camera are displayed in the Options Bar.

3. In the Options Bar, ensure that the **Perspective** check box is selected. Enter the value **5'6"** for Imperial or **1676** mm for Metric in the **Offset** edit box and then press ENTER.

4. Move the cursor down and click at a position between the **West** and **South** elevation arrows to specify the camera location. For the location of the camera, refer to Figure 9-59.

Figure 9-59 Structural plan view showing the location of the camera and its target

5. Move the cursor between the grid G, G.1 and 2, 3 location and press ENTER, refer to Figure 9-59; the project view gets changed and a view similar to the view shown in Figure 9-60 is displayed.

Figure 9-60 Camera view displaying the structural model in wireframe

6. In this view, ensure that the crop region of the 3D view is selected and the drag controls (blue dots at the midpoint of the four sides of the rectangle) are displayed.

7. Use drag controls to increase the extent of the view so that the entire structural model is visible inside the crop-region.

8. Ensure that the **Crop Region Visible** is selected in the **Properties** palette, click in the value field of the **View Name** parameter and enter **Camera-view** in it to replace the existing value. Similarly, click in the value field of the **Title on Sheet** parameter and enter **Perspective-View**, and choose the **Apply** button.

Generating Shadows

In this section, you will adjust the Sun settings and generate shadows of the structural model displayed in the camera view.

1. Ensure that the **Camera-view** view is displayed in the **3D Views** head from the **Project Browser**. And then, choose the **Visual Style: Wireframe** button from the **View Control Bar**; a flyout is displayed. Next, choose the **Hidden Line** option from the flyout displayed; the hidden line view of the structural model is displayed, as shown in Figure 9-61.

2.   Choose the **Sun Path Off** button from the **View Control Bar**; a flyout is displayed.

3. In the displayed flyout, choose the **Sun Settings** options; the **Sun Settings** dialog box is displayed.

4. In this dialog box, select the **Still** radio button in the **Solar Study** area. In the **Settings** area, ensure that the **Location** parameter is set to **Boston, MA**. Choose the **Disable Updater** button from the **Autodesk Revit 2021** message box if displayed. The **Sun Settings** dialog box is displayed again.

5. Make sure that the **Ground Plane at Level** check box is selected in the **Sun Settings** dialog box. Next, select the **Entry** option from the drop-down list displayed below this check box.

Figure 9-61 *Camera view displaying the structural model in the **Hidden Line** visual style*

6. Choose the **Apply** and then the **OK** button; the **Sun Settings** dialog box is closed.

7. In the **View Control Bar**, choose the **Shadows Off** button; a shadow is generated in the structural model. Figure 9-62 shows the camera view of the structural model displaying shadows due to the Sun settings.

Figure 9-62 Camera view displaying the structural model with shadows

Creating a Sheet

In this section, you will create a sheet in the project.

1. Choose the **Sheet** tool from the **Sheet Composition** panel in the **View** tab; the **New Sheet** dialog box is displayed.

2. In this dialog box, choose the **Load** button; the **Load Family** dialog box is displayed.

3. In this dialog box, select the specified title block **C 17 x 22 Horizontal** from the **US Imperial > Titleblocks** folder for Imperial unit system and load **A0 metric** from the **US Metric > Titleblocks** folder for Metric unit system. Choose the **Open** button from the **Load Family** dialog box. On doing so, the specified title block is added to the list in the **Select titleblocks** region of the **New Sheet** dialog box.

4. Choose the **OK** button to create the sheet view by using the loaded title block. The added sheet is now displayed in the drawing window.

Adding Project Views to the Sheet

In this section, you need to add the specified project views to the sheet by dragging their name from the **Project Browser**. Further, based on the sheet layout, you need to place the project views at their designated place in the sheet.

1. In the **Project Browser**, click on the **Entry** node under the **Structural Plans**. Next, in the **Properties** palette, click in the value field corresponding to the **View Scale** parameter and select the **1/16" = 1'-0"** option for Imperial and **1:200** option for Metric from the drop-down list displayed.

2. Now, press and hold the left mouse button on the **Entry** node in the **Project Browser** and then drag the view into the drawing sheet. Release the left mouse button when the project view appears as a rectangle in the sheet.

3. Move the cursor to the lower left area of the title block such that the corner of the rectangle get close to the lower left corner of the drawing sheet. Next, click to place the view; the **Entry** structural plan view is added to the sheet and appears enclosed in a rectangle, as shown in Figure 9-63.

4. Next, ensure that the viewport of the **Entry** structural plan view is selected in the sheet. In the **Properties** palette, ensure that the check box corresponding to the **Crop Region Visible** parameter is cleared.

5. Choose the **Edit Type** button in the **Properties** palette; the **Type Properties** dialog box is displayed. In the **Type Properties** dialog box, select the **Title Only** option from the **Type** drop-down list and ensure that the check box corresponding to the **Show Extension Line** parameter is cleared and then choose the **OK** button.

Figure 9-63 *The location of the **Entry** structural plan view in the sheet*

6. Right-click in the drawing and then choose the **Activate View** option from the shortcut menu displayed.

7. Now, in the project view, click on the **North** elevation arrow head and right-click; a shortcut menu is displayed. Choose **Hide in View > Category** from it.

8. Again, right-click and then choose the **Pan Active View** option from the shortcut menu displayed; a move icon is displayed with the cursor.

9. In the sheet, press and drag the **Entry** structural plan view and then place it at the location, shown in Figure 9-64.

*Figure 9-64 Modified location of the **Entry** structural plan view*

10. Next, right-click and choose the **Deactivate View** option from the shortcut menu displayed.

11. Click on the **Camera-view** node under the **3D Views** head in the **Project Browser** and then drag it to the sheet. Next, release the mouse button and click at a location to place the **Camera-view** view, as shown in Figure 9-65.

Figure 9-65 *Sheet displaying the structural plan, elevation, and camera view*

12. Click on the **North** node under the **Elevations (Building Elevation)** head and then specify the value of the **View Scale** parameter to **1" = 10'-0"** for Imperial and **1:100** for Metric. Next, drag the **North** node from the **Project Browser** and place it at the location, as shown in Figure 9-65. The three views are added to the sheet.

Adding Hosted Area Load

In this section, you will add a hosted area load to the structural floors.

1. Double-click on the **Analytical Model** node of the **Project Browser** under the **3D Views** head.

2. Choose the **Visual Style** button in the **View Control Bar** and then choose the **Hidden Line** option from the flyout displayed.

3. Next, choose the **Analyze** tab and then the **Loads** tool from the **Analytical Model** panel; the **Modify | Place Loads** contextual tab is displayed.

4. Choose the **Hosted Area Load** tool from the **Loads** panel. In the **Properties** palette, enter **-.5 ksf** for Imperial and **-23.94 KN/m²** for Metric in the value field of the **Fz 1** parameter and then choose the **Edit Type** button; the **Type Properties** dialog box is displayed.

5. In this dialog box, click on the **Value** field of the **Area force scale** parameter and then enter **10**. Next, choose **Apply** and then **OK**; the **Type Properties** dialog box is closed.

6. Now, in the project view, place the cursor on the edge of the structural floor at the **Roof** level, as shown in Figure 9-66. Next, click on this edge; the assigned load is displayed throughout the area of the floor at the **Roof** level, as shown in Figure 9-67.

Figure 9-66 Placing the cursor on the edge of the structural floor

*Figure 9-67 The hosted area load added to the structural floor at the **Roof** level*

7. Repeat the procedure followed in step 6 to add the area load to the structural floor on the **Second Floor** level. Press ESC to exit the tool. Figure 9-68 shows the structural model after the hosted area load is added to the structural floor at the **Second Floor** level.

Figure 9-68 *The hosted area load added to structural floor at the* **Second Floor** *level*

Saving the Project

In this section, you will save the project file using the **Save As** tool.

1. Choose **Save As > Project** option from the **File** menu; the **Save As** dialog box is displayed.

2. In this dialog box, browse to *C:\rst_2021* and create a folder with the name *c09_rst_2021_tut*. Next, open the created folder and then enter **c09_Commercial-Complex_tut1** for Imperial or **M_c09_Commercial-Complex_tut1** for Metric in the **File name** edit box.

3. Now, choose the **Save** button; the **Save As** dialog box closes and the project file is saved.

Closing the Project

1. Choose the **Close** option from the **File** menu.

   The file is closed. This completes Tutorial 1 of Chapter 9.

Tutorial 2   Industrial Complex

In this tutorial, you will set an analytical model and add boundary conditions to the project created in Tutorial 2 of Chapter 8. Also, you will add area and fabric area reinforcements to the structural floor.

(Expected time: 45 min)

The following steps are required to complete this tutorial:

a. Open the project file created in Tutorial 2 of Chapter 8.
> For Imperial   *Industrial-Complex*
> For Metric   *M_Industrial-Complex*

b. Set the Analytical Model.
c. Add boundary conditions.
d. Add area reinforcement.
e. Save the project.

Opening the Existing Project

In this section, you will open the project file created in Tutorial 2 of Chapter 8.

1. Choose **Open > Project** from the **File** menu; the **Open** dialog box is displayed.

2. In this dialog box, browse to the *C:\rst_2021\c08_rst_2021_tut* location and then choose the *c08_Industrial-Complex_tut2.rvt* for Imperial or *M_c08_Industrial-Complex_tut2.rvt* for Metric project file. You can also download this file from *https://www.cadcim.com*. The path of the file is as follows: *Textbooks > Civil/GIS > Revit Structure > Exploring Autodesk 2021 for Structure*.

3. Choose the **Open** button from the **Open** dialog box; the selected project file opens in the drawing window.

Setting the Analytical Model

In this section, you will set analytical model to check the consistency of the structure.

1. Double-click on the {3D} node under the **3D Views** head in the **Project Browser**; the 3D view of model is displayed.

2. Choose the **Analyze** tab and then choose the **Analytical Model Settings** button in the **Analytical Model Tools** panel; the **Structural Settings** dialog box is displayed with the **Analytical Model Settings** tab chosen.

3. In this dialog box, select the **Member Supports** and **Analytical/Physical Model Consistency** check boxes in the **Automatic Checks** area.

4. Choose the **OK** button; the **Analytical Model Check** window is displayed. Choose the **Yes** button; the **Warning** window is displayed. Close the warning message.

5. Right-click on the View Cube; the shortcut menu is displayed. Select **Orient to a Direction > Southwest Isometric** and the view is displayed.

Adding Boundary Conditions

1. In the **Analyze** tab, choose the **Boundary Conditions** tool in the **Analytical Model** panel; the **Modify | Place Boundary Conditions** contextual tab is displayed.

2. Choose the **Area** tool in the **Boundary Conditions** panel if not chosen by default. Move the cursor toward the left wing of the structural model and place it at the edge of the structural foundation slab, as shown in Figure 9-69.

Figure 9-69 The cursor placed at the edge of the foundation slab

3. Next, click when the edge is highlighted; the boundary conditions are added to the slab. Similarly, add the boundary conditions to the structural foundation slab of the right wing of the structural model. Figure 9-70 shows the boundary conditions added to the foundation slab of both the wings of the structural model. Press ESC to exit.

Figure 9-70 The boundary conditions added to both foundation slabs

Adding Area Reinforcement

In this section, you will add area reinforcement to the structural floor of the left wing of the structural model.

1. Double-click on the **Second Floor** node under the **Structural Plans** head in the **Project Browser**.

2. Place the cursor at the edge of the structural floor, as shown in Figure 9-71. Click when the edge gets highlighted; the **Modify | Floors** contextual tab is displayed.

3. In this tab, choose the **Area Reinforcement** tool from the **Reinforcement** panel; the **Revit** message box is displayed.

Figure 9-71 *The cursor placed at the edge of the structural floor*

4. Choose the **OK** button in the **Revit** message box; the **Modify | Create Reinforcement Boundary** contextual tab is displayed.

5. Ensure that the **Rebar Line** tool is chosen in the **Draw** panel. Choose the **Rectangle** tool from the list box in the **Draw** panel and place the cursor at the grid intersection 9 and C and click when the **Endpoint** object snap is displayed.

6. Now, drag the cursor down and place it at the grid intersection A and 8. Click, when the **Endpoint** object snap is displayed; a magenta-colored rectangular boundary is created, as shown in Figure 9-72.

Figure 9-72 The sketched boundary of the area reinforcement

7. Choose the **Finish Edit Mode** button in the **Mode** panel of the **Modify | Create Reinforcement Boundary** contextual tab.

8. In the **Properties** palette, click in the value field of the **Top Major Bar Type** parameter and select the **#8** for Imperial and **25M** for Metric value from the drop-down list displayed.

9. Similarly, click in the value field of the **Bottom Major Bar Type** parameter and select the **#6** for Imperial and **19M** for Metric value from the drop-down list displayed. Choose the **Apply** button and click on the **Finish Edit Mode** option from the **Mode** panel of the **Modify|Create Reinforcement Boundary** contextual tab; area reinforcement is created.

10. To view the reinforcement added, double-click on the **Section X** node under the **Sections (Building Section)** head in the **Project Browser**; the **Section X** section view is displayed.

11. Zoom in the floor placed in the **Second Floor** level of the left wing; the reinforcements added become visible, as shown in Figure 9-73.

Figure 9-73 The added reinforcements in the structural floor

Adding Fabric Area Reinforcement

In this section, you will add fabric area reinforcement to the structural floor of the left wing of the structural model.

1. Double-click on the **Roof** node under the **Structural Plans** head in the **Project Browser**.

2. Choose the **Fabric Area** tool from the **Reinforcement** panel of the **Structure** tab and then select the structural floor to the left wing of the structural model; the **Modify | Create Fabric Boundary** contextual tab is displayed.

3. In this tab, ensure that the **Boundary Line** tool is chosen in the **Draw** panel. Next choose the **Rectangle** tool from the list box in the **Draw** panel and place the cursor at the grid intersection 9 and C and click when the **Endpoint** object snap is displayed, refer to Figure 9-74.

4. Now, drag and place the cursor at the grid intersection A and 8 and click when the Endpoint object snap is displayed; a magenta-colored rectangular boundary is created, as shown in Figure 9-75.

5. Next, choose the **Finish Edit Mode** button in the **Mode** panel of the **Modify | Create Fabric Boundary**; the fabric area reinforcement gets done on the structural floor. You can view the fabric area reinforcement in the structural plan view as well as in the 3D view of the structural model.

Figure 9-74 *The cursor placed at the edge of the structural floor*

Figure 9-75 *The sketched boundary of the fabric area reinforcement*

Saving the Project

In this section, you will save the project file using the **Save As** tool.

1. Choose the **Save As > Project** option from the **File** menu; the **Save As** dialog box is displayed.

2. In this dialog box, browse to *C:\rst_2021\c09_rst_2021_tut* and then enter **c09_Industrial-Complex_tut2.rvt** for Imperial or **M_c09_Industrial-Complex_tut2.rvt** for Metric in the **File name** edit box.

3. Next, choose the **Save** button; the **Save As** dialog box closes and the project file is saved.

Closing the Project

1. Choose the **Close** option from the **File** menu; the file is closed. This completes Tutorial 2 of Chapter 9.

Tutorial 3   Reinforcement Model

In this tutorial, you will provide reinforcement to different elements of the *Reinforcement Model* for Imperial or *M_Reinforcement Model* for Metric.   **(Expected time: 45 min)**

The following steps are required to complete this tutorial:

a. Open the project file.
>   For Imperial   *Reinforcement Model.rvt*
>   For Metric   *M_Reinforcement Model.rvt*
b. Provide cover to different elements.
c. Provide reinforcement in column.
d. Edit sketch of reinforcement.
e. Copy the column reinforcement to other columns.
f. Provide area reinforcement and path reinforcement in floor.
g. Save the project by using the **Save As** tool.
h. Close the project by using the **Close** tool.

Opening the Project

1. Choose **Open > Project** from the **File** menu; the **Open** dialog box is displayed.

2. In this dialog box, browse to *C:\rst_2021\c09_rst_2021_tut* location and choose the project file *Reinforcement Model.rvt* for Imperial or *M_Reinforcement Model.rvt* for Metric. You can also download this file from *https://www.cadcim.com*. The path of the file is as follows: *Textbooks > Civil/GIS > Revit Structure > Exploring Autodesk Revit 2021 for Structure*.

3. Choose the **Open** button from the **Open** dialog box; the selected project file with the **3D** view opens in the drawing window.

Providing Cover to Elements

In this section, you will provide cover to columns, beams, and floor.

1. Double-click on the **Level 2** node under the **Structural Plans** head in the **Project Browser**.

2. Invoke the **Cover** tool from the **Reinforcement** panel in the **Structure** tab; the options for adding the cover are displayed in the **Options Bar**.

3. In the **Options Bar**, choose the **Pick Elements** button from the **Options Bar**; you are prompted to select an element for rebar cover.

4. Select all columns by pressing the CTRL key and then select the **Exterior - #3 to #5 <0'-1 1/2">** for Imperial and **Exterior - 10M to 16M <40mm>** for Metric from the **Cover Settings** drop-down in the **Options Bar**.

5. Select all beams and then select the **Interior (framing, columns) <0'-1 1/2">** for Imperial and **Interior (framing, columns) <40mm>** for Metric from the **Cover Settings** drop-down list in the **Options Bar**.

6. Select floor and then select the **Interior (slabs, walls, joists) #3 to #11 <0'-0 3/4">** for Imperial and **Interior (slabs, walls, joists) - 10M to 36M <20mm>** for Metric from the **Cover Settings** drop-down list in the **Options Bar**.

Note

*You need to select the **Wireframe** visual style from the Visual Control Bar to display rebars in the corresponding view.*

Providing Reinforcement to Columns

In this section, you will provide reinforcement to columns.

1. Invoke the **Rebar** tool from the **Reinforcement** panel in the **Structure** tab; a **Revit** message box is displayed. Choose the **OK** button; the **Modify| Place Rebar** contextual tab is displayed.

2. Choose the **Near Cover Reference** tool from the **Placement Plane** panel in the **Modify| Place Rebar** contextual tab.

3. Choose the **Perpendicular to Workplane** tool in the **Placement Orientation** panel in the **Modify| Place Rebar** contextual tab.

4. Select the **Fixed Number** option from the **Layout Rule** drop-down list and enter **3** in the **Quantity** edit box in the **Rebar Set** area of the **Properties** palette.

5. Now, place the rebar in the Upper left column, as shown in Figure 9-76. After placing three bars in the left of the column, place three bars on the right, as shown in Figure 9-77.

Figure 9-76 Placing rebar in the left of column   *Figure 9-77 Placing rebar in the right of column*

6. Invoke the **Rebar** tool from the **Reinforcement** panel of the **Structure** tab; the **Modify|Place Rebar** contextual tab is displayed.

7. Choose the **Near Cover Reference** tool from the **Placement Plane** panel in the **Modify|Place Rebar** contextual tab.

8. Choose the **Parallel to Work Plane** tool from the **Placement Orientation** panel in the **Modify| Place Rebar** contextual tab.

9. Select the **Maximum Spacing** option in the **Layout Rule** drop-down list and enter **0' 4"** (for Metric **150mm)** in the **Spacing** edit box in the **Rebar Set** area of the **Properties** palette.

10. Select **T1** (for Metric **M_T1)** in the **Shape** drop-down list in the **Construction** area of the **Properties** palette.

11. Now, place the rebar in the Upper left column, as shown in Figure 9-78

Figure 9-78 Placing stirrup in the column

 Note
You may need to adjust the bars in the stirrups. To do so, select them and move accordingly.

Editing the Sketch of Rebar
In this section, you will edit the sketch of reinforcement in columns.

1. Double-click on the **North** node under the **Elevations (Building Elevations)** head in the **Project Browser**.

2. Select the vertical rebar on the right in the column, as shown in Figure 9-79.

 Note
*You need to make rebar visible in north elevation view. To do so, select the rebar and choose the **Edit** option from the **View Visibility States** column in the **Graphics** area of the **Properties** palette; the **Rebar Element View Visibility States** dialog box is displayed. Select the check box in the **View unobscured** column against the **North** option in the **View Name** column. Choose the **OK** button.*

Figure 9-79 *Rebar to be selected in the column*

3. Invoke the **Edit Sketch** tool from the **Mode** panel in the **Modify | Structural Rebar** contextual tab.

4. Select the sketch and stretch it to the bottom of the footing, as shown in Figure 9-80

Figure 9-80 *Stretching the sketch of rebar*

5. Choose the **Line** tool from the **Draw** panel of the **Modify|Structural Rebar > Edit Rebar Sketch** contextual tab.

6. Draw the line, as shown in the Figure 9-81. Choose the **Finish Edit Mode** button from the **Mode** panel of the **Modify|Structural Rebar > Edit Rebar Sketch** contextual tab.

*Figure 9-81 Editing sketch of rebar using the **Line** tool*

7. Repeat steps 2 to 6 to edit the sketch of left side bars. After editing the sketch, the rebars appear, as shown in Figure 9-82.

Figure 9-82 Rebars after editing the sketch

8. Select stirrups and stretch it to the bottom of the footing, as shown in Figure 9-83.

Figure 9-83 Stirrups stretched to bottom

Copying Rebars to Columns

In this section, you will copy reinforcement in different columns.

1. Double-click on the **Level 2** node under the **Structural Plans** head in the **Project Browser**.

2. Select rebars by using window selection method, as shown in Figure 9-84; the **Modify | Multi Select** contextual tab is displayed. Next, choose the **Filter** button from the **Selection** panel in the contextual tab; the **Filter** dialog box is displayed.

Figure 9-84 *Selecting rebars*

3. Clear the **Structural Columns** check box and choose the **OK** button; rebars are selected.

4. Choose the **Copy** tool from the **Modify** panel in the **Modify | Structural Rebar** contextual tab; you are prompted to select the move start point. Click at the centre of the column where the bars are selected. Make sure that the **Multiple** check box is selected in the Options Bar.

5. Next, click at the center of the column in which the bars need to be copied. Similarly, click at the center of the remaining columns; rebars are placed, as shown in Figure 9-85. Press the ESC button to exit the tool.

Figure 9-85 *Rebars are placed on remaining columns*

Providing Reinforcement to the Floor

In this section, you will provide area reinforcement to the floor.

1. Invoke the **Area** tool from the **Reinforcement** panel in the **Structure** tab and select the floor; the **Modify | Create Reinforcement Boundary** contextual tab is displayed.

2. Choose the **Rectangle** tool from the **Draw** panel in the **Modify|Create Reinforcement Boundary** contextual tab and draw the boundary of the floor, as shown in Figure 9-86.

Figure 9-86 *Boundry of floor for reinforcement*

3. Clear the **Top Major Direction** and **Top Minor Direction** check boxes from the **Layers** area in the **Properties** palette.

4. Choose **#3** for Imperial and **10M** for Metric in the **Bottom Major Bar Type** and **Bottom Minor Bar Type** drop-downs from the **Layers** area in the **Properties** palette.

5. Choose the **Finish Edit Mode** button; the **Modify|Structural Area Reinforcement** contextual tab is displayed.

6. Choose the **Remove Area System** tool from the **Area Reinforcement** panel in the **Modify|Structural Area Reinforcement** contextual tab.

7. Choose the **Path** tool from the **Reinforcement** panel in the **Structure** tab and select the floor; the **Modify| Create Reinforcement Path** contextual tab is displayed.

8. Choose the **Pick Lines** tool from the **Draw** panel in the **Modify| Create Reinforcement Path** contextual tab and select the path, as shown in Figure 9-87.

Figure 9-87 *Reinforcement path selected using the **Pick Line** tool*

9. Choose **#3** for Imperial and **10M** for Metric in the **Primary Bar - Type** drop-down in the **Layers** area in the **Properties** palette. Enter **4' 0"** for Imperial and **1200mm** for Metric in the **Primary Bar - Length** edit boxes in the **Layers** area in the **Properties** palette.

10. Choose the **Finish Edit Mode** button from the **Mode** panel in the **Modify|Create Reinforcement Path** contextual tab.

11. Now, choose the **Remove Path System** tool from the **Path Reinforcement** panel in the **Modify| Structural Path Reinforcement** contextual tab.

12. Repeat steps 7 to 11 to complete path reinforcement for the remaining three sides of the floor.

Note
*While applying path reinforcement to the floor it may be possible that the reinforcement will fall outside of the floor. To switch the direction, choose the **Flip Path Reinforcement** tool that appears near the created line or picked line.*

Saving the Project
In this section, you will save the project file using the **Save As** tool.

1. Choose the **Save As > Project** option from the **File** menu; the **Save As** dialog box is displayed.

2. In this dialog box, browse to *C:\rst_2021\c09_rst_2021_tut* and then enter **c09_Reinforcement Model_tut3.rvt** for Imperial or **M_c09_Reinforcement Model_tut3.rvt** for Metric in the **File name** edit box.

3. Next, choose the **Save** button; the **Save As** dialog box closes and the project file is saved.

Closing the Project
1. Choose the **Close** option from the **File** menu; the file gets closed.

Self-Evaluation Test

Answer the following questions and then compare them to those given at the end of this chapter:

1. The _____ 3D view is a view of a building model in which all elements are displayed in their actual size irrespective of their distance from the source.

2. You can add information related to a project in a sheet by using the _____ tool.

3. _____ study helps you visualize and analyze the position of the Sun and the solar effects on buildings and sites in the real world.

4. Parameters for the projection planes of an analytical model are displayed under the _____ head in the **Properties** palette.

5. You can activate a view from a drawing sheet by choosing the _____ option.

6. To specify the physical properties of a material, choose the _____ tab in the **Materials** dialog box.

7. The _____ tool is used to add reinforcement throughout the area of floor or slab.

8. In Autodesk Revit, you can display the trajectory of the Sun which creates the solar study. (T/F)

9. You can place a load in the physical model view of a structural model. (T/F)

10. You cannot add an existing schedule in a project to a sheet. (T/F)

Review Questions

Answer the following questions:

1. You can invoke the **Camera** tool from the _____ drop-down list in the **View** tab.

2. You can add view and edit load case in a structural model by choosing the _____ tool from the **Analyze** tab.

3. In a concrete column, beam, structural floor, or foundation, you can place rebars parallel to the current work plane by using the _____ tool.

4. The _____ tool is used to check the consistency of the analytical and physical model of a project.

5. The _____ tool is used to adjust the alignment of an analytical structural member with reference to its adjoining analytical member.

6. You can use the _____ tool from the **Boundary Conditions** panel to create a linear boundary throughout the length of a beam.

7. To sketch a point load in a model, you need to invoke the _____ tool.

8. You can check the support stability by using the _____ tool.

9. The default analytical projection planes of columns are placed at their tops and bases. (T/F)

10. After adjusting the members of an analytical model, you can bring the structural member back to its previous state. (T/F)

EXERCISES

Exercise 1   Academic Institution

In this exercise, you will create a sheet and add it to the *Academic-Institution* project for Imperial and *M_Academic-Institution* project for Metric, created in Exercise 1 of Chapter 8. For the location of the views in the sheet, refer to Figure 9-88, use the following specifications:

(Expected time: 30 min)

1. Insert the following views in the sheet: **3D View: {3D}**, **Elevation: East**, **Elevation 1-a**, **Elevation 2-a**, and **Structural Plan: Entry**.

2. Use the desired sheet type.
   For Imperial   **E130x42Horizontal**
   For Metric   **A1 Metric**

3. File name to be referred:
   For Imperial   *c08_Academic-Institution_exer1.rvt.*
   For Metric   *M_c08_Academic-Institution_exer1.rvt.*

4. File name to be assigned:
   For Imperial   *c09_Academic-Institution_exer1.rvt.*
   For Metric   *M_c09_Academic-Institution_exer1.rvt.*

Figure 9-88 The added views in the sheet

Exercise 2   Factory Shed

In this exercise, you will add different views to a sheet for the *Factory Shed* project for Imperial or *M_Factory Shed* project for Metric created in Exercise 2 of Chapter 8. For the location of views in the sheet, refer to Figure 9-89, use the following specifications:

(Expected time: 30 min)

1. Use the desired sheet type.
       For Imperial   **E130x42Horizontal**
       For Metric   **A1 Metric**

2. Insert the following views into the sheet: **3D View: {3D}**, **Elevation: South**, and **Structural Plan: Second Floor**

3. File name to be referred:
       For Imperial   *c08_Factory-Shed_exer2.rvt.*
       For Metric   *M_c08_Factory-Shed_exer2.rvt.*

4. File name to be assigned:
       For Imperial   *c09_Factory-Shed_exer2.rvt.*
       For Metric   *M_c09_Factory-Shed_exer2.rvt.*

Figure 9-89 *Views added to the sheet*

Answers to Self-Evaluation Test
1. orthographic, **2. project information**, **3.** Solar, **4. Analytical Model**, **5. activate view**, **6. physical**, **7. area**, **8.** T, **9.** F, **10.** F

Chapter *10*

Linking Revit Model with Robot Structural Analysis

Learning Objectives

After completing this chapter, you will be able to:
- *Analyze a model using Robot Structural Analysis software*
- *Modify a model in Robot Structural Analysis software*
- *Manage analysis results*
- *Run reinforcement code check*

INSTALLING ROBOT STRUCTURAL ANALYSIS PROFESSIONAL 2021

In Autodesk Revit, after developing and annotating a model, preparing schedules, defining loads, and checking consistency, the model is ready for analysis and code checking. To analyze the model in Robot Structure Analysis 2021, you have to first install the Robot Structural Analysis Professional 2021 software in your system.

You can start Autodesk Robot Structural Analysis by double-clicking on the **Autodesk Robot Structural Analysis Professional 2021** icon on the desktop. Alternatively, choose **Start > Autodesk Robot Structural Analysis Professional 2021 > Autodesk Robot Structural Analysis Professional 2021**. The interface screen of Autodesk Robot Structural Analysis Professional 2021 is shown in Figure 10-1.

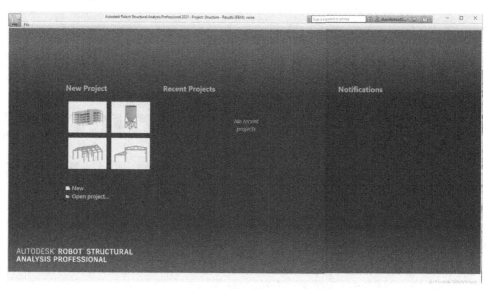

Figure 10-1 *The interface of Autodesk Robot Structural Analysis Professional 2021*

STRUCTURAL ANALYSIS INTEROPERABILITY

In Autodesk Revit, you can export the analytical model to Autodesk Robot Analysis and perform structural analysis and also check code on it. You can also perform reinforcement design process of a concrete structure directly by linking it to Autodesk Robot Structural Analysis software. The methods of linking the analytical model from Autodesk Revit 2021 to Autodesk Robot Structural Analysis software are discussed next.

Linking the Analytical Model for Analysis and Code Check

To link the analytical model from Autodesk Revit 2021 to Autodesk Robot Structural Analysis software, choose the **Robot Structural Analysis Link** tool from **Analyze > Structural Analysis > Robot Structural Analysis** drop-down as shown in Figure 10-2; the **Integration with Robot Structural Analysis** dialog box will be displayed, as shown in Figure 10-3.

*Figure 10-2 The **Robot Structural Analysis Link** tool*

*Figure 10-3 The **Integration with Robot Structural Analysis** dialog box*

In the **Direction of integration with Autodesk Robot Structural Analysis** area, the **Send model** radio button is selected by default. Choose the **Send options** button from this dialog box to send the analytical model to **Robot Structural Analysis** software for analysis; the **Integration with Robot Structural Analysis - Send Options** dialog box will be displayed, as shown in Figure 10-4. In this dialog box, the following areas are displayed: **Scope and correction**, **Specify the case that contains the self-weight**, and **Transfer (optionally)**. These areas are discussed next.

*Figure 10-4 The **Integration with Robot Structural Analysis-Send Options** dialog box*

Scope and correction Area

In this area, the **Send entire Revit project (ignore current selection)** radio button is selected by default. As a result, the entire model, except the currently selected model will be sent to Robot Structural Analysis software for analysis. Alternatively, you can select the **Send only current selection** radio button to send the currently selected models to Autodesk Robot Structural Analysis software. Note that this radio button will only be active if a model/element is selected in the project view.

Specify the case that contains the self-weight Area

In this area, the radio button on the left of the drop-down list is selected by default. As a result, you can select the load case that contains the self weight of the structural model from the drop-down list. Alternatively, in the **Specify the case that contains self-weight** area, you can select the **Ignore self-weight** radio button to avoid the self-weight of the structure to be sent with the analytical model to Robot software.

Transfer (optionally) Area

In this area, you can specify the options which can be transferred from Revit to Robot Structure. To use the plan views of Revit by the robot structure, select the **Use plan views as backgrounds** check box. Similarly, to transfer the steel connections defined in the Revit to the steel connection design module of the Robot Structure, select the **Steel connections** check box in the **Transfer (optionally)** area.

After specifying various options in the **Integration with Robot Structural Analysis - Send Options** dialog box, choose the **OK** button; the dialog box will be closed and the **Integration with Robot Structural Analysis** dialog box will reappear. In this dialog box, choose the **OK** button; the **Send model to Robot Structural Analysis** window will be displayed. This window will display the progress of sending the analytical model to Robot. When the analytical model is completely transferred to the Robot software, the **Send model to Robot Structural Analysis** window will disappear.

After analyzing the structural model in Robot, you need to update the structural model in Revit based on the design changes made in Robot Software. To do so, choose the **Robot Structural Analysis Link** tool in Autodesk Revit from **Analyze > Structural Analysis > Robot Structural Analysis** drop-down; the **Integration with Robot Structural Analysis** dialog box will be displayed. In this dialog box, select the **Update model** radio button in the **Direction of integration with Autodesk Robot Structural Analysis** area and then choose the **Update options** button; the **Integration with Robot Structural Analysis - Update Options** dialog box will be displayed. In the **Scope - consider current selection** area, the **Update the whole project (ignore current selection)** radio button is selected by default. As a result, all structural elements that had been sent to Robot for structural analysis, except the selected element, will be updated in Revit. Alternatively, if you select the **Update only the part selected in Robot** radio button, the elements selected will only be updated in Revit. To select the elements in Revit after they are updated, you can select the **Select modified elements in Revit Structure** check box in the **Scope - consider current selection** area of the **Integration with Robot Structural Analysis - Update Options** dialog box.

After specifying various options in the **Integration with Robot Structural Analysis - Update Options** dialog box, choose the **OK** button; the dialog box will be closed. Now, choose the **OK** button in the **Integration with Robot Structural Analysis** dialog box; the **Update model from Robot Structural Analysis** window will be displayed. This window will display the progress of updating the structural model in Revit. The **Update model from Robot Structural Analysis** window will disappear once the structural model is updated in Revit with the current settings. After that the **Integration with Robot Structural Analysis** message box will appear. In this message box, you can choose the **Yes** button to update the changes and the **No** button to discard any changes.

In Autodesk Revit, you can perform the reinforcement design of RCC beams, columns, and floors elements through Robot Structural Analysis software. To do so, select the elements in the project view for which you want to perform the reinforcement design and then choose the **Reinforcement Code Check** tool from **Analyze > Structural Analysis > Robot Structural Analysis** drop-down; the **Reinforcement design** window will be displayed. This window will display the progress of transferring of the selected elements to Robot software. This window will disappear once the selected model is completely transferred to the Robot software. After the **Reinforcement design** window disappears, the Robot software is opened and is ready to perform the reinforcement design for the elements that were selected and sent from Revit.

Structural Analysis in Autodesk Robot Structural Analysis Professional 2021

In the previous chapters of this textbook, you learned about various methods of modeling structural elements, imposing loads, setting boundary conditions, viewing reports, setting analytical models, and importing the structural model to a structural analysis software. Now, you will learn how to link Revit files to Autodesk Robot Structural Analysis Professional 2021, perform analysis, and view analysis results in this software. Moreover, you will also learn to update the structural model in Revit based on the analysis and design process performed in Robot.

Autodesk Robot Structural Analysis software, also known as Robot, is a structural analysis and design software that helps you achieve accurate design results for a project. This software provides a collaborative workflow and interoperability with 3D bidirectional link to Autodesk Revit and other Autodesk companion products. The various features and capabilities of Robot Structural Analysis software are discussed next.

Structural Modeling

Autodesk Robot Structural Analysis software has the capability to model a wide range of structures made up of steel, reinforced concrete, and so on. There are various tools in this software along with in-built design codes that enable the engineers to model a variety of structures based on the specification in the design codes.

Mesh Modeling

Autodesk Robot Structural Analysis Software enables the structural engineers to work with complex mesh models. The **Automatic mesh generation** tool in this software can be used for manual manipulation of the mesh, refinement of mesh, and meshing around openings of any shape and size of the structure. There are many meshing tools available in this software that enable the structural engineers to quickly create a high-quality finite element mesh.

Analysis Capabilities

Autodesk Robot Structural Analysis has the capability to perform linear static analysis of building structures. This software can be used by structural engineers to perform non-linear analysis of structures, including nonlinear analysis that includes P-delta analysis, tension/compression members and supports, cables, and plastic hinges, and so on. Autodesk Robot Structural Analysis can also be used to perform dynamic analysis of structures.

Reinforced Concrete and Steel Designing

Autodesk Robot Structural Analysis contains in-built reinforced concrete and steel design codes based on standards relevant to the country. You can use more than 40 international steel codes and 30 reinforced concrete codes to simplify the design process. These codes assist engineers in selecting and evaluating structural elements throughout the world.

Linking Revit Files to Robot

To link Revit files to Robot Structural Analysis software, choose the **Robot Structural Analysis Link** tool from **Analyze > Structural Analysis > Robot Structural Analysis** drop-down; the **Integration with Robot Structural Analysis** dialog box will be displayed. In this dialog box, ensure that the **Send model** radio button is selected and then choose the **OK** button; the **Send model to Robot Structural Analysis** window will be displayed. This window will close when the model is exported to Robot. After the window is closed, the **Integration with Robot Structural Analysis** window will be displayed, informing that the model has been transferred from Revit to Robot. In this window, you can also choose the **Yes** button to view the events report; the **Warning list** window will be displayed. Next, choose the **Close** button to close the window; the Robot Structural Analysis software containing the linked structural model from Revit will open, as shown in Figure 10-5. In the Robot Structural Analysis software, you can use various tools to analyze and design the linked model from Revit. Before performing analysis and designing, you need to set the job preferences of the structural model linked from Revit. In the next sections, you will learn to set preferences, perform analysis, view analysis results in Robot, and then update the analyzed and designed model in Revit.

Figure 10-5 *Partial view of interface of the Robot Structural Analysis software showing the linked Revit model*

Setting Job Preferences in Robot

In Robot Structural Analysis software, you can set various job preferences such as units and the codes of practices for materials to be used in the project; databases for various structural entities such as steel and timber sections, vehicle loads, and standard loads applied in the project; design codes to be used for specifying loads such as seismic load, snow or wind load, and load combinations; type of structural analysis to be performed; type of design codes to be used while designing steel or reinforced concrete structure; and various meshing parameters. To set the job preferences, choose the **Job Preferences** tool from the **Tools** menu; the **Job Preferences** dialog box will be displayed, as shown in Figure 10-6. In this dialog box, you can set job preferences.

Figure 10-6 *The* **Job Preferences** *dialog box*

Analysis in Robot

You can perform the structural analysis of a model and set the analysis type by using the tools available in the **Analysis** menu. To set the analysis type for the structural model, choose the **Analysis Types** tool from the **Analysis** menu; the **Analysis Type** dialog box will be displayed, as shown in Figure 10-7. This dialog box contains six tabs: **Analysis Types**, **Structure Model**, **Load to Mass Conversion**, **Combination Sign**, **Result Filters**, and **Buckling Deformation**. Note that the **Structural Model** tab will be displayed in the **Analysis Type** dialog box, if the **Model generation** check box is selected.

*Figure 10-7 The **Analysis Type** dialog box*

Note
*The **Analysis Types** tool in the **Analysis** menu will be displayed only when any model is opened in Robot Structural Analysis.*

In the **Analysis Type** dialog box, the **Analysis Types** tab is chosen by default. In this tab, you can specify a new load case definition, change the load case type, or modify parameters of a selected load case. While defining load cases in the structure, the linear static analysis type is assigned to all load cases by default. However, you can change the analysis type to buckling analysis, harmonic analysis, and so on by choosing the **Change analysis type** button in **Analysis Type** tab in the **Analysis Type** dialog box.

After setting the analysis type in the **Analysis Types** tab, you can specify options in the other tabs. Now, choose the **Calculations** button in the **Analysis Type** dialog box to start the calculation of the desired load cases. The calculation process is displayed in **Autodesk Robot Structural Analysis Professional- Calculations** dialog box. Once the calculation process is over, the dialog box closes automatically. Next, choose the **Calculation Restart** tool from the **Analysis** menu; the **Calculation Restart** dialog box will be displayed, as shown in Figure 10-8.

*Figure 10-8 The **Calculation Restart** dialog box*

In the **Case list** area of this dialog box, various load cases are displayed. Select the check box(es) corresponding to load case(s) of the structural project you require to perform the calculation. After selecting the desired check box(es), choose the **Restart calculations** button to perform the calculation function. After performing the calculation, you need to prepare the results of the calculation. To do so, choose the **Prepare results** tool from the **Analysis** menu; the **Prepare results** dialog box will be displayed, as shown in Figure 10-9.

Note
*While analyzing, if there is any instability in a model, the **Autodesk Robot Structural Analysis 2021** message box will be displayed. Choose the **Cancel** button to ignore warning. On doing so, the **Calculation Messages** dialog box with the number of warnings will be displayed. Choose the **Close** button.*

*Figure 10-9 The **Prepare results** dialog box*

In this dialog box, ensure that the **Activate preparation of results** check box is selected. As a result, the options in the **Prepare results** dialog box will be activated. Select an option from the **Template** drop-down list to specify a template file to be used for viewing the results. The **Analytical Model** file is selected by default in this drop-down list. You can edit it as required. To do so, choose the Browse button located next to the **Template** drop-down list; the **Composition of Template for Result Preparation** dialog box will be displayed, as shown in Figure 10-10.

*Figure 10-10 The **Composition of Template for Result Preparation** dialog box*

You can use various options in this dialog box to edit the display of the results of the analysis. Next, choose the **Save** button to save the changes in the template and then choose the **Close** button; the **Composition of Template for Result Preparation** dialog box will be closed and the **Prepare results** dialog box will be displayed again. In this dialog box, the description of the selected template will be displayed in the **Description** text box and it can be edited by specifying a new value in it. In the **Prepare results** dialog box, the **Results** area displays the table of the results contained in three columns, namely, **Result**, **Type**, and **Cases**. The **Result** column shows the list of results along with their type and cases in the **Type** and **Cases** columns, respectively. Next, in the **Prepare** results dialog box, choose the **Run preparation** button and then choose the **OK** button; the preparation of the results will be completed and the **Prepare results** dialog box will be closed. After preparing the results, you can view the calculation report. To do so, choose **Calculation Notes** tool from the **Analysis** menu; a cascading menu will be displayed. In this menu, you can choose any of the two tools: **Simplified Note** and **Full Note**. You can choose the **Simplified Note** tool to view the brief summary of the results in a window. Alternatively, you can choose the **Full Note** tool from the cascading menu to view the detailed summary of the result, refer to Figure 10-11.

Figure 10-11 *The calculation report displayed on choosing the* ***Full Note*** *tool*

Viewing Results in Robot

After preparing and calculating the results, you can view the output of the results in the form of reports and diagrams using the tools available in the **Results** menu. To view the support reactions of the structure, choose the **Reactions** tool from the **Results** menu; the output report showing the reactions at different nodes due to different load cases will be displayed in the drawing area, as shown in Figure 10-12.

Figure 10-12 *Partial view of the report of the support reaction*

In the Status Bar; the **Values** tab is chosen by default. As a result, all the values related to load cases will be displayed in the report. In the Status Bar, you can choose the **Envelope**, **Global extremes**, and **Info** tabs to view the reactions of the nodes for the envelopes, maximum and minimum reactions, and the information of the load cases and the nodes in the reaction, respectively. You can also view the displacement of the nodes, deflection of the members, forces induced in the nodes and members, and stresses induced in the nodes and members by choosing the **Displacements**, **Deflections**, **Forces**, and **Stresses** tools from the **Results** menu, respectively.

To view the diagrams of the forces, moments, and reinforcements in the model, you need to choose the **Detailed Analysis** tool from the **Results** menu. On doing so, the **Detailed Analysis** dialog box will be displayed, as shown in Figure 10-13.

*Figure 10-13 The **Detailed Analysis** dialog box*

The **Detailed Analysis** dialog box contains the following tabs: **NTM**, **Stresses**, **Reinforcement**, **Parameters**, and **Division points**. In the dialog box, the **NTM** tab will be chosen by default. In this tab, you can select the check boxes related to forces and moments that you want to display graphically in the drawing window. In the **Forces** column of the chosen tab, you can select the **Fy** check box to display the shear forces induced in the members of the project. Similarly, you can select the **Fx** and **Fz** check boxes in the **Forces** column to display the forces induced in the respective directions. In the **Moments** column, you can select the desired check box(es) corresponding to the moments you require to view in the drawing area.

In the **Elastic ground** reactions area of the **NTM** tab, you can select the **Ky** and **Kz** check boxes to view the reactions of an elastic ground for bars (the options Ky and Kz) in the drawing window. The Ky and Kz values are obtained as elastic ground reactions (R = K u, where R denotes force of reaction, K is the coefficient of elastic ground reaction, and u denotes displacement) along the member length in the local coordinate system, if elastic ground has been defined for the member. The **Reinforcement** tab of the **Detailed Analysis** dialog box displays the reinforcement in the members of the drawing window. The **Parameters** tab contains options that controls the presentation of the results displayed in drawing window. The **Division points** tab indicates the intermediate points for which the values of selected quantities are to be presented in the table in the drawing window. After specifying these options in the **Detailed Analysis** dialog box, choose the **Apply** button; the diagrams and the table for member 1 will be displayed in the drawing area, as shown in Figure 10-13. Note that the results in the diagram in the drawing window will be based on the load case that is selected from the **Cases** drop-down list in the **Selection** toolbar; refer to Figure 10-14.

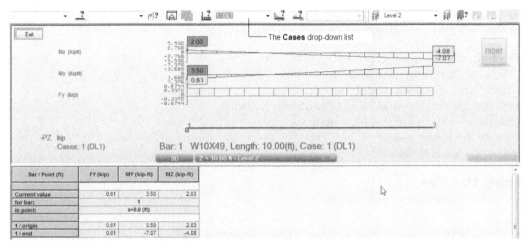

Figure 10-14 *The drawing window graphically displaying result of the moments*

Updating the Model in Revit

After working in the model, save the project in Robot, before switching back to Revit for updating the BIM model. Next, open the Revit interface containing the structural project which is to be analyzed in Robot. Next, choose the **Robot Structural Analysis Link** tool from the **Analyze > Structural Analysis > Robot Structural Analysis** drop-down in the Revit interface; the **Integration with Robot Structural Analysis** dialog box will be displayed. In this dialog box, select the **Update model** radio button. You can specify the settings for updating the model in Revit. To do so, choose the **Update options** button; the **Integration with Robot Structural Analysis-Update Options** dialog box will be displayed. In the **Scope - consider current selection** area and **Transfer (optionally)** area of the dialog box, you can specify the scope of the updating the model and also transfer the results from Robot to Revit. Next, choose the **OK** button; the **Integration within Robot Structural Analysis-Update Options** dialog box will close and the **Integration within Robot Structural Analysis** dialog box will be displayed. Choose the **OK** button in this dialog box; the model in Revit will be updated.

TUTORIAL

General instructions for downloading the model file and performing the tutorial:

1. Download the tutorial file **c10_revit_st_2021** from *www.cadcim.com*. The path of the file is as follows: *Textbooks > Civil/GIS > Revit Structure > Exploring Autodesk Revit 2021 for Structure*.

2. Next, browse to *C:\rst_2021* and create a new folder with the name **c10_rst_2021_tut**. Next, save and extract the files in this folder.

3. To perform this tutorial, you are required to download and install the **Autodesk Robot Structural Analysis Professional 2021** software.

Tutorial 1   Building Project

In this tutorial, you will perform the analysis of Revit model in Autodesk Robot Structural Analysis software.   **(Expected time: 1 hr 15 min)**

The following steps are required to complete this tutorial:

a. Open the file *Analytical Model.rvt*.
b. Check the model for consistency.
c. Check supports of the model.
d. Send the model to Autodesk Robot Analysis Software.
e. Calculate and prepare results of analysis.
f. Update the Revit model.
g. Saving the project.

Opening the File
In this section, you will open the model.

1. Choose **Open > Project** from the **File** menu; the **Open** dialog box is displayed.

2. In this dialog box, browse to *C:\rst_2021\c10_rst_2021_tut* and open the file *Analytical Model. rvt* from this folder.

Checking the Model for Consistency and Supports
In this section, you will check the consistency of the model.

1. Choose the **Analyze** tab and then choose the **Analytical Model Settings** button from the **Analytical Model Tools** panel; the **Structural Settings** dialog box is displayed.

2. In this dialog box, the **Analytical Model Settings** tab is chosen by default. Now, in the **Automatic Checks** area under this tab, select both the **Member Supports** and **Analytical / Physical Model Consistency** check boxes, refer to Figure 10-15.

Figure 10-15 *The **Structural Settings** dialog box*

3. Next, choose the **OK** button in this dialog box; the **Analytical Model Check** message box is displayed, prompting you whether to perform analytical model check or not. Choose the **Yes** button in this message box; the message box and the **Structural Settings** dialog box are closed and a warning message box is displayed.

4. In this message box, choose the **Expand warning dialog** button; the **Autodesk Revit 2021** message box is displayed, as shown in Figure 10-16. View the details of the warnings and choose the **Close** button; the message box is closed.

*Figure 10-16 The **Autodesk Revit 2021** message box*

Sending the Model to Robot Structural Analysis Software

In this section, you will send the model to Autodesk Robot Structural Analysis Professional 2021 software.

1. Choose the **Analytical Model** view under the **3D Views** node in the **Project Browser**, if the current view is different from the **Analytical Model** view.

   Note
   *To view the analytical model, make sure that the **Show Analytical Model** button is chosen from the **View Control** bar.*

2. Choose the **Robot Structural Analysis Link** tool from **Analyze > Structural Analysis > Robot Structural Analysis** drop-down; the **Integration with Robot Structural Analysis** dialog box is displayed, as shown in Figure 10-17.

3. In this dialog box, ensure that the **Send model** and **Direct integration** radio buttons are selected, and then choose the **Send options** button; the **Integration with Robot Structural Analysis - Send Options** dialog box is displayed, refer to Figure 10-18.

4. In this dialog box, keep the default settings and choose the **OK** button; the **Integration with Robot Structural Analysis - Send Options** dialog box is closed.

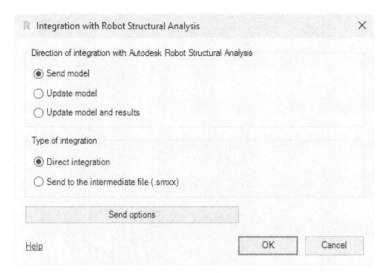

*Figure 10-17 The **Integration with Robot Structural Analysis**
dialog box*

*Figure 10-18 The **Integration with Robot Structural Analysis - Send Options** dialog box*

5. Choose the **OK** button; the **Integration with Robot Structural Analysis** dialog box is closed and **Send model to Robot Structural Analysis** window is displayed. This window displays the status of file transfer and will automatically close on the completion of the file transfer process. Once the file transfer process is complete, the **Integration with Robot Structural Analysis** window is displayed.

6. Choose the **No** button from this window; the window is closed and the model is displayed in the Robot Structural Analysis Professional 2021 application, as shown in Figure 10-19. If the Robot Structural Analysis is already running then the run time error will occur. So make sure you close the Robot Structural Analysis software.

Figure 10-19 *The exported Revit model in the Robot Structural Analysis Professional 2021*

Calculating and Viewing Results

In this section, you will calculate the results in the **Robot Structural Analysis** software.

1. Change the current view of the model to the top view by using the view cube and then select the **Load Types** option from the **Loads** menu; the **Load Types** dialog box with the list of load cases is displayed, refer to Figure 10-20. Choose the **Close** button to close the **Load Types** dialog box.

Figure 10-20 *The **Load Types** dialog box*

2. Choose the **Calculations** tool from the **Analysis** menu, refer to Figure 10-21; the **Autodesk Robot Structural Analysis Professional - Calculations** window is displayed, refer to Figure 10-22. Note that this window displays the calculation status, and is automatically closed when the calculations are completed.

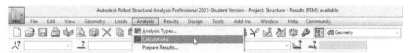

*Figure 10-21 The **Calculations** tool in the **Analysis** menu*

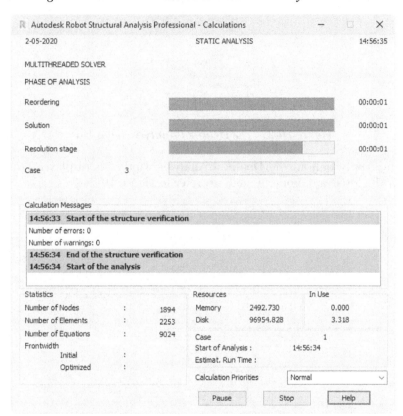

*Figure 10-22 The **Autodesk Robot Structural Analysis Professional - Calculations** window*

3. After performing calculations, choose the **Detailed Analysis** tool from the **Results** menu; the view is changed to **Detailed Analysis** and the **Detailed Analysis** dialog box is displayed.

4. In this dialog box, the **NTM** tab is chosen by default. Select the **Fx**, **Fy**, and **Fz** check boxes in the **Forces** area and the **Mx**, **My**, and **Mz** check boxes in the **Moments** area, refer to Figure 10-23.

5. Next, choose the **Stresses** tab in the **Detailed Analysis** dialog box and select the **maximum - S max** and **minimum - S min** check boxes in the **Normal - maximum** area.

*Figure 10-23 The **Detailed Analysis** dialog box*

6. Choose the **Apply** button; the **Detailed Analysis** window is displayed, showing various graphs for the force and moment analysis, refer to Figure 10-24.

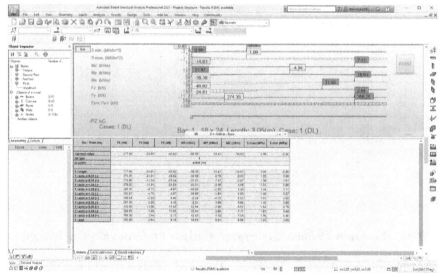

Figure 10-24 Details of the forces and moments in the changed view

7. Next, choose the **Close** button in the **Detailed Analysis** dialog box; the dialog box is closed.

Preparing Results

In this section, you will prepare results of analysis.

1. Choose the **Prepare Results** tool from the **Analysis** menu; the **Prepare results** dialog box is displayed, as shown in Figure 10-25. Choose the Browse button located next to the **Template** drop-down; the **Composition of Template for Result Preparation** dialog box is displayed.

Figure 10-25 *The* **Prepare results** *dialog box*

2. In the **Template** edit box, enter **Analytical Model** and then choose the **Save** and **Close** buttons; the changes are saved and the **Composition of Template for Result Preparation** dialog box is closed.

3. Choose the **Run preparation** button in the **Prepare results** dialog box and then choose the **OK** button; the **Prepare results** dialog box is closed.

4. Next, choose the **Save** option from the **File** menu of the **Robot Structural Analysis** application; the **Save As** dialog box is displayed. In this dialog box, save the result at an appropriate location.

Updating Revit Model

In this section, you will update the model in Revit.

1. Switch to Revit software and choose the **Robot Structural Analysis Link** tool from **Analyze > Structural Analysis > Robot Structural Analysis** drop-down; the **Integration with Robot Structural Analysis** dialog box is displayed.

2. In this dialog box, select the **Update model and results** and **Direct integration** radio buttons in the **Direction of integration with Autodesk Robot Structural Analysis** and **Type of integration** areas, respectively.

3. Next, choose the **Update options** button in this dialog box; the **Integration with Robot Structural Analysis - Update Options** dialog box is displayed, as shown in Figure 10-26.

*Figure 10-26 The **Integration with Robot Structural Analysis - Update Options** dialog box*

4. In this dialog box, select the **Reinforcement projects (beams, columns, spread footings)** and **Steel Connections** check boxes in the **Transfer (optionally)** area. Next, choose the **OK** button; the dialog box is closed.

5. Next, in the **Integration with Robot Structural Analysis** dialog box, choose the **OK** button; the dialog box is closed and the **Send Results to Revit** dialog box is displayed.

6. In this dialog box, click in the edit box next to **Model name** in the **Analysis results package** area and enter **Analytical Model**.

7. Enter **Analytical Model** in the **Model name** edit box in the **Required reinforcement results package** area, refer to Figure 10-27.

*Figure 10-27 The **Send Results to Revit** dialog box*

8. Next, choose the **OK** button; the **Send Results to Revit** dialog box is closed and the **Integration with Robot Structural Analysis** message box is displayed, as shown in Figure 10-28.

Figure 10-28 The ***Integration with Robot Structural Analysis*** *message box*

Note
The process of updating the model will take time and will depend on the processor. The status of the file updation is displayed in the ***Update model from Robot Structural Analysis*** *window.*

9. Choose the **Yes** button from this message box; the **Warning list** message box is displayed, showing update details and warning messages.

10. Choose the **Close** button to close the message box; the model is updated and is saved.

Saving the Project
In this section, you will save the project file using the **Save As** tool.

1. Choose the **Save As > Project** option from the **File** menu; the **Save As** dialog box is displayed.

2. In this dialog box, browse to *C:\rst_2021\c10_rst_2021_tut* and then enter **Analytical Model_1** in the **File name** edit box.

3. Now, choose the **Save** button; the **Save As** dialog box closes and the project file is saved.

Closing the Project
1. To close the project, choose the **Close** option from the **File** menu.

Self-Evaluation Test

Answer the following questions and then compare them to those given at the end of this chapter:

1. Which of the following check boxes in the **NTM** tab of the **Detailed Analysis** dialog box needs to be selected to view the shear force(s) induced in the structural member(s)?

   (a) **Fx**   (b) **My**
   (c) **Mx**   (d) **Mz**

2. To invoke the **Job Preferences** dialog box, choose the _____ tool from the **Tools** menu.

3. You can send the current selected model from Revit to Autodesk Robot Structural Analysis software by selecting the _____ radio button in the **Integration with Robot Structural Analysis- Send Options** dialog box.

4. The _____ tool is used to design and analyze reinforcements in a model.

5. You can link the Revit model to Robot Structural Analysis by using the _____ tool.

6. To view the support reactions of the structural model, you need to choose the **Reaction** tool. (T/F)

7. In Robot Structural Analysis, you cannot perform non-linear analysis of a structural model. (T/F)

Review Questions

Answer the following questions:

1. To view the maximum and minimum reactions in a model, which tool needs to be chosen from the Status bar?

    (a) **Envelope**   (b) **Global extremes**
    (c) **Info**   (d) **Loads**

2. After the analysis is done in Robot Structural Analysis, you can update the model and the results by selecting the _____ radio button from the **Integration with Robot Structural Analysis** dialog box.

3. In Robot Structural Analysis, you can set units and code(s) of practice for material used by using the _____ tool(s).

4. To view the graphical representation of moment(s) and stress(es) induced in a model in Revit, you need to choose the _____ tool from the Structural Analysis panel.

5. The **Parameters** tab in the **Detailed Analysis** dialog box controls the presentation of the results displayed in the drawing window. (T/F)

6. Autodesk Robot Structural analysis contains in-built reinforced concrete and steel design codes. (T/F)

EXERCISE

Exercise 1   Industrial Shade

Download the Revit file *c10_Industrial_shade_exer* from *https://www.cadcim.com*. The path of the file is as follows: *Textbooks > Civil/GIS > Revit Structure > Exploring Autodesk Revit 2021 for Structure*. In this exercise, you will analyze the Industrial shade file in Robot Structural Analysis software. Refer to Figure 10-29 to view the model in Revit window and Figure 10-30 for the graphical representation of the model in Revit. **(Expected time: 1hr 45min)**

1. Project file to be used: *c10_Industrial_shade_exer.*
2. Link the Revit model to Robot Structure Analysis software.
3. Run calculations.
4. Prepare results.
5. Update the model in Revit.
6. Use the **Result Explorer** tool to view the following results graphically in Revit:
   Rotation of the Reactions
   Displacement in members
   Deformation

Figure 10-29 *The Steel shade model in Revit window*

Figure 10-30 *Viewing results by using the **Results Explorer** tool*

Answers to Self-Evaluation Test
1. a, 2. Job Preferences, 3. Send only Current Selection, 4. Reinforcement Code Check,
5. Robot Structural Analysis Link, 6. T, 7. F

Index

Other Publications by CADCIM Technologies

The following is the list of some of the publications by CADCIM Technologies. Please visit *www.cadcim.com* for the complete listing.

Autodesk Revit Structure Textbooks
- Exploring Autodesk Revit 2020 for Structure, 10th Edition
- Exploring Autodesk Revit 2019 for Structure, 9th Edition

Autodesk Revit Architecture Textbooks
- Exploring Autodesk Revit 2021 for Architecture, 17th Edition
- Exploring Autodesk Revit 2020 for Architecture, 16th Edition

Autodesk Revit MEP Textbooks
- Exploring Autodesk Revit 2019 for MEP, 6th Edition
- Exploring Autodesk Revit 2018 for MEP, 5th Edition

AutoCAD Civil 3D Textbooks
- Exploring AutoCAD Civil 3D 2020, 10th Edition
- Exploring AutoCAD Civil 3D 2019, 9th Edition

AutoCAD Map 3D Textbooks
- Exploring AutoCAD Map 3D 2018, 8th Edition
- Exploring AutoCAD Map 3D 2017, 7th Edition

AutoCAD Textbooks
- AutoCAD 2021: A Problem-Solving Approach, Basic and Intermediate, 27th Edition
- AutoCAD 2020: A Problem-Solving Approach, Basic and Intermediate, 26th Edition

Autodesk Inventor Textbooks
- Autodesk Inventor Professional 2021 for Designers, 21st Edition
- Autodesk Inventor Professional 2020 for Designers, 20th Edition

AutoCAD MEP Textbooks
- AutoCAD MEP 2020 for Designers, 5th Edition
- AutoCAD MEP 2018 for Designers, 4th Edition

Solid Edge Textbooks
- Solid Edge 2020 for Designers, 17th Edition
- Solid Edge 2019 for Designers, 16th Edition

NX Textbooks
- Siemens NX 2020 for Designers, 13th Edition
- Siemens NX 2019 for Designers, 12th Edition

NX Mold Textbook
• Mold Design Using NX 11.0: A Tutorial Approach

Creo Parametric Textbooks
• Creo Parametric 6.0 for Designers, 6th Edition
• Creo Parametric 5.0 for Designers, 5th Edition

ANSYS Textbooks
• ANSYS Workbench 2019 R2: A Tutorial Approach
• ANSYS Workbench 14.0: A Tutorial Approach

Creo Direct Textbook
• Creo Direct 2.0 and Beyond for Designers

Autodesk Alias Textbooks
• Learning Autodesk Alias Design 2016, 5th Edition
• Learning Autodesk Alias Design 2015, 4th Edition

AutoCAD LT Textbooks
• AutoCAD LT 2020 for Designers, 13th Edition
• AutoCAD LT 2017 for Designers, 12th Edition

Autodesk 3ds Max Design Textbooks
• Autodesk 3ds Max Design 2015: A Tutorial Approach, 15th Edition
• Autodesk 3ds Max Design 2014: A Tutorial Approach

AutoCAD Textbooks
• AutoCAD 2006 (Russian Edition)
  Piter Publishing Press, Russia
• AutoCAD 2005 (Russian Edition)
  Piter Publishing Press, Russia
• AutoCAD 2000 Fondamenti (Italian Edition)

Coming Soon from CADCIM Technologies
• SolidCAM 2019: A Tutorial Approach
• AutoCAD Electrical 2020: A Tutorial Approach
• Project Management Using Microsoft Project 2019 for Project Manager

Online Training Program Offered by CADCIM Technologies
CADCIM Technologies provides effective and affordable virtual online training on architecture, animation, and GIS softwares, computer programming languages, and Computer Aided Design, Manufacturing, and Engineering (CAD/CAM/CAE) software packages. The training will be delivered 'live' via Internet at any time, any place, and at any pace to individuals, students of colleges, universities, and CAD/CAM/CAE training centers. For more information, please visit the following link: *https://cadcim.com*.

Made in the USA
Monee, IL
23 November 2021

82789803R00308